Sarah —

Enjoy the books

all the best!

JW

Healthcare Revolution:

THE PATIENT IS THE NEW PAYER

PRAISE FOR
Jonathan Wiik and *Healthcare Revolution: The Patient Is the New Payer*

"*Healthcare Revolution: The Patient Is the New Payer* is a must-read if you wish to understand how and why our healthcare payment system is so complex."

—William A. Munson, Jr., Vice President
and CFO, Boulder Community Health

"Jonathan's insight into the world of healthcare is both brilliant and captivating. His ability to make healthcare both understandable and appealing is simply remarkable. "

—Kelly Clasen, Senior Director, Business
Operations, Middle Park Medical Center

"Jonathan's energy comes to life when you read this book. He will inspire you with practical illustrations and his joyful sense of humor."

—Cheryl Curry, CFO, Littleton Adventist
Hospital, Centura Health

"Jonathan Wiik's business acumen and revenue cycle knowledge have consistently been ahead of the curve. Look to him for best-in-breed strategies."

—Cally Christensen, Principal, Christensen
& Company Consulting LLC

"Jonathan's passion for the healthcare profession lets him cut through the complexity to explain in simple terms the industry's history, current issues and future. With his well-known sense of humor, he makes the healthcare topic an interesting read—not an easy task."

—Chad Jones, MA, CFP, Principal, Trail Ridge
Wealth Management, Financial Education Director,
College of Veterinary Medicine & Biomedical
Sciences, Colorado State University

"Healthcare in the United States is clearly a confounding mess. Jonathan is uniquely qualified, in his inimitable style, to analyze and provide an understanding of this confusing and complex industry. I highly recommend this read for anyone trying to make sense of it all."

—Timothy Cashman, CFO, Estes Park Medical Center

"Go out and make positive changes in healthcare"—this is Jonathan's mantra. As an industry veteran, he's knowledgeable and well respected in his field. Healthcare is truly his passion."

—Cathy Wolff, Vice President of Financial Services/
CFO, Yuma District Hospital and Clinics

"Jonathan is the "guru" of revenue cycle and a true mentor for many. Whenever there's a need for a "subject-matter expert," Jonathan is always willing to share his knowledge."

—Pilar Mank, Director of Client Relations,
Western Healthcare Alliance, California
Critical Access Hospital Network

Healthcare Revolution:

THE PATIENT IS THE NEW PAYER

Jonathan G. Wiik

Soft Cover Edition ISBN: 978-0-9990015-2-3
Hard Cover Edition ISBN: 978-0-9990015-1-6

....

*Thank you God for your gifts provided to me to
be able to humbly prepare this book.*

*To my Family—Chelsea, Kaden, and Zane. Thank you from the
bottom of my heart for the time, encouragement and love.*

*And to my BCH and TU colleagues and to my friends old
and new (you know who you are)—without your guidance
and support this book would not be possible.*

....

FOREWORD

Healthcare operations and finance have long existed in an environment of constant change and shifting expectations. Predicting and navigating these changes is part history and part vision, based on reading the signs and setting your best-educated pathway. Given the situation, it is important that we seek information from many sources *and* that we leverage our relationships and networks. As a leader who has spent more than 25 years planning for, observing and adapting to these changes, I realize that they come now at an even more accelerated pace and level of complexity. Our current challenge is one of evolving rules and requirements, shrinking margins, and the need to constrain improper utilization and cost. At the same time, we are also facing heightened pressure to provide the highest quality, best value, and smoothest patient experience possible.

I have known Jonathan for many years, originally when he was an employee, and then when he became a peer and leader in our organization. He has taken his passion to new roads as he seeks to assist and educate others in where we have come and where we are heading. He has always been engaged and forward thinking; he has kept his eyes open and his ear to the rail. His approach and knowledge transcends the present. He truly attempts to understand and predict the possibilities of the future. He responds proactively to these possibilities by developing strategies and assessing the needs and resources required to attain the outcomes that will drive us, both clinically and financially. I have been fortunate to discuss these concepts and to debate approaches with Jonathan. His insights and clarity have helped me become more aware of, and responsive to, the inevitable changes we face.

When I first met Jonathan many years ago, he was a young man just starting on his healthcare journey. He had just come off of a number of years as a white-water rafting guide. I've ridden in his boat, and on the river he was sure and in command, he knew the hazards, and how to read the obstacles. As he began his new role in healthcare, he was inquisitive and curious. He didn't focus just on those things that were part of his position, but on a much wider set of circumstances and possibilities, looking downstream to see what lay ahead. All the things we learn in life become part of us, and in many ways Jonathan is still standing in the back of the raft, looking ahead and calling out what he sees, helping to guide us on the often rough and turbulent waters of healthcare. Hold on tight…It's going to be a bumpy ride!

As we stand now in an age of a political changing of the guard and uncertainty in who will pay for healthcare and how, and at a time of aging population and financial pressure, it is extremely important that we take on the roles of leaders, seers, protectors, and stewards. Please enjoy the past, present, and possible futures that Jonathan has so succinctly presented in this important and timely volume.

Joseph J. Mikoni BSRT, MBA
Director of Imaging and Laboratory Services
Boulder Community Health
Boulder, Colorado

PREFACE

Since an advance copy of *Healthcare Revolution: The Patient Is the New Payer* was released, I've been asked two very distinct questions. First, "Why did you write this book?", and second, "This is a great study... BUT what is the ultimate solution to the healthcare crisis?" To preface the work within, I'll tackle these questions first.

I wrote this book to offer a perspective on the state of healthcare financing, based on my tenure in the industry. I've served in many different healthcare roles and have had the privilege of viewing healthcare financing from the perspective of the patient, insurer and provider.

When I started as a hospital transporter, patients often would ask me as we traveled to and from their rooms, "How much is all this going to cost?" (Pointedly, I didn't have a good answer then, and more notably, I don't have a better answer now.)

As I obtained my master's degrees and interned as an administrative resident at a large insurance company, I observed how healthcare is covered and reimbursed. Believe it or not, insurance companies aren't these big bad businesses. They play an important role in ensuring access to coverage so employers can offer affordable plans to their employees. In that role, there are rules, and with rules, come frustrations, and winners and losers. Without "living it" it's difficult to comprehend for most, while at the same time, working within the walls of an insurance company certainly gave me a different perspective. Seeing the insurance side of the equation provided me unique insights on the insurer's role in curbing healthcare costs, as well as premiums, coverage, copays and claims risk.

When I returned to the acute care side of operations in a very large imaging department, I was able to observe costs and utilization very closely from the provider's perspective. Imaging is a lot of "ruling out" of disease processes—deductive reasoning for elimination (if we know it's not that, we can see if it's this, and so on). Lots of tests, lots of normal results, lots of costs that one would argue are unnecessary, and certainly assert as expensive.

As I gained more responsibility in admissions, patient access, and ultimately the entire revenue cycle, the relationship between cost, utilization, coverage and payment became highly visible. The myriad of elements that determine a clean versus a dirty (rejected) claim, can dramatically impact the timing or the amount of payment (if you're paid at all).

If that all went well, it became even more challenging to differentiate between a patient's *willingness* or *ability* to pay. Patients certainly should pay within their ability; however, many do not, as the bill is confusing, arrives late, or simply isn't a priority for the patient. Those who can't pay are often unaware of the help and resources that may be available.

One could argue that 20 to 25 years ago, this perhaps was inconsequential. If there was insurance, a claim flew, it got paid, and the patient paid a small copay. If the patient didn't have insurance, the hospital enrolled them in a charity program or Medicaid, and that was that. As I progressed through these various roles of responsibility, and as the market became more complex, establishing funding mechanisms for patients became increasingly difficult.

Two factors have shifted over the last few decades: The demographics of the population, and the cost of healthcare. Controlling population demographics—the number and make-up of Baby Boomers, Gen X/Y, Millennials and the underserved—is not possible. Attempts to control the costs of healthcare over the last 50 years have largely failed.

Our country spends approximately $10,000 per person per year on healthcare. If that doesn't grab you, half of American adults have one chronic disease, and one in four have two or more conditions, representing almost 90% of all U.S. healthcare costs. The majority of healthcare costs stem from lifestyle choices, while other cost drivers come from population demographics, technology, consolidation, profitability and increased regulatory constraints.

Despite this, most patients can't self-insure and approach our healthcare system with the expectation that they can afford healthcare costs without insurance. It's similar to driving a car without auto insurance. There are simply more folks that *need* health insurance and can't afford to access it, or folks that are *on* health insurance plans that they cannot afford. These factors are driving an increased focus on uncompensated care and bad debt.

According to the American Hospital Association, in 2016, uncompensated care— representing a combination of charity care and bad debt—surpassed $35 billion, with a big "B." Most hospitals and associated providers have to make up for that loss in their operations somewhere. An opportunity to offset some of this risk exists in financially engaging patients. Providing a transparent, collaborative, proactive financial discussion is an afterthought for most, but frankly, it would help patients a ton. Balance after insurance and high-deductible health plans (HDHPs) are both climbing at an alarming rate, which isn't sustainable over the next decade.

An employed worker today easily could be experiencing a $5,000 annual deductible before Medicare kicks in at 65, and if one is on an ACA plan, that deductible is already there for most plans. To make matters worse, patients have not typically saved or planned for the high costs of healthcare, and are often facing large balances that can present significant debt risk to providers.

Patients and employers have accepted high healthcare costs, as the details have not been known. When cost specifics are known, one can start a dialogue about value and choice. And after that's settled, the provider can help establish funding mechanisms for the three types of patients: those who can't pay, those who need help paying, and those who *can* pay. Knowing which type you are attending to—and how to best help each patient—is critical to engaging early regarding financial onus, and curbing some of the crisis.

Now, as far as question number two, "What is the ultimate solution?"—I think answers to that question would warrant another book someday—wait for it, it's coming. Our government, the private sector, and anyone with a good head about them have been trying to talk about solutions for decades. There doesn't seem to be much alignment or agreement, other than there's a tremendous need to cut costs and improve outcomes.

Single Payer, Medicaid reform, value-based care, restricted benefits, curbing big pharma, limiting end-of-life care, malpractice reform caps and a myriad of other reparations…the beat goes on. Misaligned incentives complicated the issue.

As of this writing, The Affordable Health Care Act passed the House, and the Senate pulled the Better Care Reconciliation Act (BCRA) from a vote. Politics aside, these bills had the potential to impact tens of millions of Americans' coverage, and reduce payments to providers by hundreds of billions of dollars (with another big "B"). I'm not certain that was the outcome we anticipated from an ACA repeal, while at the same time, healthcare spending and tax dollars have been relatively unbridled since the inception of health insurance.

I'll make one suggestion: The patient, the payer, the employer and the insurer are going to have to come together to develop solutions that serve a community, versus themselves. All will have to give a little to make it right. Prices will have to level, costs will need to come down, coverage will have to be restricted, plans will have to narrow, and how our society funds healthcare (publicly or privately) will need to revamped significantly.

A revolutionary shift must occur that delivers better care more efficiently—clinically and financially. Patients must be at the center of this paradigm, driving decisions and payment. If these things do not occur, the path we're on is clear. The Centers for Medicare & Medicaid Services (CMS) have projected healthcare spending to outpace U.S. gross domestic product (GDP) growth by 1.2 percentage points over the next 10 years. At that rate, spending on healthcare will surpass 20% of GDP in 2025. One dollar out of every five will go to healthcare.

Simply put, the path we're on is not sustainable—it's time for a revolution and the patient as the payer, will once again be the driver of change. I hope you enjoy the book.

CONTENTS

HOW WE GOT HERE

CHAPTER 1
....

HISTORY OF HEALTHCARE FUNDING

Paying for healthcare has always been with us; it is not a new concept. Since the beginning, society has had various ways of paying for medical services. Those methods have evolved from trade of goods, to taxation, to employer funding, to health savings accounts (HSAs). There was a time—before health insurance, before big pharma, before health insurance exchanges and fitness trackers—when there were only two elements of payment in healthcare: the patient and the physician. So how did we get to where we are now from where we started?

In early America, the patient typically was the payer, but not all of the time. As the healthcare industry in the United States began to develop, there were examples of patient-as-the-payer models; charity care for the poor; and in some cases, early versions of "universal coverage" in which the community supported a healer available to all.

Native Americans provided one of the first payment models for healthcare. They relied on tribal healers to treat injuries and disease and to promote health and wellbeing.[1] For their healing practices—which included magic, prayers, ceremonies, rituals, and the use of medicinal herbs—compensation practices varied.[2] In some cases, the role of healer was considered a full-time job, but healthcare was most certainly not "free." Accordingly, the tribe took care of the healer's needs, including providing the healer with the food, shelter, supplies, and services he or she needed to live. In other cases, patients paid healers directly with gifts that might include blankets, furs, weapons, or horses.[3]

3

When the first English settlers came to America, they brought their physicians with them. Among the original settlers in Jamestown, Virginia, in the early 1600s were two "chirurgeons," Thomas Wotton and Will Wilkinson.[4] Chirugeons were colonial-era surgeons. They performed surgical operations, pulled teeth, and set broken bones. They learned their trade by apprenticing with a butcher or a barber.[5] Patients paid with goods or services, if they were able. But even then, charity care existed. Captain John Smith, one-time president of the Jamestown colony, wrote about one early physician who "freely imparted to all gratis, but most bountifully to the poore."[6]

It wasn't until nearly 100 years later that the first hospital was established in the American colonies. In 1751, Dr. Thomas Bond, in partnership with American statesman Benjamin Franklin, founded Pennsylvania Hospital in Philadelphia. The legislation established that the hospital was needed "to care for the sick poor of the Province and for the reception and care of lunaticks."[7] Historical records indicate the hospital primarily provided charity care; however, there were still rules in place that governed patient admissions:

> Those wishing admittance to the hospital also had to be sponsored by two tax-paying citizens in order to provide "burial or travel deposits to indemnify the hospital, either from the expense of burial in case they die, or to defray the expense of carrying them back to their place of abode, that they may not become a charge to the city."[8]

Even 250 years ago, there were provisions governing the hospitals' obligation to treat their community, as well as provisions for their citizens to fund their care where they could. That said, most people in the 1700s—and well into the 1800s—were treated by physicians in the patient's home, not in a hospital. Most patients paid for physician services with goods or labor, in addition to cash. A leather-bound journal of patient payments, kept by Philadelphia physician William Shippen Jr., is in the collection of the Library of Congress.[9] The journal, spanning 1775 to 1793, gives a glimpse into physician compensation in the 18th century:

Patients without ready cash paid Shippen with goods: coffee, tea, wine, and beer; lengths of muslin, linen, and calico; handkerchiefs, silk stockings, a tablecloth, looking glasses, crockery, a tea table. Sometimes Shippen took a chance on things of dubious or uncertain value: once he accepted a lottery ticket in payment; another time he took what he described as a "bad painting." People who had neither goods nor cash to spare paid in labor. Bakers paid in bread, carpenters with woodcraft, tallow chandlers with candles and a barber with "dressing, [etc.]" Mr. Bates, "horseman," housed Shippen's mare in exchange for advice on his nephritis. Some people never paid. After the name of one patient Shippen wrote "bankrupt," after another, "gone."[10]

Shippen's wealthier clients paid in cash. Shippen even anticipated the advent of concierge medicine by 200 years. In 1789, Shippen's payment records indicated that a certain "General Stewart" agreed to pay 15 guineas per year for Shippen's "advice & attendance."[11]

Early American historian Julie Miller points out that, "With no pool of insurance premiums to draw on, Shippen flexibly adapted to his patients' abilities to pay. But the records also show that access to medical care was dependent on who could pay for you if you could not pay for yourself."[12]

There was wide variability in the scope of medical services and the charges for those services during this time. There was not much standardization or regulation surrounding licensure, payment, benefits, or obligations. In 1848, a group of 12 physicians in Charlottesville, Virginia, published what could be one of the first physician fee schedules.[13] The physician group agreed to set minimum fees for a list of standard services and then published the fees (figure 1.1). Fees included prescription prices ranging from $0.25 for a single pill to $1.00 for a dozen. To see the physician was $1.00, and it was $2.00 if you lived more than two miles away. An amputation of the leg was a mere $20.00.

Converting these dollar amounts to 2017 values, the fee schedule below would probably represent somewhat reasonable rates for services provided today, if you compared them to other retail markets. One dollar in 1848 is worth roughly $20 now, meaning it would cost about $4,000 for a delivery today. One most certainly would argue the services are much more advanced, safer, and comfortable now, but the average cost for delivery is almost twice that today, at $8,775 for a routine vaginal delivery and $11,525 for a C-section.[14]

Figure 1.1 Agreed Rate of Medical Charges. Source: Physician price fixing in 19th century Virginia. (n.d.). Retrieved from http://blog.hsl.virginia.edu/feebill/

The Birth of Insurance

The patient-as-payer system continued through the early 1900s. Many reasons contributed to the stagnancy in payment models, given there was not an access or cost hurdle during these times for most. Medical practices remained relatively primitive in America through this century. Elaine Breslaw, author of *Lotions, Potions, Pills, and Magic: Health Care in Early America*, wrote, "Before modern medicine, the understanding of disease and other bodily afflictions was based on ideas that were at least 2,000 years old but lacked any scientific basis ... The medical scene in the nineteenth century was a chaotic free-for-all."[15] One common practice at the time was bloodletting: cutting a vein open and allowing blood to drain as a cure for a number of diseases and conditions. In fact, the red and white stripes on a barber's pole originally indicated to patrons that bloodletting was one of the services available from your local barber (figure 1.2). The red stripes stood for the blood, and the white stripes stood for the bandages used to stop the bleeding.[16] Barbers performed a dual role: They could cut your hair and cure your disease as your barber-physician—all in the same place.

Figure 1.2 The Barber Pole. Source: Safran, B. (Circa 1962-72). Woman and barber pole [Photography]. Retrieved from http://www.safran-arts.com/photographs-new-york-barber-pole.html

Questionable practices, such as the use of bloodletting and the huckstering of various potions and pills, meant that early American healthcare treatments were not particularly effective, and the outcomes were not always positive. Patients were not going to pay for something that did not work, a concept that will be revisited later in this book.

In addition, most Americans did not have to spend much on healthcare prior to the early 1900s. Journalists Alex Blumberg and Adam Davidson note that, "In 1900, the average American spent $5 a year on health care ($100 in today's money). No one had health insurance, because you don't need insurance for something that costs $5 a year."[17] Big pharma, MRI scanners, and large facilities did not exist yet—the technological costs of healthcare had not materialized. Another factor

7

was that prior to 1920, the financial losses associated with sickness were primarily related to lost wages due to missed work versus the actual cost of care. A study done in 1919 indicated that the cost of lost wages due to illness was four times greater than the cost of treating the illness.[18]

Given this, there was little demand for health insurance from consumers in the 20th century. Although commercial insurance companies existed, they were not inclined to offer health insurance:

> Commercial insurance companies did not write health insurance policies in 1908; they saw no way to avoid the risks of adverse selection (those who were sick would seek coverage, and those who were healthy would not) and moral hazard (coverage would encourage the insured to seek unnecessary services), and they lacked the means to calculate risks accurately and set appropriate premiums.[19]

During this time, the number of hospitals in the United States was growing, and their role in healthcare was certainly changing. Many early hospitals, like Pennsylvania Hospital, operated as charitable institutions. As such, they faced the financial challenges of being largely funded by donations and foundation efforts from the wealthy. As modern medicine began to evolve, hospitals transitioned from a place where the poor went to die into becoming a place that the middle class went to receive effective care. According to *America's Essential Hospitals*:

> Not-for-profit hospitals at this time began reducing their traditional charitable role in favor of creating prestigious institutions attractive to an upper middle class clientele ... All hospitals before the 1920s had operated without much money. Physicians donated their time, and costs for nurses and staff tended to be low. For the first time, hospitals required significant funds, just as doctors and surgeons began getting paid and nursing and staffing were professionalized.[20]

As hospitals evolved from strictly charitable institutions to emerging businesses, the intersection of healthcare delivery and financing became more complex. Ironically, the first health insurance plan in the United States was developed by a hospital. In 1929, Justin Ford Kimball, vice president of Baylor University, undertook a charge "to shore up the shaky finances" of Baylor University Hospital.[21] Kimball reviewed the hospital's unpaid bills and found that many of them were incurred by Dallas schoolteachers. He created an insurance plan to address the problem:

> In 1929 ... [Kimball] developed a not-for-profit insurance plan whereby Dallas schoolteachers could prepay, at 50 cents a month, or $6.00 a year, for 21 days of inpatient care in a semi-private room at Baylor Hospital. The plan would take effect after a patient's first week in the hospital, with payments being $5.00 a day. On its first day of subscription, 1,356 teachers signed up for the plan, and by December 1929, 75% of Dallas teachers were enrolled in the plan. Within 5 years, the "Baylor Plan" provided health insurance coverage for some 408 diverse employee groups, totaling 23,000 members, eventually covering 3 million people within a decade.[22]

The Baylor plan was the first prepaid hospital insurance plan in the United States.[23] After the success of the Baylor plan other hospitals began to develop similar plans. These plans were defined by "periodic payment of a fixed amount in exchange for a certain amount of service in that hospital when needed."[24] The concept was so popular that the American Hospital Association (AHA) established a Hospital Service Plan Commission in 1937 to coordinate and organize the various plans.[25] The AHA guidelines specified that affiliated plans could not be single-hospital plans, but must allow subscribers free choice of physician and hospital.[26] This marked the beginning of Blue Cross health insurance.

Physicians worried that these new third-party payers would negatively impact physician incomes by limiting their ability to set their own fees.[27] Concerned by the increasing adoption of the Blue Cross hospital insurance plans, physician groups began creating a network of plans—eventually called Blue Shield plans—to cover primary care and physician services.[28] These medical service prepayment plans were developed according to standards recommended by the American Medical Association (AMA).[29] The services of the early Blue Shield plans were financially underwritten and guaranteed by the physicians.[30]

The early growth of the Blue Cross and Blue Shield plans was facilitated by legislation that allowed the plans to operate as tax-exempt, nonprofit corporations.[31] This designation enabled the plans to avoid the laws and regulations governing for-profit insurance companies, such as maintaining traditional reserve requirements.[32] The exemption from state insurance laws helped facilitate the growth of these early health insurance plans.[33]

Enrollment in the plans grew with each passing decade (figure 1.3). The two plans merged in 1982 to form the Blue Cross and Blue Shield Association (BCBSA). Today, the BCBSA comprises 36 independent, locally operated franchises. It is the oldest—and largest—commercial payer group in the United States.[34]

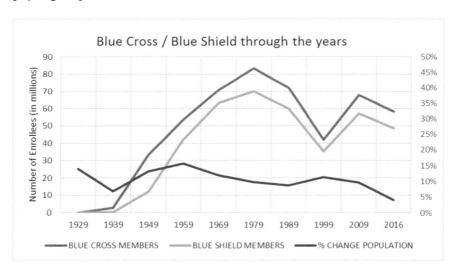

Figure 1.3 Blue Cross and Blue Shield Plans and Number of Subscribers at the Close of Each Decade. Source: Adapted by Jonathan Wiik from Cleverly, W.O. (1989). *Handbook of healthcare accounting and finance: Volume 1*. Aspen Publication.

The Rise of Employer-Based Health Insurance

By the early 1900s, many European countries—including Germany, Norway, Britain, Russia, and the Netherlands—had established "some form of nationalized, compulsory health insurance that provided income replacement and medical care in the event of accident or illness."[35] But not the United States. Even before the Baylor plan was created, early medical benefits were provided *only* in the context of a person's employment. US government funding would not come for another 50 years.

Railroad companies represented one of the more innovative funding mechanisms for healthcare during this time. They provided a lot of the initial employer-based medical care in the United States. This was because railroad work was dangerous. Traumatic injuries, such as amputations of hands and fingers, crushed limbs, and scalding from exploding boilers, were not uncommon.[36] In 1900, one of every 28 railroad employees suffered on-the-job injuries, and one in every 399 employees died.[37] As early as 1849, railroad companies began contracting with physicians to provide medical care to employees.[38]

Based on this, the earliest benefits were essentially trauma-care benefits provided by employers for on-the-job injuries. Some railroad companies even established their own hospitals to treat injured workers; others set up mutual benefits associations to cover the costs of treatment for injured employees.[39] In some cases, those benefits were extended to family members as well. For example, in 1880, the Baltimore and Ohio Employees Relief Association was formed to "extend relief" to the railroad's employees and their families "in case of sickness, injury, old age and death."[40]

Prior to Blue Cross and Blue Shield, the commercial insurance industry did not believe health insurance was feasible, due to the fear of adverse selection. If insurance became more easily available, it was highly likely that only those who needed healthcare (the sick and the elderly) would enroll in health insurance, and the risk pool would not be diversified to offset costs. Insurance companies existed, but they avoided getting into healthcare because it was volatile, expensive, and unknown. However, the success of the Blue Cross and Blue Shield plans had demonstrated to the rest of the insurance market that this was not the case. Blue Cross had overcome adverse selection and made insuring healthcare profitable. They targeted large groups of employed, healthy, and young citizens to offset the costs of covering the ill, and created a financially viable insurance product in the process.[41]

Health insurance products began to grow as the realization that marketing health insurance plans specifically to employee groups could counteract adverse selection. Divergence was already occurring between the nonprofit health insurance companies and the commercial insurance companies, as they had very different methods to set premiums for enrollees. As nonprofit organizations, Blue Cross and Blue Shield were required to "community rate" their policies. The companies were obligated to charge the *same* premiums to sick people as they did to healthy people.[42] Commercial insurers, on the other hand, were free to "experience rate" their policies, charging *lower* premiums to the healthy and *higher* premiums to the sick.[43] The lower premiums offered by the commercial plans made these plans attractive to employers.

It would be easier to defend the growth of employer-based health insurance plans if the source was good old-fashioned US capitalism, or commerce, but alas, that was not the case. The exponential increase in insurance growth was actually a by-product of legislation meant to control wage inflation during and after World War II. The Stabilization Act of 1942—and an accompanying executive order signed by President Franklin D. Roosevelt—prevented employers from increasing salaries or wages without prior approval from the National War Labor Board (NWLB).[44, 45] The purpose of the act and executive order was to prevent inflation from wreaking havoc on the American economy during and after the war. Penalties for violating the act included a fine and/or imprisonment. Insurance and pension benefits were the only types of compensation excluded from the wage and salary controls. This loophole made it possible for employers to circumvent the controls by offering health benefit packages as a fringe benefit to attract and retain employees.[46] Employers couldn't pay people more, even if they wanted to, so they had to find another way to compete for employees. Along came the health insurance and benefits wars, which catapulted employers into the role of attracting and retaining employees with fringe benefits instead of wages.

Subsequent legislation exempted employers from paying payroll taxes on contributions to employee health plans and exempted employees from paying income tax on their employer's contributions to their health insurance plans.[47] These changes made employer-based health insurance options even more irresistible to employers and employees.

The combined effect of these legislative changes drove the rapid adoption of health insurance plans over the next several decades (figure 1.4). Economic historian Melissa A. Thomasson has characterized the expansion of employer-based health insurance coverage in the United States as an "accident of history":

> Thus employer-based insurance, which started with Blue Cross selling coverage to Texas teachers and spread because of government price controls and tax breaks, became our system. By the mid-1960s, Thomasson says, Americans started to see that system—in which people with good jobs get healthcare through work and almost everyone else looks to government—as if it were the natural order of things.[48]

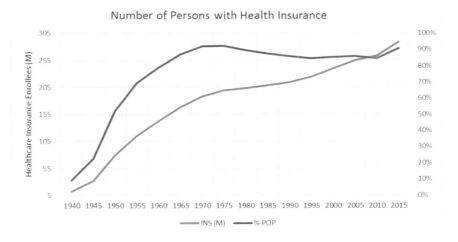

Figure 1.4 Number of Persons with Health Insurance (in Millions), 1940–2015, including all insurance types as they evolved (BCBS, other private, Medicare, Medicaid, etc.). Sources: Thomasson, M.A. (n.d.) Health insurance in the United States. *Economic History Association*. Retrieved from https://eh.net/encyclopedia/health-insurance-in-the-united-states/; Reed, L. S. (1965, Dec.). Private health insurance in the United States: An overview [PDF document]. SSA Bulletin. Retrieved from https://www.ssa.gov/policy/docs/ssb/v28n12/v28n12p3.pdf; and Cohen, R. A., Makuc, D. M., Bernstein, A. B., Bilheimer, L.T. & Powell-Griner, E. (2009, July 1). Health insurance coverage trends, 1959–2007: Estimates from the National Health Interview Survey [PDF document]. *National Health Statistics Reports, Number 17.* Retrieved from https://www.cdc.gov/nchs/data/nhsr/nhsr017.pdf

Moral Hazard Emerges

As more and more people gained employer-based health insurance coverage, moral hazard became a problem. Moral hazard theory suggests that when people become insured, they are insulated from the true costs of healthcare, causing utilization to grow significantly (more on this later). Moral hazard is similar to having a friend or boss take you to dinner: If someone else is paying the bill, you are inclined to order more food.

In the context of healthcare, moral hazard means that patients with health insurance coverage tend to go to the doctor and use other medical services more frequently than patients without health insurance coverage. This can lead to an overutilization of healthcare services and contributes to the overall costs of healthcare.

The earliest health insurance plans had less risk of moral hazard for two reasons: First, few people had health insurance coverage in the first place. But equally as important was the fact that the first health insurance plans offered very limited benefits. The benefits they did offer were in the form of specified services, rather than cash indemnity.[49] For example, the earliest health insurance plans were modeled on the Baylor plan and focused on inpatient coverage at a mere $0.75 a month for a single person, $1.50 for a couple, and $2.00 for a family.[50] Like the Baylor plan, these plans empowered consumers with an affordable way to fund inpatient hospital care.[51] Elective and primary care, however, were still funded primarily by the patient. This limited the risk of moral hazard, because you cannot over utilize health services that you do not have coverage for in the first place.

With each passing decade, insurance benefits began to cover more services. Most were still focused on "unplanned" or "catastrophic" events rather than preventative services, but the scope increased as advances in medical diagnoses evolved. By 1965, the typical Blue Cross plan covered hospital room and board, nursing, services in the operating room (OR), lab work, imaging, and other basic medical services.[52] By the mid-1960s, most plans also included emergency care. Eventually, maternity care was offered, but there were limits: It wasn't offered until after a waiting period of nine to 10 months and a maximum dollar limit was established.[53] Some plans had provisions for pre-existing conditions, while other plans excluded them.[54] Supplementary "major medical" policies were offered that provided benefits beyond the basic Blue Cross and Blue Shield policies, including private duty and visiting nurse services and nursing home care, on a deductible/coinsurance basis.[55]

Today's health insurance plans, with their long lists of mandated services, bear little resemblance to the original Baylor plan, with its benefit limited to days of care at a single hospital. The bottom line is that more insurance coverage equals increased utilization. Increased utilization means healthcare costs go up. And go up they did.

The Government Steps In

As healthcare costs started rising, the government saw that affordability was in jeopardy. The population impacted most were unemployed or underemployed people who were less likely to have health insurance through employment. Healthcare reform began to focus primarily on these two groups of consumers: the poor and the elderly.

This was not easy. Capitalism's enemy is regulation, and there simply was not much in place to control utilization or cost. Many attempts failed miserably at establishing national health insurance in the United States. The concept of "insurance" for all, whatever the cost, was not popular. This manifested in 1934, when President Franklin D. Roosevelt announced his intention to combat economic insecurity by creating a social security program.[56] The Social Security Act was signed into law on August 14, 1935. At the time, President Roosevelt said:

> We can never insure one hundred percent of the population against one hundred percent of the hazards and vicissitudes of life, but we have tried to frame a law which will give some measure of protection to the average citizen and to his family against the loss of a job and against poverty-ridden old age.[57]

Initially, national health insurance was proposed as part of the Social Security Act. However, the AMA fiercely opposed national health insurance. Supporters of the Social Security Act believed that unless they dropped the provision for health insurance, AMA opposition would kill the entire bill.[58] When the dust settled, the Social Security Act was passed without a health insurance component. Strike one.

In 1945, President Harry Truman pressed Congress for national health insurance. Truman's effort was not successful. Opposition came from the AMA again, which feared that a national health insurance program (a.k.a. "socialized medicine") would increase government control at the expense of physician autonomy. Strike two.

In 1963, the Social Security Administration of the U.S. Department of Health, Education, and Welfare, conducted a "Survey of the Aged." The survey found that "families headed by a person aged 65 or over make up one-third of all families counted as poor."[59] In addition, the survey showed that only half of the elderly had health insurance coverage, and those that had coverage had very poor coverage.[60]

The "Survey of the Aged" focused attention on the plight of the elderly with respect to healthcare access in the early 1960s. After Lyndon B. Johnson became president in 1963, one of his priorities was to address this problem by enacting a national program of health insurance for the elderly, that is, Medicare. When he pressed Congress to pass the Medicare bill, Johnson pointed out, "Our older people are likely to be hospitalized three times as often as younger people, but their income is less than half of that of people under 65."[61]

Once again, the AMA opposed the idea. Dr. Edward Annis, president of the AMA from 1963 to 1964 warned physicians that the proposed legislation would create a "socialist yoke" that would negatively impact healthcare for all Americans.[62] It would not strike out this time, although it only covered the elderly, and still did not address cost.

The original version of the Medicare bill was designed to cover hospitalization only. However, as the bill worked its way through the legislative process, proponents made revisions to ensure its passage. The final version of the bill included the following principles:

- It provided coverage to all people 65 and over regardless of income and health status (note that life expectancy at birth in the United States at that time was around 67 years for men and 73 years for women)[63]

- It prohibited any federal interference in the practice of medicine

- It covered hospital and doctor visits, paying providers for each service given to a patient (a.k.a. the fee-for-service payment model)[64]

Medicare (health insurance for the elderly) and Medicaid (health insurance for the poor) were enacted July 30, 1965. To honor former President Truman's previous attempts to implement national health insurance, President Johnson held the Medicare and Medicaid signing ceremony in Truman's hometown, Independence, Missouri. At the ceremony, President Johnson said, "We wanted you to know, and we wanted the entire world to know, that we haven't forgotten who is the real daddy of Medicare."[65]

The estimated budget for Medicare in 1965 was $10 billion; 19 million people enrolled the first year it was available.[66] As of October 2016, the Centers for Medicare & Medicaid Services (CMS) reported total Medicare enrollment (including the original Medicare plan and Medicare Advantage and related plans) at 57,351,559.[67] As of November 2016, CMS reported total Medicaid and Children's Health Insurance Program (CHIP) enrollment at 74,407,191.[68]

Today the US government, through the Medicare, Medicaid, and other government health programs, is the single largest payer for healthcare services in the United States (figure 1.5).[69] Even more astonishing, perhaps, is that the US government's current level of healthcare spending also makes it the single largest healthcare payer in the world.[70]

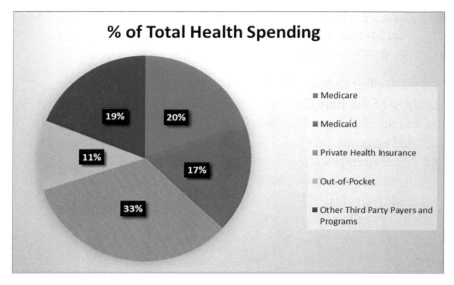

Figure 1.5 Health Spending by Major Source of Funds, 2015. Source: Centers for Medicare & Medicaid Services (CMS). (n.d.). National Health Expenditures 2015 Highlights [PDF document]. Retrieved from https://www.cms.gov/research-statistics-data-and-systems/statistics-trends-and-reports/nationalhealthexpenddata/downloads/highlights.pdf

The First Reimbursement Model: Fee-for-Service

The physician groups who created the first Blue Shield plans were careful to structure their plans to ensure profitability under their discounted fee schedules. Blue Shield plans specified that physicians could charge patients who were Blue Shield subscribers the difference between their actual charges and the Blue Shield reimbursement amount.[71] This early reimbursement methodology—called "cost plus"—still influences insurance reimbursement practices today:

> In this payment scheme, physicians were compensated according to "reasonable and customary charges" that they themselves set, and hospitals were reimbursed on a percentage of their actual costs plus a percentage of their working and equity capital. This allowed doctors to charge whatever they wanted and encouraged hospitals to increase costs so their cost-based income

would be greater. This methodology was replicated by commercial insurers and the subsequent government health insurance programs, Medicare and Medicaid.[72]

In a similar fashion, the earliest hospital expense policies (the beginnings of the Blue Cross plans) used a model that provided "reimbursement of charges for room and board and ancillary services up to specified amounts. Surgical expense policies provided for reimbursement of surgical charges up to a specified allowance for each operation."[73]

These early reimbursement strategies provided the foundation for the fee-for-services (FFS) reimbursement model that dominated US healthcare until the early 1970s. In a fee-for-services model, healthcare providers are reimbursed a fee for each particular service performed. The fee-for-service model has its own version of moral hazard built in, in that it incentivized providers to maximize the volume of services provided to consumers. In other words, during this time, often referred to as the "golden days of healthcare," the fee-for-service model provided little to no incentive for providers to offer preventative care, prevent hospitalizations, or implement other cost-saving measures.[74] It was an unbridled free-for-all; you did it, and you got paid—next patient. Healthcare costs skyrocketed.

HMOs, PPOs, and POSs

The 1950s, 1960s, and early 1970s were the glory days of healthcare reimbursement, as the majority of health insurance plans followed the fee-for-services model. There was a large workforce and the economy was thriving. Most people got health insurance coverage through their employers. This helped "chlorinate" the insurance risk pool, because good health was tied to the ability to hold a job.

Fee schedules and insurance coverage were relatively unregulated. Reimbursement was straightforward: A claim was submitted; insurance paid it; and there was little, if any, regard for utilization or cost. Once again, the affordability of healthcare became an issue. Once again, the government stepped in to provide a solution. Along came managed care, in the form of health maintenance organizations (HMOs). A few HMO plans existed prior to the 1970s, but they were not as common as the fee-for-service models. However, the HMO model got a boost when the Health Maintenance Organization Act was enacted by President Richard M. Nixon in 1973.[75] The purpose of the act was to "stimulate interest by consumers and providers in the HMO concept and to make health care delivery under this form available and accessible in the health care market."[76]

The plan authorized the government to facilitate the creation of HMO plans by committing $375 million dollars over four years (1974–1978) to support the planning, development, capitalization, and evaluation of HMO plans.[77] The act specified that HMO plans must provide certain specified services to enrollees. In addition, the act required employers with 25 or more employees who offered indemnity coverage to also offer federally qualified HMOs to employee groups.

HMOs were viewed as a way to combat escalating healthcare costs through insurance rules, by "managing the care." Instead of using a fee-for-services model, HMOs used a model in which the enrollees (whether individuals or employers) paid a fixed monthly fee for services. The monthly fees remained the same whether the services were provided or not. The HMO model incentivized efficiency, including emphasizing the use of primary care physicians (PCP) as gatekeepers to throttle the provision of services; encouraging preventive care services; and promoting less costly treatments—for example, using outpatient options versus more expensive inpatient options. HMO supporters hoped the new plan model would rein in escalating costs by incentivizing providers to offer *appropriate* services instead of just *more* services.

With the new government incentives in place, HMOs began to grab a larger share of the insurance market. The golden era of HMOs lasted from the early 1970s until the mid-1990s. By 1996, HMOs represented 31 percent of all enrollments for covered employees.[78]

Consumers, however, did not appreciate the lack of choice and troublesome restrictions that came with HMO plans. Americans began to demand health insurance plans that offered more options and fewer controls. As HMOs fell out of favor, preferred provider organizations

(PPOs) and, to a lesser degree, point of service (POS) plans rose to the forefront. These other insurance plan models still managed the care, but the patient could self-direct their care, without first gaining the blessing of a PCP. Patients could go where they pleased, at a higher cost.

The freedom of choice made consumers happier, but PPO and POS insurance plans did little to address increasing healthcare costs. Between 1973 and 1983, premiums rose from $25 billion to $111 billion—a four-fold increase in just 10 years.[79]

Consumer-Directed Health Plans

As costs to provide care continued to climb, employers were seeing double-digit increases in health plan premiums. By 2005, employers had seen six consecutive years in which premium costs rose at more than double the rate of employee earnings.[80] If managed care plans were no longer acceptable to consumers, how could employers control premium costs? Shift the cost to the patient. Put patients in control on the theory that patients will use fewer services if they have to pay for it themselves.

Consumer-directed health plans follow the logic that pushing costs back to consumers will make them more cost-conscious in their healthcare purchases. In an effort to curb premium costs, commercial healthcare benefits were soon structured to include cost-sharing mechanisms to control costs. These came in the form of deductibles, coinsurance, and out-of- pocket maximums, which specifically targeted high-cost interventions. Interventions that were expensive, experimental, or had a long treatment cycle (chronic conditions) were throttled back with these cost-shifting mechanisms.

Consumer-directed health insurance plans have become even more widespread since the passage of the Patient Protection and Affordable Care Act (PPACA, a.k.a. ACA) in 2010.[81] The passage of the ACA represented one of the largest expansions of healthcare since Medicare was enacted. It promised access, coverage, and quality healthcare for all. It also included an individual mandate, which legislated that all people who can afford health insurance (by the government's criteria) but who choose *not* to buy it are subject to a tax penalty.[82]

In order to avoid this penalty, each person in the United States must document they have qualifying health coverage, also known as minimum essential coverage or MEC. Under PPACA, all plans offered in the health insurance marketplace (health insurance exchanges) and employer-based plans are required to meet the MEC criteria. These "essential health benefits" included the typical mandated benefits package seen in most state health plans including basic inpatient and outpatient care, diagnostic testing, emergency care, prescription drugs, rehabilitation, and even preventative services.[83] It certainly reduced the uninsured rate and made healthcare more available, but alas, it has done little to address escalating healthcare costs.

As many observers have noted, "While the Affordable Care Act (ACA) has made health insurance more affordable for the uninsured, premiums and cost-sharing are still too high for many Americans. And cost-sharing has been edging ever higher for the majority of Americans who have coverage through employer-based plans."[84]

The consumer-directed health plan model is contributing to the affordability problem. As of this writing, the most widely adopted version of the consumer-directed health plan is the high-deductible health plan (HDHP) combined with an HSA. A high-deductible health plan is simply a health insurance plan with a deductible amount that is higher than a traditional health insurance plan. The HSA is designed to help the consumer plan for and pay for those high deductibles. The premiums for consumer-directed health plans are generally lower than premiums for traditional health insurance plans, making them an especially attractive option for employers.

Both HDHPs and their associated HSAs are highly regulated and must meet specific government definitions to meet ACA criteria as qualified plans. For 2017, the minimum deductible for HDHPs is $1,300 for self-only coverage and $2,600 for family coverage. The out-of-pocket maximum for HSA-qualified plans is $6,550 for individuals and $13,100 for families.[85] Proponents say shifting costs to the consumer with HDHPs will incentivize consumers to make more prudent healthcare choices. Critics say the deductibles in HDHPs are unrealistically high, and will force consumers to forego needed care.

There is no doubt that HDHPs are becoming an increasingly popular option. The Henry J. Kaiser Family Foundation (KFF) conducts an annual "Employer Health Benefits Survey."[86] The 2016 survey results show that the share of covered workers enrolled in HDHP plans with savings options (HDHP/SO) has grown from 4 percent to 29 percent in the last 10 years (figure 1.6). The report also outlines that over half of employers (51 percent) are offering an HDHP. KFF also shared that in 2016, an overwhelming majority (83 percent) of workers now have a deductible, up from 55 percent in 2006.

Distribution of Health Plan Enrollment for Covered Workers, by Plan Type, 1988-2015

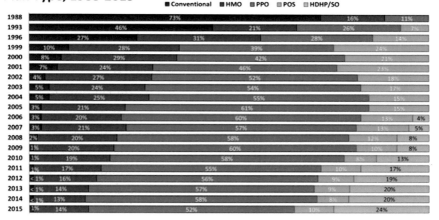

Note: Information was not obtained for POS plans in 1988. A portion of the change in plan type enrollment for 2005 is likely attributable to incorporating more recent Census Bureau estimates of the number of state and local government workers and removing federal workers from the weights. See the Survey Design and Methods section from the 2005 Kaiser/HRET Survey of Employer-Sponsored Health Benefits for additional information.

Figure 1.6 Distribution of Health Plan Enrollment for Covered Workers, by Plan Type, 1988–2016. Source: The Henry J. Kaiser Family Foundation. (2015). 2015 Employer health benefits survey, Exhibit 5.1, Distribution of health plan enrollment for covered workers, by plan type, 1988-2015 [PNG file]. Retrieved from http://kff.org/report-section/ehbs-2015-section-five-market-shares-of-health-plans/

The Age of Entitlement

In the beginning—before health insurance—there was just the patient and the physician. As healthcare became professionalized with the formation of the American Medical Association, the creation of the American Hospital Association, and the development of a credentialing process for physicians, it began to cost more. Healthcare got more organized, and it also got a lot more expensive. In addition, technology, pharmaceuticals, unnecessary procedures, incentives for volume versus outcome, administration expenses, unhealthy behaviors, and decreased competition due to consolidation have all added to the significant increase in cost.[87] These increases in cost created significant gaps in affordability. Affordability gaps brought forth a need to have more innovative reimbursement mechanisms from insurance.

As the US economy cycled through periods of prosperity and deficit, politically enhanced solutions came into play: Medicare to provide for the elderly; Medicaid to provide for the poor; HMOs to control costs when healthcare costs are too high; the passage of the PPACA to keep everyone in line; and today, the proliferation of HDHPs to shift the costs to the consumer in another attempt to exert downward pressure on rising healthcare costs.

We've progressed from a time when no one had health insurance to a generation in which the majority of the population has "always" had health insurance. US census data shows that for people under age 65, the percent of the population with *no* health insurance has remained below 19 percent since at least 1984.[88] That means the vast majority (81 percent, give or take) of the population under age 65 has learned to expect health insurance coverage as a given.

Furthermore, we expect that health insurance to be comprehensive. Our definition of what health insurance should include has changed. In the beginning, health insurance was designed to address unplanned or catastrophic events. Along the way, in a well-meaning attempt to control costs by heading off health problems early, a whole menu of preventive services was added as well.

As Americans, we expect the best. Merely having catastrophic coverage is no longer sufficient. We want health insurance coverage; we want it to be affordable; we want to have choices (no more managed care, thank you very much); and we want it to pay for the things we want it to pay for, regardless of the cost (hello, Viagra!).

In spite of all the regulations, policies, reimbursement models, and attempts at price controls that we have thrown at healthcare, costs continue to rise at an unsustainable rate. If we are spending all that money on healthcare, shouldn't we at least be healthier?

Unfortunately, the opposite is true. In the United States today, chronic diseases and conditions—including hypertension, heart disease, type 2 diabetes, and obesity—are among the most costly and common health problems.[89] Is it possible there is another aspect to rising healthcare costs that America hasn't really addressed yet? Maybe it is not actually possible to "have your cake and eat it too." More on that in Chapter 2 …

CHAPTER 2

....

AN EXPENSIVE, UNHEALTHY NATION

So how much does the United States spend on healthcare? Too much. According to the Centers for Medicare & Medicaid Services (CMS), US healthcare spending reached $3.2 trillion in 2015. That equals 17.8 percent of the US Gross Domestic Product (GDP), and works out to $9,990 per person.[90] CMS expects healthcare spending to grow 1.2 percentage points faster per year than the GDP over the next 10 years, resulting in healthcare's share of the GDP rising to 19.9 percent by 2025.[91]

Where does all of that money go? Most goes toward the typical services you would expect: Hospital care and physician and clinical services accounted for 52 percent, or $1.7 trillion of the total (figure 2.1),[92] and prescription drugs accounted for 10 percent, or about $320 billion. It is interesting to note that prescription drug spending increased by 12.4 percent in 2014 and by 9 percent in 2015, compared to a 5.8 percent increase for healthcare spending overall in 2015.[93] If you can take a pill and make it better, that seems to be the intervention of choice these days, and spending on prescription drugs reflects that.

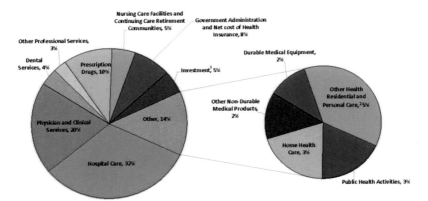

THE NATION'S HEALTH DOLLAR ($3.2 TRILLION), CALENDAR YEAR 2015, WHERE IT WENT

[1] Includes Noncommercial Research (2%) and Structures and Equipment (3%).
[2] Includes expenditures for residential care facilities, ambulance providers, medical care delivered in non-traditional settings (such as community centers, senior citizens centers, schools, and military field stations), and expenditures for Home and Community Waiver programs under Medicaid.
Note: Sum of pieces may not equal 100% due to rounding.
SOURCE: Centers for Medicare & Medicaid Services, Office of the Actuary, National Health Statistics Group.

Figure 2.1 The Nation's Health Dollar, Where it Went (2015). Source: Centers for Medicare & Medicaid Services (CMS). (n.d.). The nation's health dollar ($3.2 trillion), calendar year 2015: where it came from [PDF document]. Retrieved from https://www.cms.gov/Research-Statistics-Data-and-Systems/Statistics-Trends-and-Reports/NationalHealthExpendData/Downloads/PieChartSourcesExpenditures2015.pdf

Of course, not all healthcare spending is distributed equally. We did not each spend exactly $9,990 on healthcare in 2015. Some of us spent more than others—a lot more. In fact, healthcare spending parallels the Pareto principle (also known as the 80/20 rule), which states that 80 percent of effects come from 20 percent of causes. It turns out that is true in healthcare spending, too.

The Kaiser Family Foundation (KFF) used data from the US Department of Health and Human Services (HHS) to calculate how healthcare spending is concentrated in the US population (figure 2.2).[94] The most recent available statistics (2010) show that 1 percent of the total population was responsible for 21 percent of total healthcare spending. A mere 5 percent of the total population was responsible for nearly half (49.5 percent) of all healthcare spending. As you move across the chart, you find that Pareto was correct. Twenty percent of the population was responsible for 81.7 percent of all healthcare spending in 2010. What if the healthcare of that 5 to 20 percent of the population was managed effectively to maximize outcomes and minimize cost? I would buy that for a dollar!

Concentration of Health Care Spending in the U.S. Population, 2010

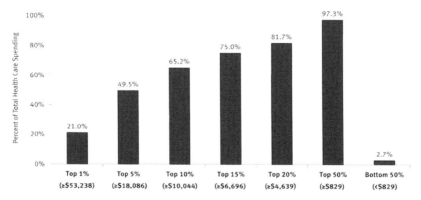

Figure 2.2 Concentration of Health Care Spending in the US Population, 2010. Source: The Henry J. Kaiser Family Foundation. (2013, March 13). Concentration of health care spending in the U.S. population, 2010 [PowerPoint slide]. Retrieved from http://kff.org/health-costs/slide/concentration-of-health-care-spending-in-the-u-s-population-2010/

It is not hard to guess which populations generate the most health expenditures. Not surprisingly, the elderly spend considerably more on healthcare than young people. With the exception of the very young (for example, newborns with serious issues), the older a person gets, the more healthcare services they consume (figure 2.3).[95]

Distribution of Average Spending Per Person, 2009

	Average Spending Per Person
Age (in years)	
<5	$2,468
5-17	1,695
18-24	1,834
25-44	2,739
45-64	5,511
65 or Older	9,744
Sex	
Male	$3,559
Female	4,635

Note: Population is the civilian noninstitutionalized population, including those without any health care spending. Health care spending is total payments from all sources (including direct payments from individuals and families, private insurance, Medicare, Medicaid, and miscellaneous other sources) to hospitals, physicians, other providers (including dental care), and pharmacies; health insurance premiums are not included.

Source: Kaiser Family Foundation calculations using data from U.S. Department of Health and Human Services, Agency for Healthcare Research and Quality, Medical Expenditure Panel Survey (MEPS), 2009.

Figure 2.3 Distribution of Average Spending per Person. Source: The Henry J. Kaiser Family Foundation. (2012, May 1). Health care costs: A primer, Figure 6. Distribution of Averages Spending per Person, 2009. Retrieved from http://kff.org/report-section/health-care-costs-a-primer-2012-report/

The fact that aging and increased health spending go hand-in-hand has an upside and a downside. On the upside, Americans are living longer than they used to. Remember Chapter 1? In 1965, when Medicare was established to provide healthcare for people age 65 and older, life expectancy at birth in the United States was around 67 years for men and 73 years for women.[96] As of 2014, US life expectancy at birth had increased to 76 years for men and 81 years for women.[97] Americans are sticking around longer, and this aging of the population has implications for healthcare costs.

The so-called "silver tsunami" in America is driven by several factors, including the aging of the Baby Boomers and Americans' longer life spans. But note that a longer life does not always mean a healthier life.

Complex health interventions and advancements in technology, treatments, and medication protocols have extended life, but also exponentially inflated costs. The US Administration on Aging (AoA) notes that in 2014, people 65 years or older numbered 46.2 million and represented 14.5 percent of the US population, or about one in every seven Americans.[98] By 2060, it is estimated that the size of this population will have increased to 98 million, representing 21.7 percent of the population, or about one in every five Americans.[99]

If you are one of those "older" Americans enjoying good health in your old age, this might be good news. But if you are concerned about healthcare costs in the United States, the news is not so good. The downside of longer life spans and the silver tsunami is that there is currently no way to fund it, other than our own government. Medicare is the second-largest federal program in terms of mandatory spending after Social Security (figure 2.4).[100] Medicare spending, at $646.2 billion, represented 20 percent of total national health expenditures in 2015 (Chapter 1, figure 1.5).[101] The Congressional Budget Office (CBO) expects this number to hit $1.4 trillion by 2027.[102] That is the equivalent of spending $3.8 billion *per day* on Medicare costs alone by 2027.

That is a lot of money, and that figure does not include government spending on other healthcare programs, like Medicaid, government-mandated health insurance subsidies, grants or tax credits, and Children's Health Insurance Program (CHIP) expenditures. When you add the spend from these other programs, US spending on major healthcare programs is expected to reach $2.1 trillion, or $5.7 billion *per day*, by 2027.[103] I cannot even wrap my head around how much money that is, per day.

Total Mandatory Spending 2015: $2.45 Trillion

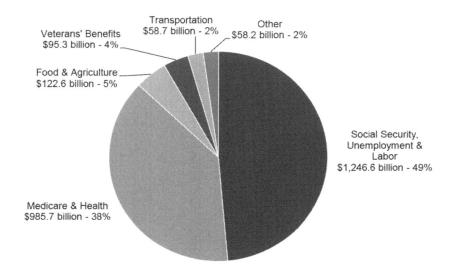

Figure 2.4 Total US Mandatory Spending, 2015. Source: National Priorities Project. (n.d.). Federal spending: where does the money go. Retrieved from https://www.nationalpriorities.org/budget-basics/federal-budget-101/spending/

Are We Any Healthier?

One of my favorite sayings is, "Follow the money." So, with all of this money being spent on healthcare, let us follow it. What *is* our ROI? In other words, what *is* the return we are getting on our investment in healthcare? Are we healthier than countries that do not spend as much as we do? Unfortunately, the data shows the United States is one of the unhealthiest industrialized nations.

The Commonwealth Fund used health data from the Organization for Economic Cooperation and Development (OECD) and other sources to conduct a cross-national analysis of healthcare spending among 13 high-income countries: Australia, Canada, Denmark, France, Germany, Japan, Netherlands, New Zealand, Norway, Sweden, Switzerland, the

United Kingdom, and the United States. A review of healthcare spending as a percentage of GDP showed the United States spent more than any of the comparison countries (figure 2.5).[104]

Health Care Spending as a Percentage of GDP, 1980–2013

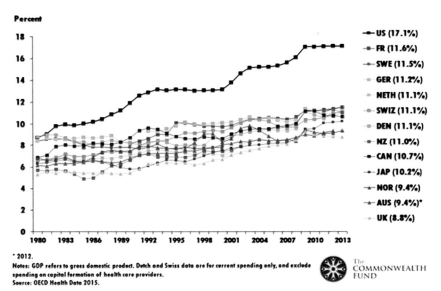

Figure 2.5 Health Care Spending as a Percent of GDP, 1980–2013. Source:
D. Squires, D., Anderson, C. & The Commonwealth Fund. (2015, October).
U.S. health care from a global perspective: Spending, use of services, prices, and health in 13 countries, Exhibit 1. Health care spending as a percent of GDP, 1980 – 2013. Retrieved from http://www.commonwealthfund.org/publications/issue-briefs/2015/oct/us-health-care-from-a-global-perspective

This depressing fact points out that for all our spending on healthcare, we are not achieving better health outcomes than those other countries. The Commonwealth Fund report notes that although both public and private spending on healthcare is higher in the United States than in the comparison countries, Americans faired more poorly on a number of population health indicators than the comparison countries (figure 2.6).[105] There is no doubt that over the last century the United States has made significant clinical and technological achievements in healthcare.

What this data says is, "so did everyone else"—compared to other industrialized nations, the United States ranks dead last, and the cost of delivery for that care is much, much more. That is a lot of money for poor performance.

Select Population Health Outcomes and Risk Factors

	Life exp. at birth, 2013[a]	Infant mortality, per 1,000 live births, 2013[a]	Percent of pop. age 65+ with two or more chronic conditions, 2014[b]	Obesity rate (BMI>30), 2013[a,c]	Percent of pop. (age 15+) who are daily smokers, 2013[a]	Percent of pop. age 65+
Australia	82.2	3.6	54	28.3[e]	12.8	14.4
Canada	81.5[e]	4.8[e]	56	25.8	14.9	15.2
Denmark	80.4	3.5	—	14.2	17.0	17.8
France	82.3	3.6	43	14.5[d]	24.1[d]	17.7
Germany	80.9	3.3	49	23.6	20.9	21.1
Japan	83.4	2.1	—	3.7	19.3	25.1
Netherlands	81.4	3.8	46	11.8	18.5	16.8
New Zealand	81.4	5.2[e]	37	30.6	15.5	14.2
Norway	81.8	2.4	43	10.0[d]	15.0	15.6
Sweden	82.0	2.7	42	11.7	10.7	19.0
Switzerland	82.9	3.9	44	10.3[d]	20.4[d]	17.3
United Kingdom	81.1	3.8	33	24.9	20.0[d]	17.1
United States	78.8	6.1[e]	68	35.3[d]	13.7	14.1
OECD median	81.2	3.5	—	28.3	18.9	17.0

[a] Source: OECD Health Data 2015.
[b] Includes: hypertension or high blood pressure, heart disease, diabetes, lung problems, mental health problems, cancer, and joint pain/arthritis. Source: Commonwealth Fund International Health Policy Survey of Older Adults, 2014.
[c] DEN, FR, NETH, NOR, SWE, and SWIZ based on self-reported data; all other countries based on measured data.
[d] 2012. [e] 2011.

 The COMMONWEALTH FUND

Figure 2.6 Select Population Health Outcomes and Risk Factors. Squires, D., Anderson, C. & The Commonwealth Fund. (2015, October). U.S. health care from a global perspective: Spending, use of services, prices, and health in 13 countries, Exhibit 1. Health care spending as a percent of GDP, 1980 – 2013. Retrieved from http://www.commonwealthfund.org/publications/issue-briefs/2015/oct/us-health-care-from-a-global-perspective

The OECD data shows that Americans' life spans are shorter; the United States has a significantly higher infant mortality rate; and the prevalence of chronic disease and obesity is higher in the United States than in any of the other high-income countries studied.[106] That does *not* make for good dinner conversation.

How Sick Are We?

This next part is going to be a little depressing, so find some sunshine before you read it. According to the Centers for Disease Control and Prevention (CDC), there were 2,626,418 deaths in America in 2014.[107] The vast majority of those deaths (74 percent) were attributable to one of 10 causes, with the top two being heart disease and cancer (figure 2.7).[108]

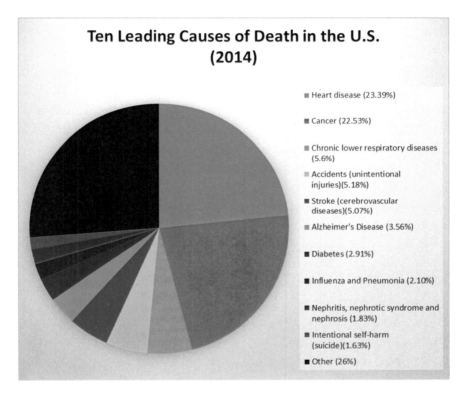

Figure 2.7 Ten Leading Causes of Death in the United States, 2014. Source: Centers for Disease Control and Prevention (CDC). (n.d.). Deaths and mortality, 2014 data. Retrieved from https://www.cdc.gov/nchs/fastats/deaths.htm

That said, mortality rates are not always the best indicator, because they mask the fact that Americans are living *longer*, but not necessarily *healthier* lives. America's afflictions have evolved over time. Prior to World War II, the focus of most US healthcare spending was acute events, trauma, and infections affecting individuals. The type of work employees did was more dangerous, and the spread of infection and disease was more prevalent in the absence of standardized vaccinations. In the last 50 years, however, a new enemy has emerged: chronic disease.[109] Chronic diseases are diseases or conditions characterized by prolonged illness, typically lasting more than three months. They do not resolve themselves in the short term and persist over time. According to the CDC, chronic diseases and conditions are "the most common, costly and preventable of all health problems."[110]

Chronic diseases include heart disease, hypertension, stroke, cancer, diabetes, obesity, and pulmonary and mental conditions. Data shows that about half the adults in the United States have at least one chronic health condition, and one in four have two or more chronic health conditions.[111] The CDC estimates that chronic disease accounts for 86 percent of all US healthcare costs.[112] The data is shocking, to say the least. This makes for fantastic dinner conversation about reasons why healthcare costs are so high in the United States.

Not surprisingly, chronic disease is also closely linked to poor lifestyle choices. America is the land of choice. We are a "have it your way" society, and we have created a retail culture where you can get most of the things you want relatively easily, whether it is healthy or not. Our "play now, pay later" culture has contributed to a perfect storm of chronic health conditions. As we go through the costs of these conditions, remember the importance of these numbers and think: How much is spent to treat these chronic conditions? Is it enough, too little, or too much? It is important to keep the prevalence and cost in mind. It is equally important to ponder incidence and cause. Some of these conditions are significantly impacted by the day-to-day lifestyle choices we make. Others are inflicted by factors beyond our control. Nonetheless, we can all agree that these chronic conditions and consumer behaviors certainly drive the majority of healthcare costs.

Chronic Conditions and Risky Behaviors

Obesity

Take a look around you and guess what the most prevalent chronic condition in the United States is: It is obesity. To put it bluntly, too many of us are overweight or obese. The most recent CDC statistics indicate that nearly 70 percent of US adults are overweight; and one-third (36.5 percent) of US adults are overweight enough to be classified as obese.[113, 114] Compare that to 1985, when not a single state in the United States had an obesity rate higher than 15 percent.[115] Sadly, the obesity rate for children and youth (ages 2–19 years) has increased at an alarming rate as well. Since 1980, childhood obesity has tripled, and now stands at 17 percent.[116]

Obesity is a multifaceted problem. It is a contributing risk factor for many chronic conditions, including several types of cancer, heart disease, hypertension, and type 2 diabetes.[117] Obesity's connection with other chronic diseases also makes it a very expensive condition. Individuals who are obese incur significantly higher medical costs than those who are of normal weight.[118] It has been estimated that obesity alone contributes as much as $210 billion dollars annually to healthcare costs.[119] That's *billion*, with a capital B in spend, on one in three adults, or 90 million adult Americans. Doing some quick math, taking dollar for dollar, that represents an additional spend of over $2,000 per obese adult annually.

What is concerning is that a large proportion of obesity costs are *preventable* and stem from personal choices. The primary causes of obesity are a lack of physical activity and poor eating habits. Recent studies have also pointed to lack of sleep as a contributing factor to obesity.[120] It sounds so easy. Reversing the obesity problem should be as simple as putting down that cheeseburger, taking a walk, and getting more sleep, right? I wish it were that simple. But we are not even through the list of chronic conditions yet.

Hypertension (a.k.a. high blood pressure)

The CDC's most recent estimates indicate one in three (33.5 percent) Americans age 20 and over have high blood pressure.[121] Even asymptomatic high blood pressure can cause long-term damage to blood vessels and the heart, leading to an increased risk of heart attack or stroke. High blood pressure is estimated to cost the United States $46 billion each year, including the cost of healthcare services, medication, and missed work.[122] That is another billion with a capital B.

Many adults develop high blood pressure as they age, sometimes with no identifiable cause. Other conditions, such as kidney disease or diabetes, can also contribute to high blood pressure. High blood pressure is kind of the poster child for lifestyle diseases, as many types of poor health choices can increase a person's risk of developing it, including eating too much, not exercising enough, smoking, consuming too much salt, drinking too much alcohol, and not managing stress. That last one is tricky, since many of us eat too much, smoke, and drink in an attempt to deal with stress. Turns out it is a vicious cycle: We make choices that compromise our health, and in turn, the consequences of compromised health stress us out even more.

Heart Disease

Heart disease includes many different types of heart conditions, such as coronary artery disease, an enlarged heart, arrhythmias, and pericarditis. Heart disease is the leading cause of death for men and women in the United States (figure 2.7).[123] Nearly one in four deaths each year is attributable to heart disease.[124] In 2015, US life expectancy actually dropped slightly from 78.9 years to 78.8 years, and one of the contributing factors was an uptick in mortality due to heart disease.[125]

Many different factors can cause heart disease, including congenital defects and infections caused by bacteria or viruses. Like obesity, lifestyle factors also play a significant role. Three key risk factors for heart disease are high blood pressure, high cholesterol, and smoking. About half of American adults (49 percent) have at least one of these risk factors.[126] Other risk factors include diabetes, obesity, poor eating habits, physical inactivity, alcohol abuse, excessive use of caffeine, and unrelieved stress. See the pattern?

Heart disease provides yet another example of how increased healthcare costs are often associated with lifestyle choices. Heart disease represents an estimated cost to the United States of approximately $207 billion each year, including healthcare services, medication, and lost productivity.[127] (That's the third billion with a capital "B," for those counting.) In a recent article published in the *Journal of the American Medical Association (JAMA)*, the authors studied 150 different health conditions and isolated the health spend associated with each condition. One particular type of heart disease—ischemic heart disease (also known as coronary artery disease)—came in second (after diabetes) in terms of disease-related healthcare spending.[128] The authors estimated that ischemic heart disease alone accounted for $88.1 billion in spending in 2013.[129] There's one of those Bs again.

Diabetes

Diabetes refers to a group of conditions that impair the body's ability to produce or use insulin, resulting in increased blood sugar (glucose). Diabetes can lead to a number of additional health problems, including increased risk of heart attack, increased risk of stroke, blindness and eye problems, lower limb amputations, and kidney disease including kidney failure.[130]

Diabetic conditions include prediabetes, type 1 diabetes, and type 2 diabetes. Type 1 is more frequently diagnosed in children.[131] Type 2 is the most common form of diabetes and is usually diagnosed after age 35.[132] The causes of type 1 diabetes are not well understood, although a disorder of the immune system is known to play a role. The causes of type 2 diabetes are not well understood either, however studies show that "being overweight is strongly linked to the development of type 2 diabetes."[133] Risk factors related to diabetes vary by the type of diabetic condition, but among the risk factors for prediabetes and type 2 diabetes are weight, lack of physical activity, high blood pressure, and abnormal cholesterol and triglyceride levels.[134]

The prevalence of diabetes varies by age, with a higher incidence in the elderly than in young adults (figure 2.8).[135] That means that the silver tsunami will likely lead to a higher number of Americans with diabetes. Indeed, the prevalence of diabetes has been increasing in the overall US population and in all subgroups (gender, ethnicity, age, education level, and socioeconomic level) over the past several decades.[136] It is the gift that keeps on giving.

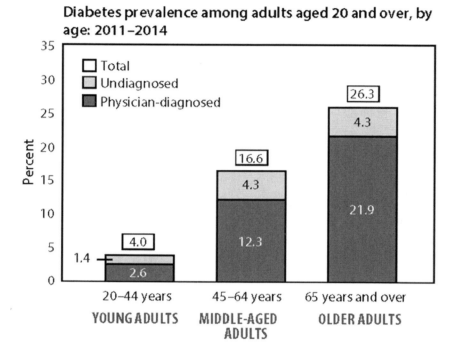

Figure 2.8 Diabetes Prevalence Among Adults Aged 20 and Over, by Age: 2011–2014. Source: Centers for Disease Control and Prevention (CDC). (2016). Health, United States Spotlight, Health Status and Determinants, Spring 2016 [PDF document]. Retrieved from https://www.cdc.gov/nchs/data/hus/hus_spotlight_spring16.pdf

To make matters worse, diabetes is a very expensive disease to treat. In the aforementioned *JAMA* article, diabetes was identified as generating the highest healthcare costs out of all 155 disease categories studied.[137] The authors estimate that diabetes was responsible for $101.4 billion in healthcare spending in 2013.[138] Of that, 57.6 percent was spent on pharmaceuticals and 23.5 percent was spent on ambulatory care.[139] Furthermore, in the past 18 years, spending on diabetes increased at a very fast rate—by an estimated $64.4 billion—second only to spending on low back and neck pain.[140] Alas, two more Bs.

Diabetes is also the most common cause of end-stage renal disease (ESRD), or kidney failure.[141] (High blood pressure is the second most common cause).[142] When ESRD occurs, a person has only two options left: dialysis or a kidney transplant. Both of these options are very complex and very expensive.

What you may or may not know is that ESRD is covered by Medicare, even for people who are under age 65. The Social Security Act of 1972 modified Medicare to include coverage for people with ESRD who were under 65 years old and had worked enough quarters to qualify for Social Security.[143] At that time, only about 10,000 people were receiving dialysis.[144] By 2014, that population had increased to 399,455. Even though ESRD patients represent less than 1 percent of the total Medicare population, they represent 7 percent of Medicare fee-for-service spending at $30.9 billion.[145, 146] That is yet another B.

Alcohol Abuse

Alcohol abuse makes our list because excessive drinking is associated with a long list of chronic health conditions, including: cirrhosis of the liver; high blood pressure; heart disease; diabetes; and increased risk of mouth, throat, liver, colon, and breast cancer.[147] According to the CDC, 23.4 percent of adults over 18 years of age have had at least one heavy drinking day (five or more drinks for men; four or more drinks for women) in the past year.[148] The rate for men has hovered around 30 percent since about 1997; however, the rate for women has increased significantly over that same time period, from 12.1 percent in 1997 to 17.4 percent in 2015.[149]

The CDC estimates that the cost of excessive alcohol use in the United States reached $249 billion in 2010, or the equivalent of $2.05 per drink.[150] Ever wonder why it costs so much to buy a drink in a restaurant or bar? (Just kidding, although there is another one of those pesky

Bs again). The calculation actually comes from estimated losses from workplace productivity (72 percent of the total cost); healthcare expenses for problems caused by excessive drinking (11 percent); criminal justice expenses (10 percent) and costs related to motor vehicle crashes (5 percent).[151]

Smoking

Cigarette smoking is the leading preventable cause of death in the United States.[152] Smoking is a risk factor for many different kinds of cancer, including cancers of the head and neck, lung, stomach, kidney, pancreas, colon, bladder and cervix, and blood cells (leukemia). Smoking is also a risk factor for many chronic diseases, including stroke, heart disease, hardening of the arteries, and chronic lung disease and asthma.[153]

Because of smoking's association with death from cancer, respiratory disease, and vascular disease, the life expectancy for smokers is about 10 years shorter than it is for nonsmokers.[154] It has been estimated that smoking accounts for almost $170 billion annually in medical care.[155] That is yet another B, although somewhat smaller when compared to the other conditions we talked about. One can infer this is likely due to the 10 less years of life (and healthcare delivery) caused by taking up smoking.

In spite of these grim statistics, smoking may be the one bright spot in our chronic disease story. The CDC's latest statistics indicate that only 15.1 percent of US adults age 18 and older still smoke cigarettes.[156] This represents a significant decline over the past 20 years; in 1997, 24.7 percent of adults smoked cigarettes (figure 2.9).[157]

Prevalence of current cigarette smoking among adults aged 18 and over: United States, 1997-2015

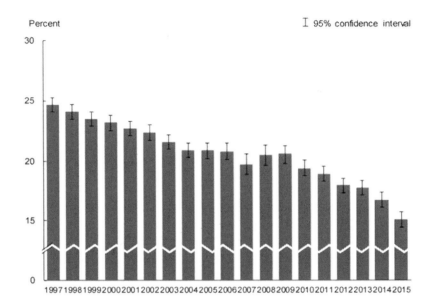

NOTES: Data are based on household interviews of a sample of the civilian noninstitutionalized popula-tion. Current cigarette smokers were defined as those who had smoked more than 100 cigarettes in their lifetime and now smoke every day or some days. The analyses exclude persons with unknown cigarette smoking status (about 2% of respondents each year). See Technical Notes for more details.
DATA SOURCE: NCHS, National Health Interview Survey, 1997-2015, Sample Adult Core component.

Figure 2.9 Cigarette Smoking Trends in the United States, 1997–2015.
Source: Centers for Disease Control and Prevention (CDC). National
Center for Health Statistics (NCHS). (2016, May). Early release of selected
estimates based on data from the 2015 National Health Interview
Survey, Figure 8.1. Prevalence of current smoking among adults aged
18 and over: United States, 1997-2015 [PDF document]. Retrieved from
https://www.cdc.gov/nchs/nhis/releases/released201605.htm#8

The price of cigarettes has increased due to an increase in "sin taxes," the practice of taxing products that are considered harmful. But it is not only the cigarettes that are expensive; these days smokers' insurance premiums tend to be more expensive as well. When the ACA was enacted, it prevented insurers from using health, medical history, or gender to differentiate health insurance premiums. However, it did allow insurance companies to charge tobacco users up to 50 percent more than people who do not use tobacco.[158] This practice is called "tobacco rating."

Smoking and alcohol abuse are both examples of behaviors that directly cause illness and disease. When patients do not follow treatment protocols, including prescribed medication regimens, it can also cause illness and disease. Read on …

Medication Nonadherence

Medication nonadherence is not a chronic condition, but it is a consumer behavior that contributes to healthcare costs. A lot of Americans are on a prescription of some sort. According to the CDC, 48.7 percent of the population has used at least one prescription drug in the past 30 days; 21.8 percent have used three or more prescription drugs in the past 30 days; and 10.7 percent have used five or more prescription drugs in the past 30 days.[159] A study by the Mayo Clinic estimated that almost 70 percent of Americans take at least one prescription medication, and more than 50 percent take at least two.[160]

Many of us have been prescribed drugs, but we struggle to make it a habit to follow our doctors' orders. That can make us even sicker. Studies show that patients who have been prescribed medications—for example, statins for high cholesterol—but who do not take those medications according to directions (or do not take them at all) can wind up with poor health outcomes. It is a choice that can lead to increased utilization of health services, like going to the emergency room (ER) to address an acute or emergent condition due to not self-administering the meds (figure 2.10).

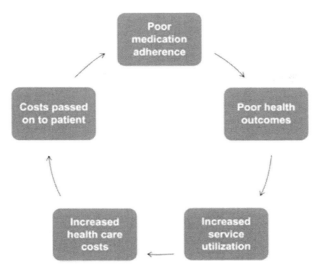

Conceptual diagram displaying a mechanism that may contribute to the maintenance of the medication nonadherence problem within the US health care system.

Figure 2.10 Medication Nonadherence Cycle. Source: Iuga, A. O., & McGuire, M. J. (2014). Adherence and health care costs. Risk Management and Healthcare Policy, 7, 35–44. doi: http://doi.org/10.2147/RMHP.S19801

Medication nonadherence varies by disease, patient characteristics, and insurance coverage, and leads to significantly increased out-of-pocket costs.[161] Medication nonadherence is also associated with poor outcomes for chronic conditions such as cardiovascular disease and diabetes, as well as other conditions and illnesses.[162] It has been estimated that between $100 billion and $300 billion in annual healthcare costs can be attributed to medication nonadherence.[163] A behavior that we all struggle with—following the doctors' orders—leads to yet another "B" in healthcare costs.

Consumer-Directed Illness

In Chapter 1, we talked about consumer-directed healthcare plans. What about consumer-directed illness? We talked about the difference between diseases and conditions that are inflicted by factors beyond the individual's control and those that are directly related to our day-to-day lifestyle choices. In this section, we're going to get real and talk about how these choices can have a direct, detrimental impact on healthcare costs.

Many of the chronic conditions affecting Americans (and contributing to escalating healthcare costs) are directly associated with lifestyle choices and consumer behavior. It has been estimated that up to 70 percent of healthcare costs can be attributed to consumer behavior, including alcohol abuse, obesity, and smoking.[164] Do not just believe the studies; believe Dr. Mehmet Oz, who said, "The biggest issue in America is that we have made it easy to do the wrong thing and if we don't address it soon, no healthcare plan is going to work."[165] Healthcare insurance is unaffordable because it is attempting to cover an unaffordable product.

Let us put our money—and our food—where our mouth is. What if we all ate properly (put down that cheeseburger!), stopped smoking, stopped drinking alcohol, went to bed early, exercised the prescribed 150 minutes per week, and used meditation instead of margaritas or maple donuts to deal with stress—what impact would that have? Are we willing to make that change?

A group of researchers recently attempted to find out. They quantified exactly what a healthy lifestyle would look like, and then used data from the "National Health and Nutrition Examination Survey" (NHNE) to see how many of us actually adhere to those guidelines.[166] Broadly, the four criteria of a healthy lifestyle included:[167]

- Moderate or vigorous exercise for at least 150 minutes per week

- Healthy eating, as measured by a score in the top 40 percent of the US Department of Agriculture's Healthy Eating Index

- Body fat percentage below 20 percent (for men) or below 30 percent (for women)

- Being a nonsmoker

Based on these guidelines, the study's authors found that only 2.7 percent of study subjects exhibited all four healthy lifestyle behaviors.[168] The flip side is that 97 percent of us prefer couches, watching TV until

2:00 a.m., and beer and half a pizza over exercise, sleep, and a healthy diet. It certainly is easier, but it costs a lot more down the road.

Who, Me? Unhealthy?

An interesting notion about our American culture is that despite all the evidence to the contrary, we think we do not have a problem. I am OK, you are OK, and we are OK. A survey by McKinsey & Company compared people's actual health risk status (based on a health profile and/or BMI) to their *perception* of their health risks. When asked— no surprise—we scored ourselves "awesome." Most people considered themselves far healthier than their actual numbers indicated. In fact, McKinsey reported that "76 percent of the participants with high-risk clinical conditions described themselves as being in excellent, very good or good health" (figure 2.11).[169]

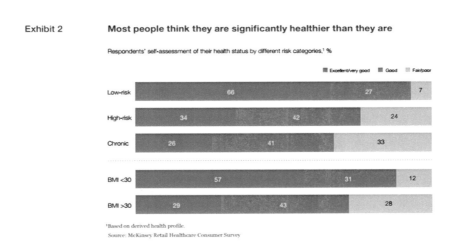

Exhibit 2 — **Most people think they are significantly healthier than they are**

Respondents' self-assessment of their health status by different risk categories.[1] %

Excellent/very good   Good   Fair/poor

	Excellent/very good	Good	Fair/poor
Low-risk	66	27	7
High-risk	34	42	24
Chronic	26	41	33
BMI <30	57	31	12
BMI >30	29	43	28

[1]Based on derived health profile.
Source: McKinsey Retail Healthcare Consumer Survey

Figure 2.11 Most People Think They Are Significantly Healthier Than They Are. Source: Dixon-Fyle, S., Gandhi, S., Pellathy, T., & Spatharou, A. (2012). Changing patient behavior: The next frontier in healthcare value [PDF document]. *Health International*, 64–73. Retrieved from http://healthcare.mckinsey.com/sites/default/files/791750_Changing_Patient_Behavior_the_Next_Frontier_in_Healthcare_Value.pdf

A clearer picture of the problem of increasing healthcare costs is emerging. As we learned in Chapter 1, more health insurance coverage brought increased utilization due to moral hazard. On the consumer side, other than things that happen *to* us (trauma, genetics, accidents, etcetera), we willingly indulge in myriad known unhealthy behaviors that contribute to chronic disease and drive up our healthcare costs. Based on the trends, there seems to be little, if any, motivation to change. In fact, we do not seem to be motivated to even acknowledge the problem. "Isn't there a pill for that?" or "I have insurance; it will cover it" have become our national mantras. The Bs we counted—in billions of dollars of healthcare spend on preventable conditions or choices—will soon be trillions. The staggering cost of this spend has not materially affected the system or consumer behavior, other than inciting some legislative patches of marginal impact and putting hospitals, insurers, and employers in the crossfire. Unless we do something fundamentally different, we are going to end up with a healthcare system that has too much spend and not enough control. (Some would argue we are already there.) This is not sustainable for the long term.

How will this play out in the context of healthcare economics? That is what we will talk about in Chapter 3.

CHAPTER 3

....

HEALTHCARE ECONOMICS

So, here is where we are: Healthcare costs were unbridled, and insurance was introduced to address it. Insurance certainly helped with access, but costs were still not contained. Think of it as a boat with lots of holes—one only has so many fingers and toes. Water came flooding into our healthcare boat, utilization and costs went up, the scope of benefits increased, and utilization went up some more.

With all that flooding of costs—why not add some more water? In the fee-for-service reimbursement model, water comes in the form of more services that a provider offers (whether a physician or a hospital), and the more services insurance (or the government) covers or reimburses. Providers had little, if any, financial incentives to provide outcome-based healthcare services for the patient, and had few restraints on orders for testing, treatments, and visits to a specialist. It was a free-for-all. So we got what we incentivized: more services than we probably needed, higher utilization than necessary, and inflated costs—more water and a higher water bill.

The government has been keeping track of per person (per capita) health expenditures for a long time. In 1960, that figure stood at $146 per person. By 2015, that amount reached $9,990 per person—a 6,742 percent increase over that 55-year period.[170] It is no wonder healthcare costs have increased from 5 percent to almost 18 percent of our GDP! For the sake of comparison, if the price of a dozen eggs had increased at the same rate as healthcare costs, a dozen eggs would now cost more than $55.[171] That may not sound like a fair comparison, but still—would you pay four-and-a-half bucks for an egg? That is breakfast, *not* an egg. Yet we, the government, or your insurance, pays for $55 "healthcare eggs" every day, and so healthcare costs keep accelerating, with no end in sight.

Why Are We in This Mess?

Medicare and Medicaid were established to address the affordability of healthcare for certain populations, specifically the elderly and the poor. There is no doubt that when these programs were enacted in 1965, they reduced out-of-pocket costs for the populations they covered (figure 3.1).

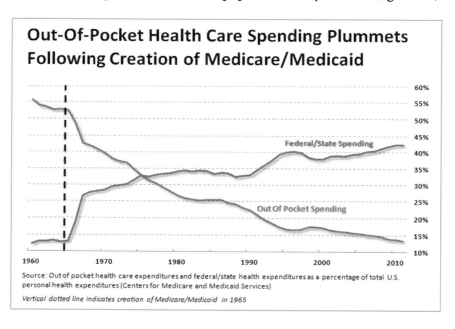

Figure 3.1 Out-of-Pocket Healthcare Spending, as a Percentage of all Healthcare Expenditures, Decreases After Medicare/Medicaid Created. Source: Davis, S. 8 Charts that explain the explosive growth of U.S. health care costs. (2013, Oct. 1). MediaTrackers. Retrieved from http://mediatrackers.org/national/2013/10/01/8-charts-explain-explosive-growth-u-s-health-care-costs

It is a classic case of solving one problem only to create another. As figure 3.1 shows, even as out-of-pocket costs dropped as a percentage of total healthcare costs, the government spend on healthcare increased dramatically. Furthermore, the enactment of Medicare and Medicaid did nothing to control the overall cost of healthcare, which also continued to rise rapidly (figure 3.2).

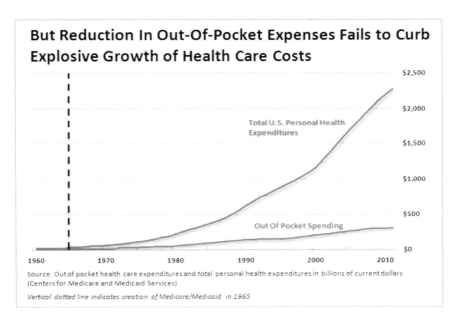

Figure 3.2 Healthcare Costs Continue to Rise. Source: Davis, S. 8 Charts that explain the explosive growth of U.S. health care costs. (2013, Oct. 1). MediaTrackers. Retrieved from http://mediatrackers.org/ national/2013/10/01/8-charts-explain-explosive-growth-u-s-health-care-costs

By decreasing out-of-pocket costs as a percentage of total healthcare costs for the covered populations, the Medicare and Medicaid programs insulated consumers from the true cost of healthcare services. And this population—the elderly and the poor—represents a significant proportion of consumers using healthcare. As of 2015, Medicaid covered 20 percent of the US population (62,384,500 people) and Medicare covered 14 percent of the US population (43,308,400 people).[172] The percent of the population covered by these programs aligns closely with each program's share of total US health expenditures. As noted in Chapter 1 (figure 1.5), in 2015 Medicare accounted for 20 percent of total health spending and Medicaid accounted for 17 percent of total health spending.[173]

The bottom line is that healthcare costs keep rising. Government health insurance programs have not contained rising healthcare costs. This is not new. Healthcare has been very expensive for some time, and as we have seen, costs continue to climb. Some might argue that government health insurance programs actually distorted the free market economy by insulating consumers from true healthcare costs. But as we will soon discover, the laws of supply and demand work backward in healthcare.

Supply and Demand Does Not Apply to Healthcare

In a market economy, the laws of supply and demand are supposed to work together to regulate the price of a service or product. As demand increases, the price goes up. When the price goes up, demand decreases. When demand is down, the price drops back down. Simple, right? Likewise, when supply increases, the price goes down. When the price goes down, demand increases, and the price rises again (figure 3.3). I know, bad flashbacks from accounting and Econ 101 courses, but stick with me. Where supply and demand meet is the sweet spot, where demand is produced to an acceptable market price (otherwise known as the equilibrium price and the equilibrium quantity). At this point—which is represented by the heart of the "X" in figure 3.3—the mar-

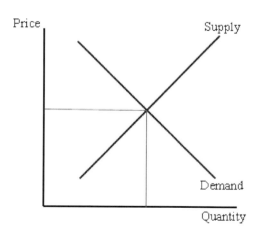

Figure 3.3 Supply and Demand

ket ensures that supply and demand meet in the most efficient way possible.

The laws of supply and demand work nicely for most consumer products. Think flat-screen televisions, for example. Remember when supersized flat-screen televisions first came out? They were expensive—like, "car" expensive. For example, a 2-inch thick TV offered by Sharp or Sony retailed for $15,000 in 1997.[174] At that price, most consumers would say, "I would never pay that much for a television!" Over time, however, prices for all sizes of flat-screen televisions dropped significantly, and now there is one in almost every home.

OK, I completely understand the challenges in comparing the healthcare market to any other market—it is not anywhere near as simple as the television market. Healthcare is not like TVs, and most certainly not like eggs, either. But some of the consumer behaviors associated with these markets are the same. The "I want it, and I want it now persona" is alive and well, with TVs, eggs (fast food breakfasts), and yes—even healthcare. On the demand side, as we have already established, increases in insurance coverage can artificially inflate the demand for services to an inefficient level. Americans want more, they want the best, and they want it right now. And when insurance absorbs much of the cost, price does not slow down consumer demand because the price is not a factor, as it simply is not visible. The current system—with the government, private insurance, and consumers all serving as payers in various scenarios—clouds visibility between cost and demand, creating a very confusing conversation on price, coverage, and cost (figure 3.4). In the model below, households are completely isolated from the fees paid between insurance and providers. Most patients prefer it this way. Patients ask, "What do I owe?" versus "What is the contracted rate between my insurance and you as my provider?" The third-party coverage blinds patients to cost, so there are not traditional supply and demand curves like we see in other markets.

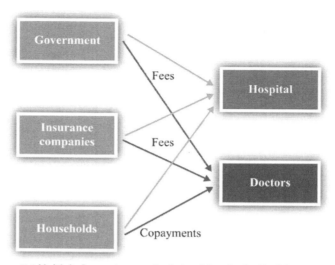

Figure 3.4 Multiple Payers Impact the Role of Cost in the Healthcare Market. Source: Cooper, R. & John, A. (2011). Ch. 15.1 Supply and demand in health-care markets. In *Microeconomics: Theory through applications*. The Saylor Foundation. Retrieved from https://open.umn.edu/opentextbooks/BookDetail.aspx?bookId=28

Confusing? OK, here is a quick example. A patient walks into the physician's office with flu-like symptoms and asks for a prescription of antibiotics. Antibiotics fight *bacterial* infections, not *viral* infections (like the flu), so presumably, they would be ineffective for the most part in this situation. But the patient demands a prescription anyway. She wants to get better now, and she wants a pill to do it. Many patients will gladly spend $10 in copays for physician office visits and prescriptions on a blind path to get rid of their diseases. No patient likes to hear, "There is nothing I can do for you. Drink fluids, get rest, and call me if your symptoms get worse." Don't believe me? Believe this—the Centers for Disease Control and Prevention (CDC) estimates that one-third to one-half of antibiotic use in humans is "either unnecessary or inappropriate."[175] That adds up to 47 million unnecessary antibiotic prescriptions each year.[176] That kind of artificial demand can certainly derail the supply and demand curves.

The Voluntary Marketplace

Another important difference between the market for healthcare and traditional markets is the source of the demand. A pure free market scenario assumes that both buyers and sellers are participating in the market voluntarily. In healthcare, that is rarely the case. For example, outside variables dramatically influence supply and demand for the TV market (a.k.a., "Yikes, the Super Bowl is on Sunday and my TV is not big enough to provide an optimal viewing experience for the two dozen friends I've invited over, so I'm going to grab my credit card and get a bigger TV today!"). Clearly, those decision drivers do not have the same impact or magnitude as drivers in the healthcare market. You may not be able to control the date of the Super Bowl, but the consequences of not having a big enough TV are unfortunate, not life-threatening (e.g., your friends go to somebody else's house on game day).

A cancer diagnosis, on the other hand, is an entirely different ball game. In Chapter 2, we touched on the difference between chronic conditions that develop as a consequence of poor lifestyle choices versus disease or injury conditions that are acquired or inflicted. A person who receives a cancer diagnosis or who develops health problems due a genetic disorder does not participate in the healthcare market voluntarily. They are not in the market for healthcare services by choice. This is where the supply/demand model breaks down. The source of this demand is fear-based, and the patient is intent on physician direction. These patients are scared, and they generally do what their physicians tell them to do. They do not "shop around."

In fact, there are few areas where healthcare services behave according to the classic supply and demand model. One example may be in the area of cosmetic surgery. Interestingly, most elective or cosmetic surgeries are rarely covered by insurance. They are all out of pocket, baby. This includes popular procedures such as liposuction, breast augmentation, and rhinoplasty (new noses). If you are seeking any of these services, your charges are dictated by what the market will bear, without any intervening insurance coverage. According to health.costhelper.com, the average cost for breast augmentation ranges from $4,000 to $10,000, including the cost of implants, the facility fee, an anesthesia fee, and a surgeon's fee.[177] Realself.

com estimates the cost at between $3,525 and $9,200 (that is the range for the United States—you can also compare by state or even country), but notes that prices vary by region.[178]

Not convinced? Check this out: At buildmybod.com you can enter your location and/or procedure of choice and get a customized estimate of your potential costs before you even book an appointment with one of the websites' recommended board-certified plastic surgeons. You can create a personal account on the website and put together a wish list that itemizes the procedures and corresponding prices for everything you want to have done. As of this writing, the home page of the website boasted the combined value of the wish lists of all the folks with buildmybod.com accounts totaled $261,446,916.[179] You can shop body improvements like car parts and pay cash on the barrel. That, my friends, is the free market economy at work. (By the way, I have no financial interest in this stuff—I just find it fascinating.)

Price Transparency and Free Choice

Let me just start by saying I hate the word "transparency." It reminds me of doing presentations in college with that big light bulb thingy and getting mad at the copier when the sheets of transparency film got stuck in there. For those of you who have no idea what I am talking about, put the book down, go watch a show called *M*A*S*H**, and then read on. Transparency in the context of healthcare is even more misunderstood, overused, and ill-defined. It has become a legislative football—which I *love*, by the way. "Hey! We can't figure out all this 'pricing' stuff, let's allow the government to define it, and call it 'transparency.'" I avoid using the word "transparency" whenever possible. I feel the T-word, if you will, inaccurately represents the scenario. I use the words "patient financial engagement" or "educating about the costs of your care," but never the T-word.

However, in talking about a market economy, it is important to note two other concepts that are critical to achieving market efficiency using the supply and demand model we talked about: choice and price, or—gulp—transparency.

Choice is self-explanatory. If you live in an urban area, look around.

There are a *ton* of doctors' offices, imaging centers, pharmacies, hospitals, free-standing emergency departments (EDs), and so on. You want it, you got it—lots of choice, almost like Starbucks. It is everywhere. Why? Because you will go, and you will go often. It is a "build it and they will come" mantra. And you typically go where you are told (by friends or your physician or where you see it—whichever comes first). There is so much supply that we are choking on it. I would bet you a beer that there is a healthcare facility of some sort being built in your town, right now. Now choice in rural healthcare is another thing, and I could write a whole book about that (and telemedicine).

The second concept, price transparency, is where it gets tricky in healthcare. When we talked about supply and demand earlier, we noted that when the supply of goods matches the demand, the equilibrium price is attained. Price transparency allows consumers to shop for the best deal—the highest quality at the lowest price. If the price is known, consumers can shop on decisions and purchase according to their financial position, wants, or needs. Simple, right? Wrong.

Unfortunately, in the US healthcare system there is very little price transparency. In fact, the supply and demand curve for healthcare might be better represented by figure 3.5, where the equilibrium price is … invisible.

Remember the published price list we saw back in Chapter 1? A group of physicians set minimum fees for standard services and then published them for all to see (figure 1.1). It would be hard to find that prevalently in the US healthcare system to-day. Even buildmybod.com, the cosmetic surgery website, does not include a public price list for procedures. You have to establish an account on the buildmybod.com website to access pricing information, and even then, they only post regional averages for each procedure.[180] Same goes for your insurance

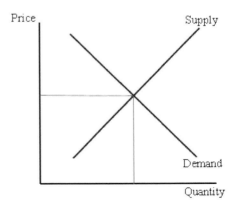

Figure 3.5 Supply and Demand in the US Healthcare System

or hospital portal—which may or may not even have the price once you get there, and if it does, it is probably list price—a meaningless number. What you owe (your cost) is what matters to you, and it is invisible.

Why is that? Why doesn't price transparency exist in the US healthcare market? And if it did, would it drive consumer decisions?

Three Drivers of US Healthcare Economics

The question of price transparency brings us to the topic of blame. Whose fault is it that we cannot see healthcare costs, anyway? Is it because they are not there in the first place? Or is it because we do not want to look? As the affordability of healthcare continues to erode, the fingers of blame have pointed in many different directions. I often hear, "With (insert T-word), we will have consumerism, and that will drive patients to make better decisions." Or, alternately, "Deductibles will drive down costs." And, "If we only had price transparency in healthcare, it would solve the healthcare cost problem."

In the meantime, it is nice to have someone or something to blame. Three healthcare cost drivers that have received a lot of media attention in the last few years are the hospital chargemaster, the healthcare insurance industry, and Big Pharma. Let us look at each of these drivers and see how each plays a role.

Driver #1: The Hospital Chargemaster

The chargemaster garnered much more attention in 2013, when *Time* magazine published a 36-page report on healthcare billing practices. It was penned by lawyer and journalist Steven Brill.[181] The article, titled "Bitter Pill: Why Medical Bills Are Killing Us," examined the role the chargemaster plays in rising healthcare costs and the impact that has on consumers, especially the uninsured and underinsured.[182] (I consider this article required reading for anyone who touches the dollars in the healthcare industry.) Brill went so far as to say, "... for patients, the chargemasters are both the real and the metaphoric essence of the broken market. They are anything but irrelevant. They're the source of the poison coursing through the health care ecosystem."[183]

So what is the chargemaster and why is it so vilified? The chargemaster—also called a charge description master (CDM)—is a master list, or catalog, of charges for each of the items, services, and procedures a hospital bills for. The charges on a chargemaster were intended to account for direct costs, indirect costs (overhead), and/or markup. In the retail world, the charge on a CDM might be compared to the list price of an item. The CDM price list only represents a base or starting price, and is typically very difficult to maintain and keep current with reimbursement. The CDM is often owned by the billing department, and finance controls when, if, and how much the prices go up each year (they rarely go down). The prices in a CDM are typically irrelevant to the out-of-pocket costs to a patient or insurance, other than setting a base price to discount from. In a retail market, the list price typically has some relation to the costs of the services.

Healthcare is different. For one thing, providers such as hospitals typically do not post their prices unless they are required to do so. That is because the chargemaster represents "prices," not reimbursement. As a billing tool, the chargemaster, by design, reflects the complexity of the cost of the services and charges to deliver care. It gets us close, but by no means should the charges be taken at face value. Reimbursement from insurance, charity, and self-pay discounting are often dramatically lower than the CDM price.

For example, there are significant differences between the CDM charge and the price a patient actually pays. In the healthcare market, the list price (a.k.a. CDM price) is the same for all—it is flat. The amount actually paid depends upon various discounts. This varies by payer, and the payer model is very complex. Payers can include combinations of the consumer (the patient), employers, private insurers, government insurers (Medicare, Medicaid, and related programs), and other providers (see figure 3.4, earlier in this chapter). In this highly complex environment, the chargemaster provides a list price as a base that can be applied to all constituents equally.

Often you hear, "Where did that price come from?" or "What interventions or procedures does this charge represent?" Also, the answers can unfortunately vary depending upon whom (or where) you ask. Prices can be highly variable in the same town! Consumers trying to navigate the system find this vagueness very troubling. That said, the chargemaster enables hospitals to charge the same, maintain it one place, and at least account for their charges (and hopefully costs). Hospitals use the chargemaster as a base to establish contracts between payer groups—contracts which account for different reimbursement rates. Reimbursement rates vary widely, depending upon the nature of the payer (self-pay patient, private insurance, Medicare, Medicaid).

Reimbursement rates are also very unstable; they change constantly, in response to changing economic and political conditions. Figure 3.6 shows aggregate hospital payment-to-cost ratios for private payers, Medicare, and Medicaid over the past 20 years. As this chart shows, Medicare and Medicaid consistently pay less than 100 percent of hospital costs. In order for hospitals to recapture this deficit, costs are shifted to private payers to subsidize the underpayments and therefore, costs for private payers keep edging upward.[184]

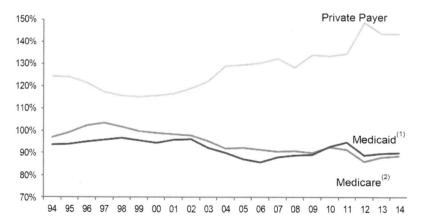

Source: Analysis of American Hospital Association Annual Survey data, 2014, for community hospitals.
(1) Includes Medicaid Disproportionate Share payments.

Figure 3.6 Aggregate Hospital Payment-to-Cost Ratios for Private Payers, Medicare, and Medicaid, 1994 to 2014. Source: American Hospital Association (AHA). (2016). Chart 4.6: Aggregate hospital payment-to-cost rations for private payers, Medicare and Medicaid, 1994 to 2014 [PDF document]. In *Trendwatch Chartbook 2016*. Retrieved from http://www.aha.org/research/reports/tw/chartbook/ch4.shtml

For hospitals, this is further complicated in that payers who reimburse at the lowest rate (Medicaid, Medicare, and other government payers) are making up an increasingly larger share of the overall payer mix (figure 3.7).

Distribution of Hospital Cost by Payer Type

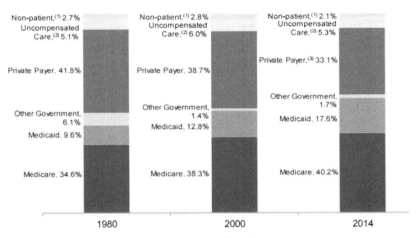

Source: Analysis of American Hospital Association Annual Survey data, 2014, for community hospitals.
(1) Non-patient represents costs for cafeterias, parking lots, gift shops and other non-patient care operating services and are not attributed to any one payer.
(2) Uncompensated care represents bad debt expense and charity care, at cost.
(3) Private payer formulas were updated in 2014 to account for the change in bad debt calculations, which is now reported as a deduction from revenue rather than a expense.
(4) Percentages were rounded, so they do not add to 100 percent in all years.

Figure 3.7 Distribution of Hospital Cost by Payer Type, 1980, 2000, 2014. Source: American Hospital Association (AHA). (2016). Chart 4.5: Distribution of hospital cost by payer type, 1980, 2000, 2014 [PDF document]. In *Trendwatch Chartbook 2016*. Retrieved from http:// www.aha.org/research/reports/tw/chartbook/ch4.shtml

Based on the above, over half (*half* gang—57.8 percent, to be exact) of reimbursement is coming from the Centers for Medicare & Medicaid Services (CMS), on average. And as we mentioned, CMS's share is growing, and its reimbursement needs to be subsidized by the commercial insurers, which are shrinking. Given this, the maligned chargemaster at least provides the hospital with a stable reference point for charges, as the payer mix and payer reimbursement rates are anything but stable. The chargemaster provides the hospital with a means of adapting to the dynamically changing reimbursement environment through trending its pricing, billing, reimbursement, and costs to the patients they serve.

The chargemaster may be a necessary artifact of the current health-care system, but that does not mean there is not room for improvement. Incomprehensible price inflation—like the $1.50 charge for one acetaminophen tablet; the $7.00 charge for a single cotton alcohol prep pad; or the $800 an hour charge for nursing care that caught Brill's attention—erodes consumer confidence and incurs the wrath of regulators.[185] I could write another book on costs of care and charge-to cost-ratios, but that would be really boring. Just trust me that hospitals are not "spinning a wheel" to establish a price, they are doing the best they can with what they have in a very dynamic market. Providing meaningful prices to a patient in a transparent and financially engaging manner is extremely challenging, to say the least.

In fact, one of the priorities of the Affordable Care Act (ACA) was to improve the transparency of hospital charges by requiring that hospitals establish and make public a list of their standard charges for items and services.[186] A little over a year after *Time* published "Bitter Pill," CMS issued its "Fiscal Year 2015 Policy and Payment Changes for Inpatient Stays in Acute-Care Hospitals and Long-Term Care Hospitals" report.[187] CMS guidelines for implementing the ACA's transparency provision are:

> … that hospitals either make public a list of their standard charges or their policies for allowing the public to view a list of those charges in response to an inquiry. CMS continues to encourage hospitals to undertake efforts to engage in consumer friendly communication of their charges to help patients understand what their potential financial liability might be for services they obtain at the hospital, and to enable patients to compare charges for similar services across hospitals.[188]

Awesome, more legislation to follow—as if healthcare did not already have enough. It is not clear how many hospitals are or are not compliant with the price transparency rule at this point. However, as more costs are pushed onto consumers via high-deductible health plans (HDHPs), health savings accounts (HSAs), and related changes in the health insurance market, consumers are clamoring for more price transparency. I am not certain patients or legislators have a clear understanding of what the T-word even means, and it still may not drive down cost. Most T-word legislation requires a charge to be provided, and the chargemaster pricing is not a reflection of out-of-pocket spend. It is a meaningless number for most consumers ("Sir, the list price for your TV is $25,000, but you have insurance, right? No? Uh oh.") We have a long way to go.

Transparency is not the only chargemaster issue under scrutiny. The accuracy, validity, and defensibility of hospital charges are important to regulators, as well. The CMS *Provider Reimbursement Manual* (PRM) contains a very specific definition of "reasonable costs." The definition allows costs to take into account both direct and indirect costs. It also allows that costs may vary between institutions due to "scope of services, level of care, geographical location, and utilization." The definition states:

> It is the intent of the program that providers are reimbursed the actual costs of providing high quality care, regardless of how widely they may vary from provider to provider, except where a particular institution's costs are found to be substantially out of line with other institutions in the same area which are similar in size, scope of services, utilization, and other relevant factors ...
>
> Implicit in the intention that actual costs be paid to the extent they are reasonable is the expectation that the provider seeks to minimize its costs and that its actual costs do not exceed what a prudent and cost-conscious buyer pays for a given item or service ... If costs are determined to exceed the level that such buyers incur, in the absence of clear evidence that the higher costs were unavoidable, the excess costs are not reimbursable under the program.[189]

In addition to defining costs, the CMS PRM also defines charges: "Charges refer to the regular rates established by the provider for services rendered to both beneficiaries and to other paying patients. Charges should be related consistently to the cost of the services and uniformly applied to all patients whether inpatient or outpatient."[190]

When CMS talks, hospitals listen, since about 41 percent of all patients treated in US hospitals are covered by Medicare.[191] But there are other good reasons besides pressure from CMS for hospitals to give their chargemasters a makeover. Traditional hospital practices such as allocating a portion of overhead to charges across the board, or marking up direct costs by a preset percentage, can be inaccurate and can cause price inflation.[192] Inaccurate cost allocation causes consequences like overpricing, which impacts a hospital's ability to compete in the marketplace, and underpricing, which impacts profitability.[193] Keeping a chargemaster relevant to the care provided from a cost perspective presents both an extreme challenge—and an opportunity—for most hospitals.

There is hope. In a report entitled "Effective Hospital Pricing Strategy," William O. Cleverley suggests that hospital prices should be set to cover:[194]

- Average reasonable costs
- Losses from payers who pay less than cost
- Reasonable return on investment (ROI)

In the same report, Cleverley concludes, "Pricing is an effective strategy for increasing hospital profitability. Across-the-board price increases, while easy to implement, are not usually as effective as selective price increases. Selective price increases typically increase profit potential by 30% to 80% and may create stronger price competitiveness if combined with detailed competitive price constraints."[195]

Price transparency in the US healthcare market is not a reality—yet. But the writing is clearly on the wall: The days of the mysterious, indecipherable chargemaster are numbered. A new and improved chargemaster that is more closely aligned to cost and marketplace realities will still play a role. Marketplace incentives are changing for consumers and providers in a way that will make increased price transparency inevitable. Patients will demand price transparency if they are the new payers.

Driver #2: Healthcare Insurance Companies

The next driver in the story of healthcare economics is the health insurance company. Health insurance companies seem to be doing OK in all of this, right? Americans love to hate our insurance companies. Annual American Customer Satisfaction Index (ACSI) surveys consistently rate health insurance companies poorly.[196] Health insurance companies also consistently rank below other types of insurance companies, including life, property, and casualty insurers.[197] ACSI's "Finance and Insurance Report 2014" went so far as to say, "According to customers, there is no area where health insurance companies offer an outstanding experience ..."[198]

Americans have been dissatisfied with health insurance companies for a long time. Back in 2009, journalist Nicholas Kristof summed up the feelings of many consumers when he wrote, "The business model of private insurance has become, in part, to collect premiums from healthy people and reject those likely to get sick—or, if they start out healthy and then get sick, to find a way to cancel their coverage."[199]

Healthcare reform, including provisions that became part of the ACA, was supposed to fix that problem. And to a certain extent, it did. Before the ACA was implemented, consumers hated health insurance companies because they denied pre-existing conditions, did not cover essential health benefits (for example, preventative care), kicked child dependents off if they were not in college, could cancel or jack up rates, could not be sued, and had astronomical out-of-pocket limits.[200]

ACSI's 2016 survey showed a slight increase in satisfaction with health insurance, including a 2 percent increase in satisfaction with "coverage of standard medical services (office visits, tests, procedures)."[201] This is not a surprise, since the ACA addressed many of the insurance coverage gaps (pre-existing conditions, annual and lifetime limits) that used to upset consumers.

But now that the ACA has addressed many of these consumer complaints, consumers have a new reason to hate health insurance: the high cost of insurance. In 2014, ACSI noted, "Health insurance has a history of lower customer satisfaction than other types of insurance due to high premiums, deductibles, and copays as well as more complex and frequently used claims processes."[202] Those premiums, deductibles, and copays have gone up considerably in the past two years.

What consumers do not seem to grasp is that when you mandate expansive coverage (eliminating pre-existing condition exclusions, eliminating annual and lifetime limits, adding preventive care benefits), the cost to health insurance companies goes up accordingly. You cannot ask your insurance plan to cover a lot more than it covered previously, and then expect premiums to go down at the same time. Insurance does not work that way. In other words, you cannot have affordable coverage for an unaffordable product.

But have the costs to insurers really gone up? Or is it just greed? Are they hiking up prices by spending unreasonable amounts on administration, marketing, and other non-claims-related costs? The answer to those questions lies in the insurance company's medical loss ratio (MLR). Per CMS, the MLR is "the proportion of premium revenues spent on clinical services and quality improvement."[203]

Prior to the passage of the ACA, insurance company MLRs were not regulated at the federal level.[204] In 2010, when the ACA was passed, only 34 states "had established some type of MLR guidelines; required the filing or reporting of MLR information; set limits on administrative expenses for comprehensive major medical insurance; or enacted a combination of such policies."[205] For those states that did enforce MLR requirements, the requirements ranged from 55 percent to 80 percent for products in the individual market, and from 60 percent to 85 percent for products in the group market.[206]

The ACA statute and accompanying regulations imposed a federal minimum MLR requirement on fully funded health plans (self-funded plans are not subject to the same insurance regulations).[207] In an explanation of the need for MLR controls, CMS noted, "Many insurance companies spend a substantial portion of consumers' premium dollars on administrative costs and profits, including executive salaries, overhead, and marketing."[208] The MLR requirement covers all licensed health insurers, "including commercial insurers, Blue Cross and Blue Shield plans and health maintenance organizations."[209] The ACA's MLR requirement is 80 percent for plans that cover individuals and small businesses, and 85 percent for large group plans.[210] As of this writing, it remains to be seen as to whether continuing health insurance reform efforts will maintain, modify, or repeal the ACA's national MLR minimums.

Where does your health insurance premium dollar go anyway? According to America's Health Insurance Plans (AHIP), your premium dollar is distributed as follows (figure 3.8)

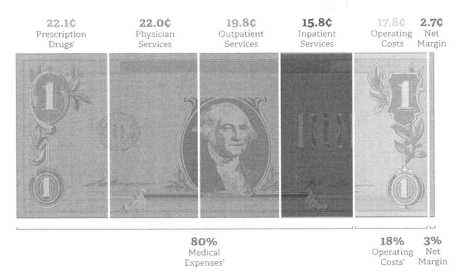

22.1¢	22.0¢	19.8¢	15.8¢	17.8¢	2.7¢
Prescription Drugs	Physician Services	Outpatient Services	Inpatient Services	Operating Costs	Net Margin

80%	18%	3%
Medical Expenses	Operating Costs	Net Margin

Figure 3.8 Where Does Your Premium Dollar Go? Source: Wick, K. (2017, March 2). Where does your premium dollar go? Americas Health Insurance Plans (AHIP). Retrieved from https://ahip.org/health-care-dollar/

Note that the largest share of your health insurance premium, according to AHIP, goes to prescription drugs. Consider this a hint as to what Driver #3 might be …

In the end, health insurance companies are businesses and they serve a role. I used to work for one, and I completely understand why they are here and exist. They have to manage risk for the populations they serve. If health insurance premiums do not adequately cover the company's claims risk, they will go out of business. What would a world without health insurance look like? By spreading risk across hundreds of thousands of people, health insurance companies increase access to the healthcare system. You often see stories in the media about the one claim that was denied, or the experimental drug that was not covered, but you do not hear about the hundreds of thousands of people who did get the coverage they needed, or the hundreds of thousands of prescriptions that were filled, and the hundreds of millions of claims that were paid.

Insurance also serves a cost containment role in the US healthcare system. Insurance companies negotiate discounted prices for hospital and physician services. Insurance companies also pay much better and consistently than a patient ever would. The size of the insurance company, with its tens of millions of customers, allows employers to negotiate rates in a way that individual consumers would never be able to. Because of that, we are better off having insurance companies than not having health insurance at all. It is easy to hate them, but when you look deeper, it is hard to imagine healthcare without healthcare insurance.

Driver #3: Big Pharma

Gallup regularly conducts research on which business sectors consumers view most favorably, and which business sectors they view most negatively. The pharmaceutical industry is *not* an industry adored by many.[211] In Gallup's most recent poll (August 2016), the only business sector that scored lower than the pharmaceutical industry was "the federal government."[212] That is a lot of hate, people.

The percentage of people who have a "very negative" view of the pharmaceutical industry has been increasing steadily over time, from 14 percent in 2001 to 30 percent in 2016.[213] Why do Americans view the pharmaceutical industry so negatively? Drugs are expensive and Big Pharma is big money. As we discussed in Chapter 2, prescription drugs accounted for 10 percent (about $320 billion) of the total US healthcare spend in 2015. Prescription drug spending increased more rapidly (up 12.4 percent in 2014 and up 9 percent in 2015) than overall healthcare spending (up 5.8 percent in 2015).[214]

Those kinds of price increases get the attention of consumers *and* lawmakers—and not in a good way. In October 2014, Rep. Elijah E. Cummings and Sen. Bernie Sanders released the results of an investigation into the escalating prices of 10 common generic drugs.[215] Price increases on the 10 drugs examined ranged from a "low" of 388 percent over two years (for Nitropress, used to treat congestive heart failure and reduce blood pressure), to a high of 8,281 percent in one year (for doxycycline hyclate, an antibiotic).[216]

Often those individual drug price hikes end up on the front pages. In 2015, price hikes involving the drug Daraprim made headlines. Daraprim is a drug used to treat patients with human immunodeficiency virus (HIV) and acquired immune deficiency syndrome (AIDS). Prior to 2010, the cost for Daraprim was $1 per pill. In 2010, the price was raised to $13.50 per pill.[217] In 2015, the price was raised again—to $750 per pill, a 5,000 percent increase.[218] In 2016, the EpiPen took center stage, increasing from $100 per two-pack to $608 per two-pack in less than 10 years.[219] In that case, the company CEO was even summoned to a congressional hearing to explain the price increase to the House Committee on Oversight and Government Reform.[220]

Studies have shown that Americans pay consistently higher prices for the same pharmaceuticals than other countries around the world. A 2015 study by the International Federation of Health Plans showed the United States is in the 95th percentile for price (not a good thing) compared to the other countries studied for many commonly prescribed drugs.[221]

Why has this occurred? Well, between protections on patented drugs and the Medicare Modernization Act of 2003 (MMA), which banned Medicare from negotiating on prescription drug prices, there are very few cost-containment mechanisms influencing the industry.[222] In "Bitter Pill," Brill pointed out that, "The difference between the regulatory environment in the U.S. and the environment abroad is so dramatic that McKinsey & Co. researchers reported that overall prescription drug prices in the U.S. are '50% higher for comparable products' than in other developed countries."[223]

The pharmaceutical industry is trying to let consumers and regulators know there is more to the story than the headlines people read in the daily news. This year, the Pharmaceutical Research and Manufacturers of America (PhRMA) launched a national, multiyear advertising and public affairs initiative in an attempt to fight back against Big Pharma's bad press. In a press release announcing the initiative, PhRMA stated the campaign "will showcase the industry's unsung heroes driving cutting-edge advances in science."[224] The press release also notes that:

The Pharmaceutical Research and Manufacturers of America (PhRMA) represents the country's leading innovative biopharmaceutical research companies, which are devoted to discovering and developing medicines that enable patients to live longer, healthier and more productive lives. Since 2000, PhRMA member companies have invested more than half a trillion dollars in the search for new treatments and cures, including an estimated $58.8 billion in 2015 alone.[225]

John Lechleiter, chairman, president, and chief executive officer of Eli Lilly and Company, has pointed to spending on research and development (R&D) as a significant component of the cost of drugs. Writing in *Forbes*, Lechleiter said:

> ...the pharmaceutical industry accounts for 21 percent of all R&D spending by all U.S. businesses—creating and sustaining hundreds of thousands of jobs while serving as a the engine of biomedical progress for the entire world. This level of investment is what is required today to bring forth new medicines.[226]

So what is the true face of pharma? Is it the intention to make money whatever the cost? Well, the pharmaceutical industry is a business. Businesses exist to make a profit. Businesses experience pressure from shareholders—and also hold a fiduciary responsibility—to maximize profits. These drugs make people lives better, and even save them—often, I might add. Drugs cost money to produce, people most certainly need them, and pharma has a lot of the cards. It is not necessarily fair, and neither is life.

And yet, you cannot have an effective healthcare system without pharmaceuticals. And you cannot have pharmaceuticals if you do not have the resources to do R&D. Like the other cost drivers in this story—the chargemaster and health insurance—pharma is a cost we hate, but it is a necessary cost. Pharmaceuticals are an essential part of the healthcare economy and care delivery. Can pharmaceutical costs be bridled? As of this writing, that topic is being hotly debated in the legislature. Regardless of the sources or causes, pharmaceuticals are a large driver of cost, and the current spend and profitability is simply not sustainable in the long-term. None of the current payers in the healthcare ecosystem—patients, insurers, or the government—has the capacity to continue absorbing increasing pharmaceutical costs. Because of this, how much we spend and whether we can continue to spend it will unfortunately persist as questions. If the "market" cannot find an answer to these questions, we may see the government step in again. That is yet to be determined.

Consolidation is King

Back in the beginning of this chapter, we mentioned that one of the concepts important to the functioning of a free market economy is choice. Consumers need choices for the laws of supply and demand to work, for if there is only one choice or one supplier, the consumer cannot "pay with their feet" and shop elsewhere to force prices down. At first blush, it seems we have a lot of choice in healthcare. When you look around, you see lots of healthcare facilities and lots of insurance plans. However, the bigger picture clarifies an industry trend toward consolidation, and that is beginning to cause monopolistic pricing among both providers and insurers. The result is that the healthcare economy is eroding consumer choice on a number of fronts.

Community hospitals are the free and proud, home of the brave—but they are a dying breed. They are losing their leverage in negotiating contracts, and their patient volume is leaking to other systems with larger footprints. In the context of an increasingly diluted payer mix, commercial insurance rates may not cover the costs for stand-alone providers, and that will be passed on to patients through narrower networks.

Health insurance companies are abandoning the health insurance exchanges established by the ACA. There is no profit in it. An analysis by AP and Avalere Health determined that about one out of three US counties will have only one health marketplace insurer in 2017.[227] According to ACSI data, lack of choice in both the individual and group health markets can have a significant negative impact on customer satisfaction.[228] Medicaid expansion and funding is also in for another roller coaster ride, which may limit choices for patients and providers in this market as well.

And it is not just the health insurance exchanges or Medicaid that are seeing options disappear. In February 2017, a proposed merger between Anthem and Cigna (two of only four insurers offering a nationwide network that can serve large employers) was blocked by a federal judge on the grounds the merger would violate antitrust laws.[229] The companies are expected to appeal the decision. A planned Aetna and Humana merger was also blocked by a federal judge, due to concerns the merger would harm consumers.[230] Merger mania among insurers is due, in part, to merger mania among providers. The larger the entity, the more the negotiating power. Mark Pauly, a professor of healthcare management at Wharton, described it this way:

> ... the ACO [Accountable Care Organization] part of the Affordable Care Act has stimulated, among other reasons, consolidation on the provider side. What we're seeing here is a reaction to that consolidation by insurers saying, well, if the providers are now going to gang up on us, we better gang up on them.[231]

Providers are indeed "ganging up." A report on provider consolidation by Deloitte noted that "regulatory changes, technological innovations and market dynamics are setting the stage for what may be a period of rapid consolidation among health systems."[232] A report by Irving Leven Associates Inc. stated that, "health care mergers and acquisitions posted record-breaking totals in 2014," with a total dollar value of $62 billion, up from $52.7 billion in 2013.[233]

Providers need a bigger footprint to survive in a rapidly changing healthcare economy where everything is changing—payer mix, payment models, the regulatory environment, and technology imperatives that require economies of scale. For providers to survive, they need the throughput that a larger system provides; without throughput, you do not have reimbursement; without reimbursement, you do not have revenue; without revenue, you do not have profits; and without profits, you do not have viability. Remember when I said, "Follow the money?" Follow the allegiance of the healthcare facility: When a provider collects money from patients and provides care, is the money flowing back or somewhere else? Is it going to the community and its needs or going to a shareholder? These are important things to consider as patients choose where they pay with their feet based on price, quality, or access.

Deloitte estimates that by 2024, independent hospitals will all but have disappeared, and that the total number of health systems in the United States will be halved, from 1,833 in 2014 to 926 in 2024.[234] Consolidation may be essential for insurer and provider survival, but what is the upside for the consumer? Free market theory holds that competition is essential to contain costs to consumers. Healthcare costs are already unsustainable. Where will the dynamics of the US healthcare economy lead us to next?

WHERE WE ARE NOW

CHAPTER 4
. . . .
THE GOVERNMENT

The United States government has had a hand in healthcare since 1935, when there were proposals to include a national health insurance component with the Social Security Act. That failed, as have most single-payer proposals, and since then, and as we talked about in Chapter 1, the government has been involved in various healthcare interventions in the name of providing for the greater good. Some of those interventions have been large-scale and broad in scope, like the Patient Protection and Affordable Care Act (PPACA, a.k.a. ACA and Obamacare). Other interventions have been targeted in scope, like the Women's Health and Cancer Rights Act (WHCRA) of 1998, which is a federal law that ties health insurance coverage for cancer-related mastectomies to coverage for breast reconstruction.[235]

Do Americans really want the government to intervene in healthcare? The answer to that depends on whom you ask, when you ask them, and what you want. A Gallup poll conducted in May of 2016 found that 58 percent of US adults were in *favor* of "replacing the [ACA] law with a federally funded healthcare system that provides insurance for all Americans."[236]

Is a government-run, single-payer system a slam-dunk then? Actually, no. Only a few months earlier, in November 2015, Gallup asked a slightly different question about Americans' preferences for the US healthcare system. In that poll, 55 percent of Americans expressed a preference for privately run healthcare in the United States, compared to 41 percent expressing an interest in a government-run healthcare system.[237]

Healthcare has been a frequent topic of debate and a key platform initiative this year. Gallup, the Associated Press (AP), and the Kaiser Family Foundation have each inquired about Americans' opinions during the presidential election campaign, and they all came up with slightly different answers.

For at least 15 years, Gallup has been asking questions about the government's role in ensuring Americans have health insurance. The Gallup data shows that Americans' opinions tend to change with the political and economic climate (figure 4.1).[238] Up until 2006, around 61 percent of Americans felt it was the government's responsibility to ensure all Americans have healthcare coverage. As of Gallup's most recent poll (November 2016), that figure has dropped to 52 percent.[239]

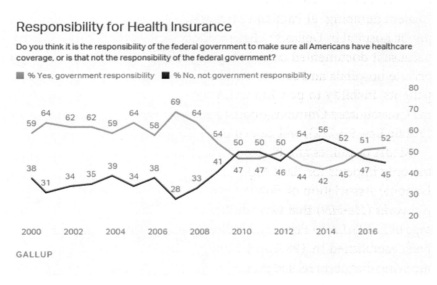

Figure 4.1 Gallup Poll Data on Whether the Government Should Ensure Americans Have Health Insurance, 2000–2016. Source: Gallup. (n.d.). Healthcare system, Responsibility for health insurance, 2000 -2016. Retrieved from http://www.gallup.com/poll/4708/healthcare-system.aspx

Regardless of what the citizens think, the government has intervened again and again in the name of the greater good and with the intention of trying to right a healthcare system that is seriously out of whack. In this chapter, we are going to look at a few of the more significant government interventions in the healthcare system—or maybe I should call them great ideas that went horribly wrong—and their effects on consumers, providers, and the health insurance marketplace.

The Emergency Medical Treatment and Active Labor Act, 1986

The Emergency Medical Treatment and Active Labor Act (EMTALA) is a small law (four pages) that has had a large impact on healthcare providers. Prior to the passage of EMTALA, hospital emergency departments could turn away or transfer patients to other hospitals whether or not the patient was in stable medical condition, including when a patient was in active labor. A 1985 episode of the CBS show *60 Minutes* focused on "patient dumping" at Parkland Memorial Health and Hospital System, a public hospital in Dallas.[240] The episode was titled "The Billfold Biopsy," because it documented cases in which patients were turned away from private hospitals and sent to Parkland—a public hospital—due to the patients' inability to pay. EMTALA was introduced in 1985 as part of the Consolidated Omnibus Budget Reconciliation Act of 1985 (COBRA) (Public Law 99-272), and passed in 1986.[241]

Media headlines and horror stories about patient dumping were not the only impetus for EMTALA. Larry S. Gage, former president of the National Association of Public Hospitals, stated in *Hospitals & Health Networks* (*H&HN*) that two additional reasons contributed to the passage of EMTALA.[242] First, the Medicare prospective payment system had been established in 1983, and Congress was concerned that hospitals receiving diagnoses related group (DRG) based bundled payments would limit more services than would be necessary for Medicare patients. A second impetus was the impending expiration of some hospitals' obligations to provide indigent care per the 1946 Hospital Survey and Construction Act (or the Hill-Burton Act).[243] Quoted in *H&HN*, Gage said, "EMTALA was a vehicle that was designed, in large part, to provide protection to Medicare and Medicaid patients. The fact that, in the end, it applied to all patients in all hospitals, even undocumented immigrants, was interesting. And it was good that it did get applied to all patients, especially those whose transfers were economically motivated."[244]

EMTALA requires all hospitals that participate in Medicare to screen and stabilize anyone who presents to the hospital campus and requests emergency services, regardless of their ability to pay.[245],[246] EMTALA has had some unintended consequences. Indeed, it provides great protection for patients, but has had a negative impact on hospitals' fiscal health, since it is, for the most part, an unfunded mandate. A Centers for Disease Control and Prevention (CDC) study published in 2012 found that uninsured adults were more likely to visit the emergency room because they had "no other place to go" (61.6 percent), compared to adults with private insurance (38.9 percent) or adults with public health plan coverage (48.5 percent).[247] The unintended consequence is that hospital emergency departments have become the source of a significant amount of bad debt and uncompensated care. Patients have to go somewhere, and under EMTALA, hospitals are obligated to treat them. Payment discussions are taboo, at least at the time the patient presents, because of the risk of violating EMTALA. A medical screening exam (MSE) must be conducted by a licensed physician, and stabilization of the patient must occur and be documented prior to any financial discussions. EMTALA violations can result in civil fines, exclusion from participation in the Medicare and Medicaid programs, and lawsuits from patients who assert their rights were violated.[248]

EMTALA is a well-known piece of legislation and—interestingly— still results in a large bunch of folks getting busted for violations. Between 2002 and 2015, the Centers for Medicare & Medicaid Services (CMS) investigated a total of 6,035 EMTALA complaints, averaging 431 investigations per year.[249] A total of $6,357,000 in fines was assessed against hospitals and physicians for EMTALA violations during that time period.[250] It places providers in a "catch-22" situation, since the area of the hospital most likely to generate bad debt and uncompensated care is the very same area where conversations with patients about the costs of care have the most hurdles—administratively and clinically.

Hillarycare (Health Security Act), 1993

Healthcare reform was a major theme of President Bill Clinton's election campaign. Soon after taking office in 1993, President Clinton appointed a healthcare reform task force to work on the issue. He named First Lady Hillary Rodham Clinton as chair and charged the task force with having a proposal prepared within 100 days of his inauguration.[251] Initially, the goals were for the plan to limit both public and private healthcare spending, and to provide health insurance coverage for the estimated 36 million Americans uninsured at the time.[252]

The eventual proposal, called the Health Security Act of 1993, was introduced to Congress in November 1993, but it never gained substantial support.[253] It never had a chance. Opponents derisively nicknamed the bill "Hillarycare." There was fierce opposition to the bill, particularly by the health insurance industry, which stood to lose the most if the bill passed. The Health Insurance Association of America (HIAA) created a series of successful television ads—known as the "Harry and Louise" ads—that portrayed a negative impact on average Americans if Hillarycare were to pass.[254] The tagline for the commercials was, "If we let the government choose, we lose."[255] The commercials specifically called out provisions for flat community rating or, as the fictional "Louise" described it, "everyone pays the same rate, no matter their age, even if they smoke or whatever."[256] (You may recall, from Chapter 1 on the history of health insurance, that as nonprofit organizations, the Blues were required to community-rate their policies.)[257]

Key provisions of the Health Security Act included universal coverage for all Americans, with very comprehensive benefits. Employers were to pay 80 percent of the premiums (wow), and health plan competition was to be the driver for cost controls. We saw our first proposed employer mandate with this bill, and it included regional purchasing pools (across state lines).[258]

Ultimately, the Clinton reform healthcare effort never came to a vote. There are many opinions about why it failed, but more than one analyst has suggested that the Healthcare Security Act's downfall was that it was *too* comprehensive. Dr. Jonathan Oberlander, writing in the *New England Journal of Medicine*, said:

> I think the major problem is they [the Clinton healthcare reform plan] tried to do too much. They tried to do everything at once. They wanted to insure everybody. They wanted to have an employer mandate. They wanted to control costs. They wanted to change the delivery system so more people enrolled in HMOs and other managed care plans. Any one of those is very, very difficult to achieve ... they wrapped it all up in a single legislative package, and it was just too much to bite off. [259]

So Hillarycare is gone, but not forgotten. On the election trail in 2016, Hillary Clinton said, "It was called Hillarycare before it was called Obamacare."[260] Though that assertion has been disputed, healthcare economist Jonathan Gruber, quoted by journalist Sahil Kapur of *Bloomberg*, said, "I think the success of the ACA would not have been possible without some of the key lessons learned during the Clinton era debates ... So she gets important credit for setting the political groundwork."[261] The bills proposed and debated today, including the American Health Care Act, which was pulled before vote under the Trump legislation in March of 2017, outlined some of the same elements introduced in Hillarycare.

Health Insurance Portability and Accountability Act (HIPAA), 1996

HIPAA is the acronym for the Health Insurance Portability and Accountability Act of 1996. Important point here: The acronym is 'HIPAA,' not 'HIPPA.' It is an act of legislation, not an animal! (Here is a tip: Think of it as a Hawaiian word: *hipaʻa*.)

HIPAA is a complex piece of legislation that has been revisited many times since it was first enacted. The original Act (Pub. L. 104-191, 110 Stat. 1936) is a 169-page document that covers everything from restrictions on pre-existing condition exclusions to healthcare fraud to administrative simplification to the tax treatment of medical savings accounts (MSAs) and long-term care insurance.[262] Its birth came out of "portability"—making insurance changes more portable and fair for patients. Privacy concerns, payment standards, and others are also parts of the act, which has grown to become a household name. The language of the act states that the purpose was:

To amend the Internal Revenue Code of 1986 to improve portability and continuity of health insurance coverage in the group
and individual markets, to combat waste, fraud, and abuse in
health insurance and healthcare delivery, to promote the use of
medical savings accounts, to improve access to long-term care
services and coverage, to simplify the administration of health
insurance, and for other purposes.[263]

Today HIPAA is best known for its rules regarding the privacy and
security of patients' health information. HIPAA's Privacy Rule created
national standards for how protected health information (a.k.a. PHI) can
be used and disclosed.[264] (Later iterations of HIPAA include electronic
protected health information, or ePHI). Similarly, HIPAA's Security Rule
established national standards that the healthcare industry must use to
protect the privacy of consumers' health information.

Obviously, it is outside the scope of this book to address all of the
aspects of HIPAA, but I wanted to touch on a few points that particularly impact consumers and providers with respect to health insurance
coverage, as HIPAA touches a lot more than people think.

Pre-Existing Conditions

HIPAA addressed insurance portability in part by enacting reforms to
the group health insurance market that placed limits on pre-existing
condition exclusions. Group health plans could still exclude pre-existing
conditions if certain criteria were met. For example, if the patient's diagnosis or treatment occurred within six months prior to the plan enrollment date, coverage for the condition could be excluded for up to 12
months (18 months for a late enrollee).[265] It made insurance accessible as
a consumers transitioned between plans, and set standards for ensuring
insurers played fair as qualifying events (job, marriage, births, etcetera)
occurred. This is an oversimplification, but the point is that HIPAA began to address concerns about obtaining coverage for pre-existing conditions by placing limits on insurers' exclusions.

Medical Savings Accounts

HIPAA promoted the use of MSAs by establishing tax deductions for contributions to medical savings accounts. Medical savings accounts were linked to high-deductible health plans (HDHPs) and were the forerunners of today's health savings accounts (HSAs). It is interesting to note what qualified as an HDHP in the 1996 legislation:

(2) HIGH DEDUCTIBLE HEALTH PLAN.—

(A) IN GENERAL.—The term 'high deductible health plan' means a health plan—

(i) in the case of self-only coverage, which has an annual deductible which is not less than $1,500 and not more than $2,250,

(ii) in the case of family coverage, which has an annual deductible which is not less than $3,000 and not more than $4,500, and

(iii) the annual out-of-pocket expenses required to be paid under the plan (other than for premiums) for covered benefits does not exceed—

(I) $3,000 for self-only coverage, and

(II) $5,500 for family coverage.[266]

Remember these numbers when we get to the 2017 definition of an HDHP (in the ACA section—hint, these are waaaaay lower!). Could it be that 1996 was the good ol' days?

Claims Processing

The original HIPAA legislation had a whole section on what was called "Administrative Simplification." The point was to promote standards for the electronic transmission of health information, including payment-processing transactions. Nine types of covered transactions are spelled out in the original legislation, including health claims attachments, enrollment and/or disenrollment in a health plan, eligibility for a health plan, healthcare payment and remittance advice, health plan premium payments, health claims status, and referral certification and authorization (a.k.a. "auths").[267]

Now 20 or 30 years ago, when I first started in healthcare as a transporter, these transactions were largely on paper. Everything in healthcare was on paper. We had paper, and pens, and film, and faxes, and those old dot matrix printers that made a lot of noise. Remember those? The ones that went, "Eee! Eee! Eee!" The printer paper was perforated on the edges to accommodate the tractor feed, and these long reports would end up in a giant wad on the floor every morning. The hospital would have a giant pile of papers, and I imagine the insurance companies had a giant pile of papers in their office, as well.

I would describe the relationship between hospitals and insurance companies not so much like war, but more like a game of chess. That is what a lot of these transactions are about. On one side of the chessboard, you have the insurance company and their medical managed care department, their medical officers, their actuaries, and their analysts. They are all charged with keeping an eye on risk, and making sure that claims are managed in a way that will keep premiums in check. The insurance company's moves are to pay what is covered under the plan and keep everything else in check.

On the other side of the chessboard, you have the physicians and providers who have patients coming to them for medical services. Frankly, at that point in time, providers were not really looking much at the funding mechanisms or the insurers' claims-denial patterns proactively. No one could sift through those giant pieces of paper coming off the dot matrix printer and give them to someone to work on. Also, this was well before any "big data" analytics or business intelligence. The rules and data evolved in an antiquated manner, where a large bolus of information was difficult to analyze and prioritize and frankly, just plain hard to understand. It was very reactive—"Hey! We got more denials from X insurance last month. Go pull that report from the cabinet and highlight ones that look funny." It was awful.

As claims processing evolved, denials evolved, too. Back then, claims got denied for different reasons than they do now—originally denials were all about coverage and benefits. We used paper claims that got folded in thirds, stuffed in an envelope, and then somebody licked a stamp and sent it. A person in the insurance office checked to see if the patient's plan was on file, and if the services were covered or not. If the services were covered, they stamped it "processed" and threw it in a bin, and it was paid. If not, a denial letter or a phone call happened and it was all pretty simple. At that time, denials were pretty black and white. Was the patient on the plan eligibility roster or not? Was the treatment or service covered by that particular plan or not?

As transactions became electronic instead of paper-based, denials became more complex. The care got more complex, too—CTs, MRIs, oncology treatments, cardiac cases, and so on all involved "new technologies" and raised eyebrows at insurance companies for their "expensive" costs. In the beginning, when claims processing was about paper and labor-intensive manual transactions, "the juice wasn't worth the squeeze." That is, denials based on complex plan rules were less frequent, because it took too much time to administer them, and insurance did not want to hold up payment while the patient was getting sicker.

But as technology has evolved, claims processing has become faster, less labor-intensive, and more sophisticated. Insurers have been able to codify the most complex plan designs using electronic databases and algorithms. They have been able to use data analytics to refine their risk management strategies, and now they generate these enormous electronic provider manuals that go into detail about plan benefits and coverage. The expectation is that there is someone at the hospital who (1) understands what the language is; (2) has time to read it; and (3) has time to operationalize the changes in the rules so the next time a patient comes in, they can follow those new standards.

The threshold for payable claims has gotten higher and higher as insurance benefit plans have become more sophisticated. Now you can have a claim rejected not just because of plan eligibility or covered benefits, but also because you are missing medical precertification or authorizations or not meeting medical necessity requirements. That is why hospitals are now put in the position of prescrubbing appointments, claims, and charges before they go out—to make sure that charge integrity and documentation is there in the first place, because if it is not on the claim, or not documented, you are not going to get paid.

Where HIPAA fits into all of this is that the regulations governing healthcare data transactions have become enormously complex. Paper transactions have nearly become extinct; today everything is about electronic data interchange (EDI). President Donald Trump famously said in 2016, "I think that computers have complicated lives very greatly."[268] That most certainly applies to healthcare claims processing. HIPAA's most recent version of electronic transaction standards, Version 5010, became effective January 1, 2012. After 5010 was implemented, claim rejections increased.[269] Here are just a few of the fun reasons claims can be rejected under HIPAA 5010:

- No detailed description of an unlisted Current Procedural Terminology (CPT) or Healthcare Common Procedure Coding System (HCPCS) code

- Lack of drug units when a National Drug Code (NDC) is present

- ZIP codes are only five digits instead of nine

- Billing provider address is a P.O. Box instead of a physical address[270]

Insurance companies really have the upper hand in the claims payment chess game right now. HIPAA specifications are very exacting as to which fields must be completed, which codes should be used, and how those codes should be used when submitting claims in order to be compliant. Overlook any one of those things, and the provider strikes out, by either not getting paid enough, or not getting paid at all. I am not a big fan of paper, but at least there was more time and visibility into the claim elements—one could "see" things that are unseen now, as it has become just a data stream. Without adapting that stream to stop or monitor for valid data elements, the claims just fly and many things get missed.

In the original HIPAA legislation, the section on Administrative Simplification was covered in about 13 pages.[271] As of 2013, the combined text for all of the regulatory standards related to the HIPAA Administrative Simplification (as published by the Department of Health and Human Services), runs about 115 pages.[272] (And no, I have not, nor will I ever, read it.) Once claims processing went digital, it was going to become more complicated, whether or not the government got involved. In this instance, when it became clear that standards needed to be established to regulate healthcare transactions, HIPAA came to the rescue.

Self-Pay Opt-Out

One last footnote to the HIPAA story that many patients and providers are unaware of is an opt-out option for consumers who choose to pay out of pocket for medical tests or treatment. This provision was part of the HIPAA Omnibus Rule that was published in the Federal Register in 2013.[273] The rule is titled "Right to Restrict Certain Disclosures to a Health Plan," and it requires providers to comply if an individual wants to restrict disclosure of healthcare services to the health plan (insurer) in situations where the patient has paid the provider in full, out of pocket.[274]

I like to refer to this provision as the "windshield or car wreck principle." If you get into a fender bender, you have this scenario going through your head. You think, "How much is this going to cost? And do I want to submit it to my insurance company or not? Because if I do, my rates are going to go up. But if I just pay out of pocket, my rates won't go up."

This kind of consumer option was not available in healthcare until this new HIPAA rule came out. You could hide your insurance card, or not declare it, but there were ways of finding that coverage, and there still are today. But now, if the patient wants an MRI of their back, or a head CT for their sinusitis or something, and the insurance company will not authorize it for the diagnoses, the patient now has an option to opt out of the insurance rules and pay cash on the barrelhead for it themselves without disclosing it to the insurance company. It gives the patient a little bit more freedom. It also makes the patient the payer—not the insurance. With more freedom can come more payment, but with less administrative insurance restrictions.

The catch-22 is that if a test finds something requiring further medical treatment, but the insurance company was not involved from the get-go, the insurer is well within their rights to deny future care related to that test, because the insurer was not allowed to manage the care. Insurance can deny things that they believe fall outside the usual course of treatment, as the patient "went off course." Sometimes the risk proves worth it for the discount or removal of the insurance burdens, sometimes it does not. Patients also cannot change their mind and submit a claim to insurance later. There is risk assumed when the insurance is removed from the care, in that they are no longer managing it if the patient is the only payer; the contract is between patient and the provider.

I call it the "three doors." You have three doors of funding: yourself, the insurance company, or some sort of third party like motor vehicle or workman's comp insurance, or some sort of subrogation. Once you go in through one of those doors, the door locks behind you and you cannot come out of that room. You cannot submit a claim multiple places and get paid multiple times. It does not work that way. You pick one, and that is who pays.

This option puts the onus on providers, like hospitals, to have self-pay case rates. Some consumers want to pay out of pocket and avoid all the rules associated with insurance, and now, because of HIPAA, they do not have to. Providers need to be able to accommodate those patients. If the price is something that the consumer feels is valuable and affordable, this rule allows that to happen without going through the hoops of insurance company rules.

Romneycare (An Act Providing Access to Affordable, Quality, Accountable Health Care), 2006

Mitt Romney (former GOP presidential candidate) championed healthcare reform when he was Governor of Massachusetts (2003–2007). Romney developed and enacted innovative healthcare reform legislation—the "Massachusetts Model"—in 2006 that provided near-universal health insurance for Massachusetts residents via state subsidies and individual mandates to purchase insurance. Key provisions of the legislation, which was officially titled An Act Providing Access to Affordable, Quality, Accountable Health Care, included:

- An individual mandate requiring all adults to purchase health insurance or pay a penalty.

- Requirements for employers to contribute toward health insurance coverage for employees or pay a per-employee "fair share" contribution to the state.

- Creation of a health insurance exchange website (considered the model for the health insurance exchanges that were part of the ACA implementation). The exchange, called the Commonwealth Health Insurance Connector, offered both sliding-scale subsidized insurance for low income individuals and nonsubsidized private health insurance.

- Insurance market reforms, including guarantee issue, community rating, and coverage and affordability standards.

- Expansion of eligibility for the state's Medicaid program and the Children's Health Insurance Program (CHIP).[275]

"Romneycare" is widely considered to be the legitimate forerunner of the ACA, rather than Hillarycare, which was forgotten soon after the Clintons left office. Romneycare has been recognized for reducing the number of uninsured in the state. However, as with many of the national efforts at healthcare reform that have both preceded and followed Romneycare, the legislation, alas, again did not impact healthcare costs. A 2012 Kaiser Family Foundation study on Massachusetts' reform noted, "Massachusetts made the decision in 2006 to focus health reform on expanding insurance coverage not on controlling health costs. As a result, rising costs remain a serious problem."[276]

Health Information Technology for Economic and Clinical Health Act, 2009

In April 2004 President George W. Bush declared, "Within 10 years, every American must have a personal electronic medical record."[277] In the same month, by executive order, he created the Office of the National Coordinator (ONC) for Health Information Technology (HIT), establishing "one person in the Federal government responsible for implementing the goal of health information technology."[278] I often compare this to President John F. Kennedy's proclamation about getting a man on the moon in the 1960s. It was bold, it was good idea, but it was also very expensive.

President Bush strongly believed in the potential benefits of digitizing healthcare and moving from paper medical records to electronic health record (EHR) systems—also synonymously referred to as electronic medical record (EMR). As he stated in his 2004 State of the Union Address, "By computerizing health records, we can avoid dangerous medical mistakes, reduce costs and improve care." Bush's commitment to this goal initiated a slow but steady increase in the adoption of EHR systems among healthcare providers across the country.

The effort to spur adoption of EHR systems among US healthcare providers received a significant boost when President Barack Obama committed an estimated $20 billion (another one of those Bs we talked about in Chapter 2) to healthcare information technology as part of the American Recovery and Reinvestment Act of 2009 (ARRA). The Health Information Technology for Economic and Clinical Health (HITECH) Act that was part of ARRA authorized CMS to award incentive payments to providers and eligible professionals who demonstrate "meaningful use" of certified EHRs.[279] The timeline for the incentive program was designed to quickly spur the adoption and implementation of EHR systems. The CMS incentive program was front-loaded so that early adopters (2011 and 2012) saw the largest incentive payments.[280] Incentive payments decreased over time, and financial penalties began to take effect in 2015 for providers who did not move to EHRs.[281]

Like many of the government initiatives we have discussed, the HITECH Act worked better on some levels than on others. It most certainly spurred an increase in EHR adoption, particularly among acute care hospitals (figure 4.2).[282]

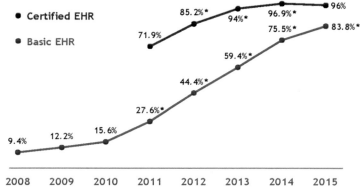

Basic EHR adoption increased while certified EHR adoption remained high

Figure 1: Percent of non-Federal acute care hospitals with adoption of at least a Basic EHR with notes system and possession of a certified EHR: 2008-2015

NOTE: Basic EHR adoption requires the EHR system to have a set of EHR functions defined in Table A1<#appendix>. A certified EHR is EHR technology that meets the technological capability, functionality, and security requirements adopted by the Department of Health and Human Services. Possession means that the hospital has a legal agreement with the EHR vendor, but is not equivalent to adoption. *Significantly different from previous year (p<0.05).
SOURCE: ONC/American Hospital Association (AHA), AHA Annual Survey Information Technology Supplement

Figure 4.2 EHR Adoption After the Passage of the HITECH Act and Implementation of the Meaningful Use Program Incentives and Penalties. Source: Henry, J., Pylypchuk, Y., Searcy T. & Patel V. (2016, May). Adoption of electronic health record systems among U.S. non-federal acute care hospitals: 2008-2015. *ONC Data Brief 35*. Retrieved from https://dashboard.healthit.gov/evaluations/data-briefs/non-federal-acute-care-hospital-ehr-adoption-2008-2015.php

Thanks to the HITECH Act, doctors are no longer roaming hospital hallways *St. Elsewhere*-style, with a clipboard and paper patient chart in hand. These days they are more likely to be carrying an iPad. And even though detractors sometimes like to refer to the program as "meaningless use" instead of "meaningful use," there have been positive outcomes. The adoption of EHRs has increased patient and physician access to medical records; reduced medical record errors; facilitated legible, complete documentation including prescriptions; and enhanced the interchange of medical records between providers.[283]

So clinically, and from a patient safety standpoint, EHRs have been a win. From a cost containment standpoint however, although EHRs were supposed to increase efficiency in a way that could lead to lower healthcare prices, what really happened is that providers ended up spending millions of dollars purchasing and implementing EHR systems while healthcare costs continued to climb. This is another case of technology driving healthcare costs upward. I will not lie—it helped hospitals financially in a tough time, too. Many sustained profitability through those meaningful use incentive payments or avoiding the penalty. Care got more efficient and safer, but it cost the government a lot of money. All in all, I think we are in a better place, but it was at a tremendous outlay of cost.

Another issue with EHR systems is that in the rush to meet the incentive timetables, the systems' designs centered on optimizing clinical support, while details related to billing, claims, and revenue cycle management (RCM) got neglected. Most of the big EHR vendors did not focus on billing and claims at all. Now, obviously, clinical functionality should be prioritized in the spirit of care delivery and safety, but the revenue cycle elements were left at the station in their entirety. Paper processes may have been inefficient, but providers evolved processes over time that supported clinical outcomes and the back office as well. If meaningful use was the locomotive, RCM was the caboose, and the two got uncoupled the minute the meaningful use regulations came out.

Revenue cycle leaders ended up with their shoulders against that caboose, trying to push it down the track to get it hooked up again, because that documentation has to support not only clinical outcomes, but billing and reimbursement as well. Many providers have had to turn to third-party systems to make certain that claims-specific processes—like obtaining authorizations or documenting medical necessity electronically—can be documented in a way that supports and meets the insurance plan rules for reimbursement.

Claims fly a lot faster now, too. It is like having a lot of pingpong balls bouncing around in a fishbowl, and you do not always have the stop gates you need to make sure a claim is clean before it is submitted. With claims, you are constantly going upstream to find the information that you need downstream to get paid, and meaningful use did not help with that much. In fact, I think it made it worse, from a payment perspective, because it was not designed for that. Similar to the ACA, it solved some problems and created some others.

Affordable Care Act (PPACA-Obamacare), 2010

We talked about ACA in each of the previous chapters. From a consumer's perspective, the primary goal of the ACA was to expand health insurance coverage. The ACA used several strategies to expand access to health insurance coverage. One strategy was the development of health insurance exchanges, where consumers could compare and purchase health insurance coverage. To meet ACA requirements, all plans have to meet minimum essential coverage (MEC) requirements—also called essential health benefits.

Some, but not all, of the plans on the ACA health insurance exchanges qualify as HDHPs per Internal Revenue Service (IRS) rules, which qualifies plan enrollees to participate in HSAs as well. Remember what defined an HDHP when medical savings accounts were created in 1996? Figure 4.3 shows the difference between then and now.

Plan characteristic	Definition from 1996 HIPAA legislation	Definition from 2017 IRS code
Self-only, minimum deductible	$1,500	$1,300
Self-only, maximum deductible	$2,250	Not specified
Self-only, maximum out of pocket	$3,000	$6,550
Family, minimum deductible	$3,000	$2,600
Family, maximum deductible	$4,500	Not specified
Family, maximum out of pocket	$5,500	$13,100

Figure 4.3 Change in Definition of High-Deductible Health Plan, 1996–2017. Source: Health Insurance Portability and Accountability Act of 1996 (HIPAA), Public Law 104-191, Title III, Subtitle A. (1996). Retrieved from https://www.gpo.gov/fdsys/pkg/PLAW-104publ191/pdf/PLAW-104publ191.pdf; and U.S. Department of the Treasury. Internal Revenue Service (IRS). (2016). 26 CFR 601.602: Tax forms and instructions (Also: Part 1, § 1, 223), Rev. Proc. 2016-28. Retrieved from https://www.irs.gov/pub/irs-drop/rp-16-28.pdf

ACA health exchange plans are offered in four tiers, with bronze offering the lowest premiums and highest deductibles, and platinum offering the highest premiums and lowest deductibles. Low-income health exchange enrollees are eligible for income-based premium subsidies. Nevertheless, the plans still hit consumers hard with high deductibles and high ceilings on out-of-pocket costs. Figure 4.4 shows the results of an analysis by healthpocket.com for average deductible and out-of-pocket costs for the four tiers for 2017.[284]

Plan type	Individual, avg. deductible	Individual, max. out of pocket	Family, avg. deductible	Family, avg. out of pocket
Bronze	$6,092	$6,904	$12,393	$13,810
Silver	$3,572	$6,449	$7,474	$12,952
Gold	$1,197	$4,889	$2,745	$10,168
Platinum	$405	$2,159	$809	$4,318

Figure 4.4 ACA Plans, Average Deductible and Out-of-Pocket Costs, by Tier. Source: Coleman, K. (2016, Oct. 26). Aging consumers without subsidies hit hardest by 2017 Obamacare premium & deductible spikes. HealthPocket. Retrieved from https://www.healthpocket.com/healthcare-research/ infostat/2017-obamacare-premiums-deductibles#.WNn_svkrl2w

It is interesting to see the dramatic increase in deductibles on the bronze and silver plans over the years (20 percent increases in just three years), whereas the gold and platinum plan deductibles have stayed relatively flat. The 2017 premiums in the silver plans are in the $300 to $750 per month range, an increase of 17 percent on average from 2016. The 2017 platinum premiums are in the $550 to $1,300 per month range, increasing 15 percent from 2016 (depending on the type of plan, age, and number dependents).[285]

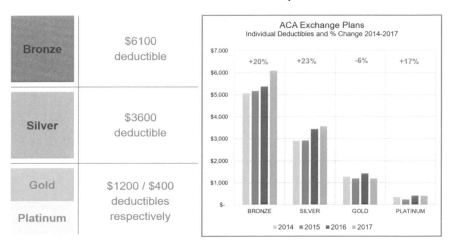

Figure 4.5 ACA Exchange Plan Deductibles Are Resulting in More Funding Gaps for Patients in 2017. Source: Graph by Jonathan Wiik; adapted from Coleman, K. (2016, Oct. 26). Aging consumers without subsidies hit hardest by 2017 Obamacare premium & deductible spikes. HealthPocket. Retrieved from https://www.healthpocket.com/healthcare-research/infostat/2017-obamacare-premiums-deductibles#.WNn_svkrl2w

Although the private health insurance plans offered on the ACA exchanges did result in many uninsured consumers becoming insured, the ACA strategy that was most significant for expanding coverage was the Medicaid expansion.

Under the ACA, states were given the option to expand Medicaid eligibility to cover children to at least 138 percent of the federal poverty level (FPL), as well as the option to extend eligibility to adults with incomes at or below 138 percent of the FPL.[286] As of January 2017, 32 states adopted the Medicaid expansion and 19 states did not.[287] Figure 4.6 illustrates the coverage gap for low-income adults in states that did not expand Medicaid eligibility.[288]

Gap in Coverage for Adults in States that Do Not Expand Medicaid under the ACA

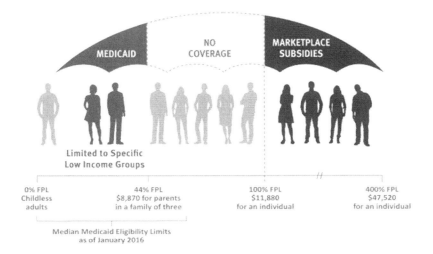

Figure 4.6 The Medicaid Expansion Coverage Gap. Source: Garfield, R., & Damico, A. (2016, Oct. 19). The coverage gap: Uninsured poor adults in states that do not expand Medicaid. The Henry J. Kaiser Family Foundation. Retrieved from http://kff.org/uninsured/issue-brief/the-coverage-gap-uninsured-poor-adults-in-states-that-do-not-expand-medicaid/

This expansion of Medicaid affected providers by diluting their payer mix, but also by decreasing uncompensated care. A 2015 report by the US Department of Health and Human Services, Office of the Assistant Secretary for Planning and Evaluation (ASPE) concluded, " … the large observed declines in the uninsured and increases in Medicaid coverage have led to substantial declines in hospital uncompensated care in 2014. Medicaid expansion states account for $5 billion of the estimated $7.4 billion reduction in uncompensated care costs attributed to ACA coverage expansions."[289] Hospital margins got a boost as well. In 2009, hospital total margins were at 2.6 percent and jumped to 8.3 percent by the close of 2014 (figure 4.7).

Chart 4.2: Aggregate Total Hospital Margins[1] and Operating Margins,[2] 1994 – 2014

Source: Analysis of American Hospital Association Annual Survey data, 2014, for community hospitals.
[1] Total Hospital Margin is calculated as the difference between total net revenue and total expenses divided by total net revenue.
[2] Operating Margin is calculated as the difference between operating revenue and total expenses divided by operating revenue.

Figure 4.7 AHA: Aggregate Total Hospital Margins(1) and Operating Margins(2), 1994–2014. Source: American Hospital Association (AHA). (2016). Table 4.1 Aggregate total hospital margins and operating margins; percentage of hospitals with negative total margins; and aggregate non-operating gains as a percentage of total net revenue, 1994-2014 [PDF document]. In *Trendwatch Chartbook 2016*. Retrieved from http://www.aha.org/research/reports/tw/chartbook/2016/table4-1.pdf

Essentially, the ACA shifted costs around, but did not contain them. As "Bitter Pill" author Steven Brill stated, "…with Obamacare we've changed the rules related to who pays for what, but we haven't done much to change the prices we pay."[290]

American Health Care Act (AHCA), 2017

The American Health Care Act of 2017 (a.k.a. Ryancare or, alternatively, Trumpcare) was introduced in March 2017 as the Republican Party's replacement for the ACA. The original bill included the following provisions:

- Eliminated ACA taxes on prescription drugs, over-the-counter medications, health insurance premiums, and medical devices

- Eliminated the individual and employer mandate penalties

- Eliminated the ACA health insurance premium subsidies and replaced them with age-based tax credits

- Eliminated federal matching dollars for enrollment in the Medicaid expansion (beginning in 2020)

- Limited federal funds for Medicaid to an amount based on per capita enrollment, beginning in 2020

- Required health insurers to increase premiums by 30 percent for one year for enrollees who have not maintained continuous coverage over the previous year

- Revised rules governing HSAs[291],[292]

The Congressional Budget Office (CBO) released a cost estimate for the bill on March 13, 2017.[293] The CBO estimated enacting the legislation would reduce federal deficits by $337 billion between 2017 and 2026, with the largest savings coming from reductions in outlays for Medicaid and elimination of ACA subsidies for nongroup health insurance.[294] Although the CBO outlined that it would save federal dollars, the Joint Committee on Taxation indicated a $600 billion price tag over the next decade.[295] (*That* is a lot of Bs). More costs with more legislation. Once again, the bill had no provisions that tackled rising healthcare costs head-on. It was more a matter of cost-shifting back to the patient. As one blogger characterized it, "There is no real 'repeal and replace.' There is just a lot of heavy handed meddling."[296]

In addition to ducking out on cost, the CBO indicated the bill would swiftly return the uninsured rate to pre-Obama rates (figure 4.8). A double whammy: more costs *and* less access. That means that Ryancare would have increased the uninsured rate to almost 20 percent from the lowest point in history (10.9 percent in the fourth quarter of 2016) in a matter of eight years.[297] According to Gallup, 10.9 percent is the lowest uninsured rate "since Gallup and Healthways began tracking insurance coverage in 2008."[298]

Republican plan would have led to rise in uninsured Americans
Percentage of people aged under 65 without health insurance

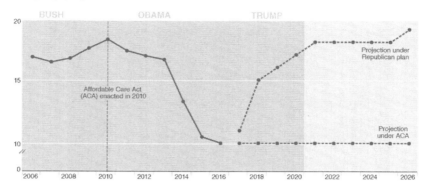

Figure 4.8 Republican Plan Would Have Led to Rise in Uninsured Americans. Source: BBC News, U.S. & Canada. (2017, April 28). Trump tracker: How much has the president achieved so far?" Retrieved from http://www.bbc.com/news/world-us-canada-38663043

The bill was opposed by the American Medical Association (AMA), as well as America's Essential Hospitals, the American Hospital Association, the Association of American Medical Colleges, the Catholic Health Association of the United States, the Children's Hospital Association, the Federation of American Hospitals, and the National Association of Psychiatric Health Systems.[299] No doubt these hospital groups saw the writing on the wall: A significant reduction in government support would mean more cost-shifting to patients and providers, leading to less access, more bad debt, and rising uncompensated care costs.

The bill was to come before the House of Representatives for a vote on March 24, 2017, but was withdrawn at the last minute when it became clear it did not have enough support to pass.[300] After substantial modifications, a revised version of the AHCA was passed by the House of Representatives on May 4, 2017. As of this printing, the Senate was working on its own version of healthcare reform, which may bear little resemblance to the version of the AHCA that passed the House.[301]

The ongoing disagreements around the components of the AHCA demonstrate the challenges in achieving consensus with healthcare. At the time of this writing, we are still waiting for a healthcare reform solution, with round one going to Obamacare.

The government has not been able to solve the healthcare cost problem, yet. No doubt they will keep trying. In the meantime, two interconnected trends continue: (1) healthcare costs keep escalating, and (2) costs keep shifting back to the consumer, solidifying them as "the patient as the new payer."

CHAPTER 5

· · · · · · · · · · · · · · · · · · ·

THE PATIENT
AS THE PAYER

"Patient is the new payer." This may sound odd when you first hear it. After all, within the healthcare industry, the term "payer" usually refers to an insurance carrier, or another third party—not the patient. But in the new healthcare reality, the patient most certainly *is* the new payer. It is a paradigm shift. Traditionally, providers have depended on cash flow through the back end from their insurance carriers (aka, "payers"), but in this new reality, the patient is a payer as well. Patients do not pay like traditional payers. They sometimes struggle to pay their medical bills; they take longer to pay when they do pay; and they subordinate medical bills to other bills. As shown in figure 5.1, consumers rank paying medical bills below paying their mortgage or rent; their utilities; their car payments; and even their cable, cellphone, and Internet bills.[302]

In spite of every historical development and every attempt at healthcare reform outlined in the previous chapters, the fact is that healthcare costs keep rising, and the patient keeps taking on more and more of those costs. Employers and insurance companies continue to shift costs to the patient by increasing deductibles, copays, and coinsurance. Figure 5.2 illustrates the increase in deductible costs alone over the past five years compared to workers' earnings and overall inflation.

Consumers prioritize paying their health insurance premiums, but not their medical bills

Percent of customers ranking the following expenses in their top two choices

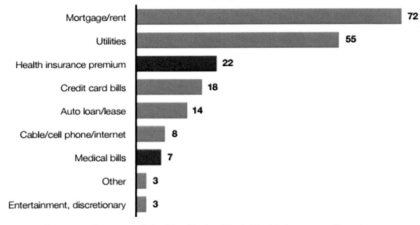

Figure 5.1 Consumer Prioritize Paying Their Health Insurance Premiums, but Not Their Medical Bills. Source: Pellathy, T., & Singhal, S. (2010, March). Revisiting healthcare payments: An industry still in need of overhaul [PDF document]. McKinsey & Company. Retrieved from http://healthcare.mckinsey.com/sites/default/files/776489_Revisiting_Healthcare_Payments_An_Industry_Still_in_Need_of_Overnaul.pdf

Cumulative Increases in Health Insurance Premiums, General Annual Deductibles, Inflation, and Workers' Earnings, 2011-2016

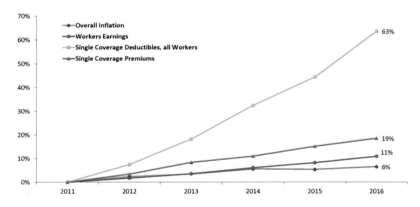

Figure 5.2 Increase in Health Insurance Premiums and Deductibles, 2011–2016.

Source: The Henry J. Kaiser Family Foundation. (2016, Sept. 14). Cumulative increases in health insurance premiums, general annual deductibles, and workers' earnings, 2011-2016. 2016 Employer Health Benefits Survey. Retrieved from http://kff.org/health-costs/report/2016-employer-health-benefits-survey/

As figure 5.2 illustrates, deductibles have increased 63 percent since 2011, outpacing both earnings (11 percent increase) and inflation (6 percent increase).[303] Furthermore, the percentage of covered workers with a general annual deductible (for single coverage) has increased from 55 percent in 2006 to 83 percent in 2016.[304] The size of that deductible has also increased, from an average of $584 in 2006 to $1,478 in 2016.[305] It would be nice if we all got raises as our healthcare premiums and out-of-pocket expenses grew, but alas, that is not the case. These increases in patient payments are not sustainable in the long term.

The shift of costs to patients is a growing problem for patients, and for the providers who care for them. Revenue collected directly from patients is making up an increasingly larger share of overall patient revenue (figure 5.3).[306] Over the past decade, the percentage of revenue collected from patients has increased from less than 10 percent to more than 30 percent.[307] This trend has a direct impact on providers because patients do not behave like traditional payers.

Figure 5.3 The Patient Is the New Payer. Source: Jonathan Wiik adapted from Wyatt, C. (2015, May). Increasing patient responsibility requires a modern billing approach. Retrieved from http://www.hfma.org/Content.aspx?id=30965; and Margolis, J., & Pope, C. (2010, April). Perspective on patient payments. *MGMA Connexion.* Retrieved from https://www.mgma.com/Libraries/ Assets/Practice%20Resources/Publications/MGMA%20Connexion/2010/ Perspective-on-patient-payments-MGMA-Connexion-April-2010.pdf; and InstaMed. (2015). Trends in healthcare payments: Sixth annual report, 2015 [PDF document]. Retrieved from http://www.instamed.com/wp-content/ uploads/Trends-in-Healthcare-Payments-Annual-Report-2015.pdf

Death to the Deductible

Deductibles are an innovative concept, right? "Let's keep healthcare premiums in check while creating a large amount of cash the patient has to front, making them more responsible for their healthcare spend. That way they will shop for care and make better healthcare choices." Uh-huh. Or maybe you will buy this piece of propaganda: "Deductibles empower patients to make better healthcare decisions." Riiiiiight. Patients did not ask for high-deductible health plans (HDHPs). They have been inflicted on consumers, and they are just a symptom of the overall disease of unaffordable healthcare costs.

Patients want lower costs and shop on lower-cost premiums. Although premium costs have not dropped, premium increases have slowed somewhat in the last few years per the 2016 Kaiser Family Foundation (KFF) "Employer Health Benefits Survey."[308] Premiums increased 63 percent between 2001 and 2006, but increased by only 20 percent between 2011 and 2016 (figure 5.4).[309] This slowdown in premium growth is due, in part, to more employees moving into HDHPs, which have lower average premiums.[310]

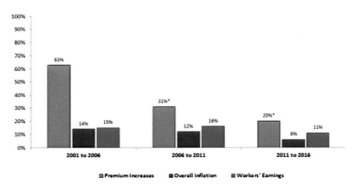

Cumulative Premium Increases for Covered Workers with Family Coverage, 2001-2016

Figure 5.4 Cumulative Premium Increases for Covered Workers with Family Coverage, 2001–2016. Source: The Henry J. Kaiser Family Foundation. (2016, Sept. 14). Average annual workplace family health premiums rise modest 3% to $18,142 in 2016: More workers enroll in high-deductible plans with savings option over past two years. Retrieved from http://kff. org/health-costs/press-release/average-annual-workplace-family-health-premiums-rise-modest-3-to-18142-in-2016-more-workers-enroll-in-high-deductible-plans-with-savings-option-over-past-two-years/

Deductibles did what they could to slow skyrocketing premiums, but alas, there is a lot of fuel in the healthcare cost rocket. From 2006 to 2016, premiums for family coverage climbed from $2,973 to $5,277, representing an alarming 78 percent increase, per the KFF survey (figure 5.5).[311]

Exhibit D:
Average Annual Health Insurance Premiums and Worker Contributions for Family Coverage, 2006-2016

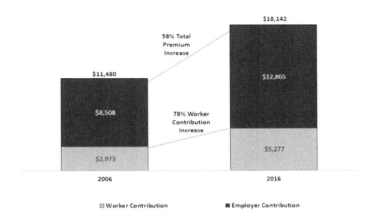

SOURCE: Kaiser/HRET Survey of Employer-Sponsored Health Benefits, 2006-2016.

Figure 5.5 Average Annual Health Insurance Premiums and Worker Contributions for Family Coverage, 2006–2016. Source: The Henry J. Kaiser Family Foundation. (2016, Sept. 14). Summary of findings. 2016 Employer Health Benefits Survey. Retrieved from http://kff.org/report-section/ehbs-2016-summary-of-findings/

As a means of controlling healthcare costs, deductibles have failed miserably. In part, it is because when physicians tell patients they need something—a test, procedure, or prescription, for example—patients are typically focused on the *clinical* aspects of the conversation, not the *financial* ones (more on that in a minute).

One problem, as the previous figures illustrate, is that HDHPs are pushing the boundaries of affordability for many people. As noted above, the average deductible for individual coverage was $1,478 in 2016.[312]

Compare that to a recent survey conducted by the Board of Governors of the Federal Reserve System (aka, "the Fed"), which showed that 46 percent of US adults said they could not cover an emergency expense costing just *$400*.[313] (And today's average deductible for individual coverage is three-and-a-half times that amount!) I am even seeing plans with deductibles as high as $15,000 to $20,000. That is like walking onto a car lot and paying cash. That does not happen often. The same Federal Reserve System survey showed that 22 percent of respondents had experienced a "major unexpected medical expense" for which they had to pay out of pocket in the previous year; and 46 percent of those respondents stated they still owed debt from that expense.[314] Patients cannot afford the out-of-pocket expenses under the benefit plans they have purchased after the bills come.

If that does not raise an eyebrow, ponder this: Most interventions and procedures at a hospital *start* in the several hundred dollars range. I did a quick search of some common procedures for my zip code on healthcarebluebook.com, and found the following:

- Physician office visit (60 minutes for a new patient): $402

- CT scan, abdomen and pelvis, with and without contrast: $828

- Emergency room (ER) visit, level IV (severe issue): $2,483

- Vaginal delivery, three-day inpatient stay: $9,625

- Appendectomy (general surgery): $13,589

- Hip replacement with inpatient stay: $32,994

Using the typical benefits available through a health plan today and a typical worker's disposable income ($400), I thought it would be instructive to show how "underwater" a patient would be in funding their own care in several different scenarios (figure 5.6). The examples below assume a $1,500 deductible, 20 percent coinsurance, a $25 physician copay, and a $250 emergency department copay. I also assumed each visit only happened once in that plan calendar year (the deductible reset).

Scenario	Average cost	Relevant coverage	Patient responsibility	Amount underwater (patient responsibility minus $400)
Physician office visit	$402	Basic copay	$25 copay	Not underwater
CT scan	$828	$1,500 deductible	$828 out of pocket	$428 underwater
ER visit	$2,483	$250 copay + 20% coinsurance	$697 out of pocket	$297 underwater
Birth (vaginal delivery)	$9,625	$1,500 deductible + 20% coinsurance	$3,125 out of pocket	$2,725 underwater
Appendectomy (general surgery, outpatient)	$13,589	$1,500 deductible + 20% coinsurance	$3,918 out of pocket	$3,518 underwater
Hip replacement with inpatient stay	$32,994	$1,500 deductible + 20% coinsurance	$7,799 out of pocket	$7,399 underwater

Figure 5.6 How Far Underwater for Typical Hospital Scenarios? Source: Jonathan Wiik.

This is not news to hospitals, healthcare systems, physician groups, and other providers. The reality is that high deductibles are not changing patient behavior, or if they are, they may be changing it in a counterproductive way. Patients cannot afford the "insurance" plan that they purchased, let alone the climbing deductible. The results of a 2014 study by The Commonwealth Fund found that insured adults with HDHPs were more likely to delay or decline necessary care, due to cost concerns (figure 5.7).[315]

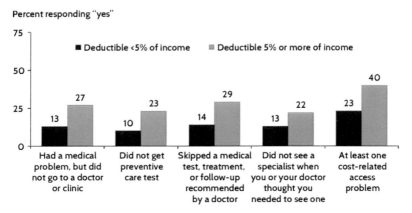

Percent responding "yes"

■ Deductible <5% of income   ■ Deductible 5% or more of income

	Had a medical problem, but did not go to a doctor or clinic	Did not get preventive care test	Skipped a medical test, treatment, or follow-up recommended by a doctor	Did not see a specialist when you or your doctor thought you needed to see one	At least one cost-related access problem
Deductible <5% of income	13	10	14	13	23
Deductible 5% or more of income	27	23	29	22	40

Privately insured adults ages 19–64 who have a deductible

Base: Respondents who reported their income level and deductible for their private insurance plan (includes those who are currently covered by employer-provided insurance, a marketplace plan, or a plan they purchased through the individual market outside of the marketplaces).
Source: The Commonwealth Fund Health Care Affordability Tracking Survey, September-October 2014.

Figure 5.7 Two of Five Privately Insured Adults with Deductibles That Comprise Five Percent or More of Their Income Reported Delaying or Avoiding Needed Health Care Because of Their Deductible. Source: Collins, S. R., Rasmussen, P. W., Doty, M. M., Beutel, S. & The Commonwealth Fund. (2014, Nov.). Too high a price: out-of-pocket health care costs in the United States: Findings from the Commonwealth Fund Health Care Affordability Tracking Survey, September-October, 2014 [PDF document]. Retrieved from http://www.commonwealthfund.org/~/media/files/publications/issue-brief/2014/nov/1784_collins_too_high_a_price_out_of_pocket_tb_v2.pdf

To make matters worse, there is a level-of-care problem with these delays. The patient delays their care, gets sicker, and then has to go to an emergency department instead of seeing a physician (or even being treated in an urgent care center). It has been well documented that effective preventative care upfront can reduce costs later down the line, but cost and affordability concerns can disrupt that. For example, diagnosing and successfully treating metabolic syndrome (a group of conditions including high blood pressure, high blood sugar, obesity, and abnormal cholesterol and/or triglyceride levels) can prevent bigger, more complex health problems from developing later. If not addressed early, metabolic syndrome can lead to more complex and more expensive problems—like heart disease, stroke, and diabetes—down the line.

It is the same with medication nonadherence, as we discussed in Chapter 2. If you do not take your cholesterol medication, or you do not follow your inhaler regimen because of cost concerns, you may end up in the ER.

So HDHPs can actually be a short-sighted approach to controlling healthcare costs. If patients forgo preventative care because of cost concerns, you are not really controlling costs at all. You are just kicking the can down the road. Granted, most health plans have been structured to make physician office visits and preventative services more affordable, but once things get complicated after that first visit (cancer, shortness of breath, broken bones, heart arrhythmias, etcetera), the costs get exponentially more complex, as well. That is when that deductible kicks in. Patients are then faced with a funding choice (that is, if they are even thinking about the costs at all). The deductible either causes the patient to delay the care or causes the patient to delay payment, or to not pay at all, due to a lack of affordability. HDHPs are simply not sustainable over the long-term as a mechanism to curb healthcare costs or premiums. It is a dysfunctional spiral; keep premiums affordable through high deductibles, which allows more patients to purchase insurance to gain access to care, but the patients cannot afford the deductible to get the care, so they do not.

A 2015 Kaiser Family Foundation issue brief made the critical point that coverage does not always translate to care (or payment):

> Asking enrollees to pay a portion of costs at the point of service may encourage them to make consumer health care more wisely and to weigh the costs and benefits of alternative treatment options and providers. At the same time, cost sharing that seriously stresses family budgets may act as an impediment to seeking needed care, frustrating a primary reason people seek to be insured in the first place. For these families, having coverage would certainly reduce the ultimate financial consequences of serious illness, which is important both for the family and for providers delivering care, but this is a bargain that may look better in hindsight, after an illness has occurred, than it does when the family is trying to decide whether or not to pay for such a plan in the first place. Particularly as we extend private cover-

age to more families with lower incomes and limited resources, we need to be cognizant of their financial capacity to use the coverage that they are being asked to buy. [316]

Even consumers who can presumably "afford" to pay the deductibles on those HDHPs do not change their behavior much. A study by the Employee Benefit Research Institute (EBRI) showed that only 33 percent of adults enrolled in an HDHP were likely to check the price of a service before getting care, compared to 26 percent of adults enrolled in a traditional plan.[317] That is an increase of only 7 percent, and it means that two out of three patients did not check prices at all, even when enrolled in an HDHP.

That is consistent with what I experienced in my role at the hospital, and with what I experience when networking or speaking at industry events. When I am doing a presentation, I always ask how many people in the audience can tell me what their health plan deductible amount is, and only a few raise their hands. I also ask how many are asking patients for money before they come back into the clinical area—about a third raise their hands. And how many collect it? Less than one in 10. That is why I say, "death to the deductible." It simply does not work the way it is intended to.

Patients Do Not Shop for Kidneys Like They Shop for Cars

Cost does not drive consumer behavior in healthcare as much as our legislators and some industry leaders think. As I mentioned earlier, when patients are presented with a disease diagnosis or treatment options, they are focused on the clinical aspects of that, not the financial aspects. Given this, it is still interesting how cost concerns for patients rank high among all other fears. Per a Kaiser Family Foundation report, more people were worried about not being able to afford healthcare services than were worried about losing their jobs or not being able to pay their rent or mortgages (figure 5.8).[318]

Apparently, there is a "concern" for costs, but this concern is not linked to a change in behavior. Patients still seek healthcare when they feel sick or are scared, and then they fear the costs. They will forgo some things, but when a situation gets complicated, they seek care and worry about the cost later.

Cost Concerns, Including Health Care Costs, Top List of Worries

Percent who say they are worried about each of the following:

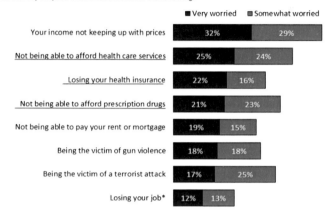

Figure 5.8 Cost Concerns, Including Healthcare Costs, Top List of Worries. Source: DiJulio, B., Kirzinger, A., Wu, B., & Brodie, M. (2017, March 2). Data note: Americans' challenges with health care costs. The Henry J. Kaiser Family Foundation. Retrieved from http://kff.org/health-costs/poll-finding/data-note-americans-challenges-with-health-care-costs/

Physicians typically are not thinking about costs when they are treating their patients, either. (I think this is a good thing for the most part, but there is some opportunity for improvement here, as we will discuss in later chapters). CMI/Compass performed a survey of more than 800 physicians over six different physician specialties and found that when prescribing medications—a relatively nonurgent practice—cost is not a consideration.[319] Doctors pick the drug that is needed, without considering cost. The survey also pointed out that physicians are having to field some questions about the cost, but not a lot. Primary care physicians ranked costs as "an important consideration," which makes sense, since they see a lot of patients at a high frequency, and pharmaceutical treatments are often the first line of defense (take this pill and call me in the morning). I am certainly not suggesting that the out-of-pocket cost does not come into play for some patients, but it is not the majority, as we learned earlier. Most clinical care is not planned; it is a surprise. Cost is not the first thing on a patient's (or physician's) mind when they get the surprise of a medical diagnosis; getting better is.

When a doctor tells us we are sick, there is something in our human DNA that makes us feel compelled to do whatever we need to do to get that fixed. We want to get better; we want to be made whole again—no matter the cost. If you want to buy a house or car or take a vacation, cost generally factors into that decision right up front. But with healthcare—for better or for worse—it is different. Costs take a back seat.

I will qualify this by saying that with elective procedures, cost can be a factor. Take, for example, total knee replacement surgery (aka, arthroplasty). One study found that arthroplasty is the most commonly performed surgery during a hospital stay.[320] Knee replacement surgery can make a huge difference for patients in terms of eliminating pain and restoring mobility, however, knee replacement surgery is not considered an emergency—that is, a compromised knee is typically not considered a life-threatening condition.

With elective procedures, there is evidence that patients will "shop around"—somewhat. Not to the degree that they would when buying a car or house, but more so than they would with other types of medical issues. Patients have the gift of time with electively scheduled procedures, e.g. "My knee hurts. I'm going to go see the orthopedist." They may decide to go to the orthopedist to get some imaging studies, get a diagnosis, and schedule a procedure for a few weeks down the road. One study found that 30 percent of consumers with traditional health plans; 35 percent of consumers with consumer-driven health plans (defined as plans with a deductible of $1,000-plus for individual plans or $2,000-plus for family coverage, combined with an HSA or HRA); and 39 percent of those with HDHP plans sought cost information about outpatient procedures and surgeries (figure 5.9).[321]

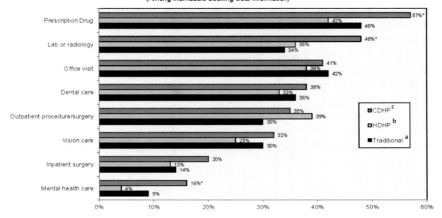

**Types of Cost Information Sought,
by Type of Health Plan, 2013**
(Among Individuals Seeking Cost Information)

Source: EBRI/Greenwald & Associates Consumer Engagement in Health Care Survey, 2013
a Traditional = health plan with no deductible or <$1,000 (individual), <$2,000 (family)
b HDHP = High-deductible health plan with deductible $1,000+ (individual), $2,000+ (family), no account
c CDHP = Consumer-driven health plan with deductible $1,000+ (individual), $2,000+ (family), with account
* Difference between HDHP/CDHP and Traditional is statistically significant at p ≤ 0.05 or better

Figure 5.9 Types of Cost Information Sought, by Type of Health Plan, 2013. Source: Fronstin, P. (2013, Dec.) Findings from the 2013 EBRA/Greenwald & Associates Consumer Engagement in Health Care Survey. EBRI Issue Brief, No. 393. Retrieved from https://www.ebri.org/pdf/briefspdf/EBRI_IB_012-13.No393.CEHCS.pdf

With nonelective procedures, however, cost is rarely a part of the upfront conversation. If you start noticing something is wrong—an ache in your abdomen, a pain in your neck, an itchy rash—the first thing you are going to do is ask your family and friends (your social network), if they know anyone who has had similar symptoms and, if they did, who they saw to get it fixed. You are not thinking about costs at that point; you are just looking for the best place to get better.

After you talk to your family and friends, you consult with a doctor, if you have one. What does he or she recommend? Ninety-nine percent of the time that is what the patient is going to do. The doctor says, "You need this stuff," and you go get it. You do not shop for it; you just get it. I call it the "grocery-store-at-night" scenario. Imagine you are at your doctor's office and the doctor says, "I need you go to this grocery store with me. I'm not going to tell you the name of the store, but we're going to go there together, and I'm going to push your cart and put a bunch of stuff in it, because there is something wrong with you and we need to get it fixed."

So you show up at the grocery store, and it is dark, the lights are all off, and the doctor is saying, "You need this, and you need this, and you need this ..." You keep hearing things going "clunk" in your cart. You get to the register and you hear the "beeps" as the prices are being scanned, but you cannot see any of the prices. At the last minute, after you have been rung up, the lights come on. You look in the cart. You do not really know what any of that stuff in there is or how much any of it costs, but that cart is *full*. The cashier hands you your receipt—it says "$10,256." Then she smiles and says, "Don't worry, we'll just bill you." And you say, "Thanks," and you leave. That is healthcare, right there.

That it is also why transparency—the "T" word—is not going to solve the problem. Publishing prices is not going to solve the consumer's issue with healthcare, because price does not mean anything unless there is also coverage, fundability, affordability, and acceptance from the patient. Most patients do not understand their benefits; they do not understand what the prices mean, just like the grocery store example. Just putting prices out there does not help. I will give you an example: "Mr. Wiik, you need a cardiac catheterization. The price is $10,000." Um, do I say "OK" or "yikes!"? My point is that stating a price does not garner funding, just like creating transparency legislation does not cause a lowering of healthcare costs for providers; it just adds administrative burdens. Stating a price is just that—a price. What do we gain by that? What does the patient gain? It scares the heck out of the patient, but it does not solve anything. The system needs to look more holistically at the larger issues—affordability and funding mechanisms—along with rising (somewhat uncontrolled) healthcare costs. It is a complex issue, and knowing the prices is a start, but not a solution. Discussing costs and treatment options in tandem, as well as funding mechanisms, may help drive some change.

Entitled to Healthcare?

Healthcare is "legalized shoplifting." You are either laughing with me, or really angry at me right now, but think about it. In what other industry can you get pretty much whatever you want (with a doctor's order) and not have to pay a dime of it until much later (if at all)? Healthcare has evolved into a services-*now*, figure-out-payment-*later* industry. It is somehow culturally unacceptable to talk about costs before care is provided, yet patients are accustomed to knowing the costs in advance (and paying them) in all other industries. People do not show up at the airport and expect to hop on a plane and deal with the bill later. People do not show up at a car dealership, jump into a car, and drive it off the lot without first thinking about the cost and how they are going to pay for it. They do not order anything they want at a restaurant and then not expect a bill to be paid before they leave. They have a backstop with those purchases; they know the costs and make decisions about what goods they are going to purchase and act accordingly. There is an inferred agreement in place—if you want these goods, you have to pay for them—sometimes before, sometimes during, but hardly ever after. Even a car or home purchase requires a loan in advance before you get to keep it, unless you are paying cash.

But people do not seem to have that kind of a backstop with respect to healthcare. They might not have insurance; or they may be underinsured, with a $10,000 deductible; or they may have great insurance that does not cover the one thing they want. But they come in anyway. When I worked at a hospital, we would try to call as many patients as possible in advance of elective procedures and let them know, to the best of our ability, what the anticipated out-of-pocket patient cost was going to be. We would get all kinds of responses, from "thank you" to "how dare you." Over time, patients became more appreciative of us for helping them navigate their costs, but it was a journey.

The toughest patients were the ones who said, "Well, I do not really have the money." We would then move into a dialogue about whether they needed financial assistance and, if not, how they planned to pay for the services. Some would say they had been saving, or planned to pay over time, or they were getting insurance soon, or—my personal favorite—"Well, I do not really have a plan." They would just come in and let the system do what the system was going to do. Healthcare is different than any other industry—payment is an afterthought. Imagine this scenario in another industry: "Well, I don't have any money or any plans to pay you, but I still need this." If you took (stole) it, and walked out, you would get tackled or arrested faster than you can say, "Bill me." It would not work. Yes, healthcare is different; there is pain and wellness, and some level of duty (or entitlement) to care, while at the same time, costs and affordability have been taboo topics with most hospitals. Why?

The societal question is, does the patient have access to imaging, the lab, the operating room, and all of the other resources of the hospital for any purpose they want, at any hour of the day, without having any financial obligation to pay for it?

By way of illustration, let me tell you about "Mr. Smith" (not his real name). This story was shared by a healthcare colleague about something that happened at his facility, and it is a good example of the kinds of dilemmas hospitals face every day. Mr. Smith was scheduled for an elective procedure. The procedure was scheduled for several weeks out, but Mr. Smith did not have any insurance coverage. The procedure was expensive—representing maybe $30,000 to $70,000 on the high end in charges. Fees for the diagnostic studies alone for this procedure can run between $10,000 and $25,000.

The exact costs for this procedure—like many other hospital procedures—are difficult to estimate until doctors actually "get into" the patient. There are a lot of nuances in the art and science of medicine, and a lot of variables that do not make themselves known until you actually begin a procedure or operation. Because of that, insurance reimbursement and out-of-pocket costs are highly variable for this procedure. It would be typical for a person with insurance to still have thousands of dollars of patient responsibility after insurance paid, and an uninsured patient could easily face tens of thousands of dollars in patient responsibility.

Mr. Smith was an entrepreneur. He did not have employer-sponsored coverage or any other kind of health insurance coverage. He was self-pay, or "self-insured." He could afford insurance, but chose not to purchase it. The process at this particular hospital was to prescreen patients that presented as self-pay in an attempt to establish a funding mechanism prior to service. As I have mentioned, many hospitals consider it important for patients to understand their financial position *before* they come in for services, rather than just sending them a surprise bill afterward and expecting them to pay it.

One of the hospital's financial counselors called Mr. Smith a couple of weeks before his procedure was scheduled. They told him: "Mr. Smith, we see you are on the schedule with Dr. Jones for procedure "X". We would like to help you understand your financing situation. This is obviously a procedure that you need, otherwise Dr. Jones would not have ordered it, but we also need to figure out whether you might be eligible for our hospital's charity program, or Medicaid, or another funding resource. It's important we have a plan to fund your care for this scheduled procedure prior to your visit so you can focus on getting better and not worry about the bill."

The financial counselor went through the standard litany of questions: "Are you employed? Did you lose your job? Are you disabled?" All of those fun questions they use to screen patients for funding programs that are available.

Mr. Smith turned out to be what I call a "doughnut hole" patient. He did not have insurance, and he also made too much money to be eligible for any type of assistance program like the Affordable Care Act (ACA) exchange plans or Medicaid. He was stuck. He was in his late 30s or early 40s, with a wife and a couple of kids, and—per the financial counselor—he had made the gamble of not electing coverage. He opted not to spend money on health insurance. And now he needed it.

He started trying to negotiate the price down with the financial counselor, as if he was buying a car. I can appreciate that—at least he was asking, and trying to figure out what he could pay prior to coming in—that is better than what most patients do. The financial counselor told him the hospital could discount it down to cost. Hospitals do not want to lose money on an elective procedure that is scheduled; they need to be paid for the services being provided. Some hospitals have found a way to discount procedures down to the fixed costs and eat the labor/variable costs as an exception to get as low as one can to bridge the affordability gap. This only works for scheduled, elective procedures, as hospital personnel need time to talk to the vendors, to talk to the physician(s), and to calculate the cost of the supplies and the room, etcetera.

Typically, in this scenario, the finance and the billing departments have to do some really complicated math to calculate what the actual cost would be to perform the procedure, weighing the time, materials, risks, etcetera, and excluding any possible insurance reimbursement.

In Mr. Smith's case, the hospital got the charges down to around $18,000, which was slightly less than the $20,000 they would have been reimbursed from an insurance company, and it covered the cost of the procedure, the medical supplies, pre- and post-op services, and the like. It was basically a "break-even" price. Providers have some discretion to discount care, but there are still certain fixed costs they have to cover. They cannot provide free care for everyone—if they did that all the time, they would eventually have to close their doors.

You actually see that happening with a lot of rural health centers these days. They do not have a choice—they take what they can get, and many patients cannot, or will not, pay. Doing a lot of procedures (or services) for free (in any business) leads to reduced income and ultimately, bankruptcy. Hospitals have a mission to treat those in need. I hate the saying, "no margin, no mission," but you need a margin to get to that mission, otherwise your hospital's ability to continue to provide care to the community really is jeopardized over the long term.

When the hospital presented Mr. Smith with the discounted price, he said, "I don't want to pay that. I think someone else should pay that." Wow. I am not sure how I would have reacted to that. Then it got more interesting. The hospital's financial counselor said, "Well, Dr. Jones thinks you need this procedure, so it needs to happen and it can, but we want to avoid a very large bill coming to you later in the mail. You do not have insurance, but you do have an ability to pay. We could set you up with a payment plan, and help you figure out how to fund your care." Mr. Smith refused assistance. Wow, again.

Wait, it gets better. Two weeks later Mr. Smith walked into the hospital's ER and said, "I'm scheduled for a procedure a couple of weeks from now, but my chest hurts …" which of course, are the magic words in an ER (as they should be). And, of course, because of the Emergency Medical

Treatment and Labor Act (EMTALA), they were obligated to treat him. He got his procedure that afternoon and was admitted to the hospital. A procedure that could have been done in an outpatient setting turned into an emergency department (ED) procedure followed by an inpatient stay. I find it interesting that depending upon where a patient presents—in this example an ED versus for a scheduled outpatient procedure—the care can differ somewhat (whether the patient has the clinical indications or not).

When the financial counselors who had spoken to him earlier saw that he was on the hospital census, they were upset about the turn of events, but Mr. Smith's behavior was not all surprising. When patients go to the ED, they are generally pretty scared. This patient must have been scared too (although I am not sure if he was more scared about the condition, the cost, or both). And I get that. From a clinical standpoint, I do not know how much danger Mr. Smith was in—I was not there, and I am not a doctor. If he had not gotten the procedure, would he have been fine, or would he have had a life-threatening event occur? Maybe he was not in that much danger, but he felt he was, so he went to the place everybody goes when they are in danger: the ER.

Afterward, the financial counselors explained to him that the bill would be even more expensive because of his choice to come through the emergency room—like, a *lot* more expensive. ED visits for this condition range in the $10,000 category at most hospitals, and the inpatient stay easily represents $5,000 a day. After all the unnecessary tests and physicians that came to see him unexpectedly, he was looking at another $100,000, on top of the $18,000 the hospital initially quoted him for the procedure at cost.

Mr. Smith told the hospital staff that he did not care, and that he knew if he came into the ER he would get the care he needed. They attempted to collect, but they could not. He may have paid partially on it—I do not really know—but eventually, it got written off as bad debt as it did not meet charity care assignment. Double wow. Free care, from someone who could have paid but refused to, and there was nothing anyone could do. And turning him over to collections could have made a bad situation even worse. How often do situations like this occur in hospitals today? Probably more often than you think.

When October came around, and the health insurance exchange enrollment period had opened, the hospital called him and encouraged him to get a plan for his family. They told him, "This incident was something that happened to you, but something could happen to your son or daughter, where they would need care, and you would be back in the same boat again. I know premiums are expensive, but healthcare is, too. And you need something to offset the cost." He thanked them for calling, and he did end up enrolling his family in coverage through the exchange, but it was too late to remedy his earlier situation.

Cannot Pay Versus Will not Pay

Insurance carriers are reasonably consistent when it comes to payment. Providers know that Medicare may pay them only 30 cents on the dollar, but, if they follow the rules, Medicare pays consistently and on time. Private insurers may pay 60 cents on the dollar, but it can be more complicated to collect because of denials related to eligibility, the scope of coverage, precertifications, authorizations, and things like that. But eventually, private insurers pay providers most of the time as well. (Hint: If they are not paying most the time, it might be a good time for providers to revisit that contract and renegotiate with better terms.)

Patients-as-payers are in a completely different ballpark. In the first place, all patients are not the same. There are three types of patients:

1. Patients who can pay you. They do not really want to be bothered, but they will always pay you.

2. Patients who want to pay you, but who really cannot afford to pay, or need help paying their balances over time.

3. And patients like Mr. Smith, who can pay, but will not.

4. I believe that most patients want to pay, and will pay, if you help them do so. Differentiating between a patient's willingness and ability to pay is critical to understanding how you collect (or can collect) from your patients.

Income and Ability to Pay

The federal government publishes an annual list of poverty guidelines (aka, the federal poverty level, or FPL) that determines eligibility for assistance programs such as Medicaid and subsidy-eligible ACA exchange plans. Guidelines take into account household size, household income, and state of residence (Alaska and Hawaii have higher poverty thresholds).[322] The guidelines for 2017 are as follows (figure 5.10):

Figure 5.10 2017 Poverty Guidelines and Approximate Federal Poverty Levels (200 Percent, 400 Percent) for the 48 Contiguous States and the District of Columbia

Persons in family/ household	Poverty guideline* (100%)	200%	400%**
1	$12,060	$24,120	$48,240
2	16,240	$32,480	$64,960
3	20,420	$40,840	$81,680
4	24,600	$49,200	$98,400
5	28,780	$57,560	$115,120
6	32,960	$65,920	$131,840
7	37,140	$74,280	$148,560
8	41,320	$82,640	$165,280

*For families/households with more than eight persons, add $4,180 for each additional person.
** Note that ACA Marketplace subsidies do not apply to households earning above 400% of the FPL.[323]

Figure 5.10 2017 Poverty Guidelines and Approximate Federal Poverty Levels (200 Percent, 400 Percent) for the 48 Contiguous States and the District of Columbia. Source: "Annual Update of the HHS Poverty Guidelines; Notice," 82 Federal Register 19 (31 Jan. 2017), pp. 8831-8832; and The Henry J. Kaiser Family Foundation. (2016, Nov. 1). Explaining health care reform: Questions about health insurance subsidies. Retrieved from http://kff.org/health-reform/issue-brief/explaining-health-care-reform-questions-about-health/

According to KFF, in 2015, 14 percent of the US population had incomes at less than 100 percent of FPL.[324] Another 18 percent of the population is under 200 percent of the FPL, and an additional 29 percent is under 400 percent of the FPL.[325] Doing the math, that is 61 percent of the US population under 400 percent of FPL. We have an affordability issue.

Traditional Medicaid eligibility is limited to specific low-income groups (see figure 4.6 from Chapter 4). ACA Marketplace subsidies phase in at 100 percent of FPL and phase out at 400 percent of FPL.[326] What this means is that there are coverage gaps. Low-income households can fall into the gaps between Medicaid eligibility and ACA subsidies, particularly in states that chose not to expand Medicaid eligibility.[327]

Middle-class families can fall into coverage gaps, too. At 400 percent of FPL, people do not qualify for premium subsidies. The insurance premium alone can take out a significant portion of their income at that level, and it is hard for people to think about spending that much money on something that they may or may not need when it means they may not have the money for rent or groceries. And besides being out of income level for subsidized premiums, they are also probably out of the income level for most hospital charity plans as well.

According to The Advisory Board Company, "patients aren't likely to pay medical bills greater than five percent of their household income."[328] Let us expand on this for a minute. The median household income in 2015 was $55,775, per the US Census Bureau.[329] Multiply that by 5 percent, and you get $2,788.70. Compare that to the average deductible for family coverage in an HDHP plan in 2015—$4,332—and it is clear we have a problem.[330]

Deductible Size and Propensity to Pay

Household income is only one factor that impacts whether or not a patient is likely to pay a bill for healthcare services. In revenue cycle management terms, that likelihood is called the patient's "propensity to pay." Propensity to pay is impacted by a number of factors, including household income, net worth, disposable income, available credit, and whether the patient has insurance coverage or not.

The size of the deductible (there is that useless "D" word again) also impacts a patient's propensity to pay (figure 5.11).

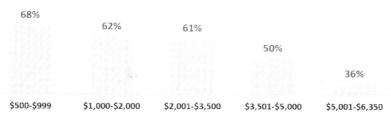

Figure 5.11 Patient Propensity to Pay by Deductible Size. Source: Eyestone, J., & Rozen, M. (2016, May 3). Patient payment optimization: Practical considerations for optimizing patient payment processes and performance. Retrieved from https://commercial.jpmorganchase.com/pages/commercial-banking/executive-connect/patient-payment-optimization

The higher the deductible, the lower the propensity (or likelihood) of payment. A patient is only 36 percent likely to pay off a bill over $5,000.[331] While there is an appeal to lower premiums, especially with the ACA plans, they have a hidden, very high dollar deductible. This is not surprising, considering deductible costs are typically inversely related to premium costs. Lower income households are more likely to choose lower premium plans (even if they come with higher deductibles) than high premium plans. This makes matters worse. A family with very little income and propensity to pay has a very large deductible. That quickly translates into medical debt and household bankruptcies.

Age of Account and Likelihood of Collecting

An average of 50 percent of all patient financial responsibility goes uncollected.[332] Naturally, the older the account receivables (A/R), the harder they become to collect. In fact, at about the 180-day mark, the cost of collecting exceeds the value of the account. A dollar today in collectable is only worth 5 cents in a year, as the cost to collect it, as well as the likelihood of collecting it, outweighs the amount collected. One of my favorite sayings is, "The least expensive time to collect is right now … it gets real expensive to collect money tomorrow!"

What This Means for Providers

Patients do not pay like insurance carriers. They pay slower and take longer and hence, take more resources to collect, which drives up the cost to collect. A McKinsey & Company survey indicated, "Costs are likely to be significantly higher when collecting from individual patients on a per-transaction basis than when collecting from payors—on average, healthcare consumers pay more than twice as slowly as commercial payors."[333]

Per a TransUnion healthcare report released in June of 2016, 51 percent of patients owed more than $1,000 in out-of-pocket costs, and 77 percent owed more than $500.[334] Patients also represented a large amount of downstream debt when faced with large bills. In an isolated study, for patients that owed $3,000 or more, only 2 percent of the patients paid their bill in full. Eight percent of patients partially paid their bill. Inversing those numbers, 92 to 98 percent of the time patients did not pay their bill in full or at all when they owed more than $3,000.

Equally troubling is the fact that there is less credit to fund the debt. Per the report: "TransUnion Healthcare's proprietary ratio comparing available revolving credit to select healthcare costs declined to 17.2 to 1 in Q1 2016. The ratio means that for every $100 in healthcare costs, consumers had $1,720 in revolving credit to potentially make those payments at the end of March 2016. Just one year prior, consumers had $2,250 in revolving credit for medical costs as the ratio stood at 22.5 to 1 in Q1 2015."[335] That is alarming.

To add fuel to the fire, patients who did not like their healthcare experience did not like paying for it, either. McKinsey conducted a survey in 2008 to identify what the drivers were behind insured consumers' nonpayment of medical bills (figure 5.12).[336] Although the information is somewhat dated, what is important for providers to note is that the majority of the reasons for nonpayment are addressable. That is, the vast majority of consumers just needed help to pay; they needed a more patient-friendly bill, a more timely statement, or financing options. McKinsey also shared through a 2013 JPMorgan Chase & Co. report that, "52 percent of consumers would pay from $200 to $500 or more by credit or debit card when they visit a physician, if an estimate was provided at the point of care."[337]

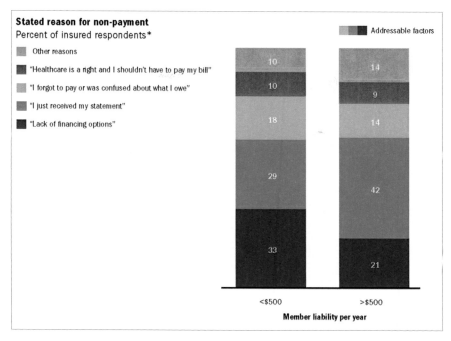

Figure 5.12 Drivers of Consumer Nonpayment. Source: Finn, P., Pellathy, T., & Singhal, S. (2009). U.S. healthcare payments: remedies for an ailing system. In McKinsey on Payments, No. 4, April 2009 [PDF document]. Retrieved from http://healthcare.mckinsey.com/sites/default/files/762679_US_healthcare_payments_Remedies_for_an_ailing_system.pdf

This points to the fact that hospitals and healthcare systems are largely behind every other industry in terms of meeting the customer where they are at. Healthcare is not a retail consumer experience.

Think about the last time you went to a car mechanic to have your car repaired. Now, I am embarrassed to admit this, but I do not know anything about cars. I have never even changed my own oil. I could change a battery or a tire, and I know where the oil and other fluids are, and I know what the gauges are, but I have no idea how it all really works. I am a revenue-cycle guy, I know hospitals, not cars. I am a mechanic's dream when I walk in. They could tell me whatever they wanted, and I would probably believe them.

When your car breaks down, and you are not familiar with it, you are going to talk to someone who knows something about cars. You might call a buddy, or a mechanic who you know, and have a conversation that is very similar to a conversation you might have with your physician. The same dialogue happens, whether it is "my stomach hurts" or "I'm hearing this clunky noise from the right rear tire." The mechanic then says, "Tell me about the noise," and the physician says, "Tell me about your pain." It is the same. They both are working up a diagnosis—only one is mechanical and one is clinical.

But at the auto repair shop, something interesting happens, and that is where the process is different from healthcare. At the auto repair shop, some nice lady or gentleman at the front desk takes all of your information, and then they give you an estimate, if they can. If they cannot, they might say, "We are not sure what is wrong with it, we might have to get in there and figure it out. I'll call you with an estimate once we have it figured out. What number would you like us to call?" And with some shops, they go a step further, and they say, "At what level would you like us to do the work without bothering you?" I love it when they ask that, because if it is under $500, I will just say, "Do it" or, "Please call me if it is over this much."

A couple of hours later, the phone will ring, and you start this all-too-familiar thought process in your head: "How much are they going to tell me this going to be? How much is it going to be in parts? How much is it going to be in labor? Do I have to get a new part? Oh, please let this be a cheap, understandable thing that just goes away!"

I have had times where the mechanic has said, "It was nothing, we did this and this, and there is no charge," and I have had other experiences where the mechanic says, "You have to replace this thingamajig and it's going to cost about $600, plus five hours of labor to put it in." I never have any idea whether they are lying to me or not. But if it is expensive, I will say, "Hold off on that; let me call around and compare rates." (That is code for, "I better tell my wife about it so she can call and get the best deal before I do something stupid and pay too much." My wife is way smarter than I am).

On certain things—clutches, tires, brakes, transmissions, and things like that—I have learned to call around and check prices. You are starting to see that a little bit in healthcare, calling around for things like MRIs or CT scans, or maybe knee or hip surgeries—things that are more elective. But that critical moment, that differentiator, is when the mechanic calls the consumer back to say, "This is what I think is going wrong, based on the test results, and *this is how much it's going to cost to fix it*." That does not happen in healthcare very often. Only 35 percent of hospitals are doing preservice estimates per a 2015 Availity report.[338]

What happens instead is the "grocery store in the dark" scenario I described earlier. You get referred to the lab to diagnostic testing and to specialists, or to other services, but the conversation about cost rarely happens. It does not happen like it does with the car mechanic—the process of receiving an estimate before starting the work in healthcare is still evolving. In healthcare, it is not until after you have been treated the "discussion" happens, and it is a one-sided discussion at that—just a bill in an envelope.

Aligning Patient and Provider Interests

The McKinsey data mentioned previously included another data point that is relevant to the conversation about patients as payers. McKinsey noted that provider collection rates vary depending on the amount owed, and produce different outcomes as the consumers' ability and willingness to pay are considered (figure 5.13).[339] A patient who has a bill of less than $500 is almost always (92 percent) willing to pay his or her bill, and the provider is likely to collect it (65–75 percent). Conversely, a patient who has a bill that is over $500 may only be willing to pay half the time (54 percent), and the yield to the provider drops significantly (50–60 percent). Three percent of patients with bills higher than $500 lack an ability to pay the bill at all, and the provider only collects 20 percent of the time. In other words, as the bill gets higher, the patient's willingness and ability to pay diminishes, as does the provider's ability to collect it.

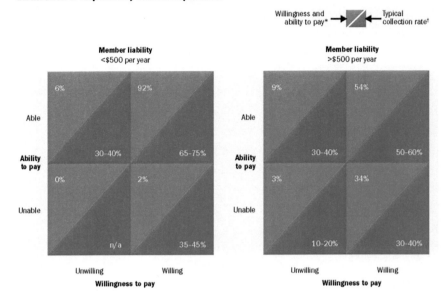

Figure 5.13 Collection Rates Lag Consumers' Ability and Willingness to Pay. Source: Finn, P., Pellathy, T., & Singhal, S. (2009). U.S. healthcare payments: remedies for an ailing system. In McKinsey on Payments, No. 4, April 2009 [PDF document]. Retrieved from http://healthcare.mckinsey.com/sites/default/files/762679_US_healthcare_payments_Remedies_for_an_ailing_system.pdf

Patients who do not like their healthcare experience do not like paying for it, either. A separate study noted that dissatisfied patients are less likely to pay than satisfied patients (figure 5.14).[340]

On balances over $100, patients who were fully satisfied with their care paid in full 70 percent of the time, or paid a portion with the intent to pay in full 95 percent of the time. Those who were very dissatisfied paid in full only 22 percent of the time, and paid a portion with the intent to pay in full only 50 percent of the time. They may *intend* to pay it, but they do not, and it delays collections significantly and ultimately drives up the cost to collect. Happy patients equal paying patients equal lower collection costs. This represents yet another reason to discuss financial plans in advance so everyone is on the same page—happy, paying, and getting paid. Saying nothing creates confusion, and confusion

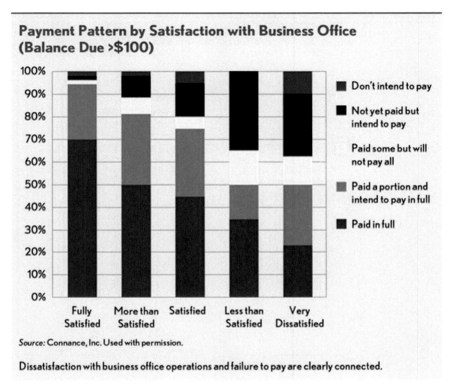

Payment Pattern by Satisfaction with Business Office (Balance Due >$100)

Source: Connance, Inc. Used with permission.

Dissatisfaction with business office operations and failure to pay are clearly connected.

Figure 5.14 Dissatisfied Patients Are Less Likely to Pay. Source: Fifer, J. J. (2014, Sept. 18). Staying ahead of the curve: Revenue cycle change. 2014 MAHAP-MPAA-HFMA, Michigan Revenue Cycle Conference. Retrieved from http://www.mahap.org/2014-2015+Programs

brings forth frustration, dissatisfaction, and ultimately slow or no payment. Patients need to be treated as paying customers, as they are the new payers.

What providers need to do is to educate and engage patients. Educate them about their eligibility, benefits, coverage, and costs. Along with helping patients navigate clinical information, we also must find a way to engage them in a discussion about the financial aspects of their care. That will help both the patient and the provider. It is important that the patient experience includes a patient financial experience along with clinical experience.

The goal is not necessarily to collect more money from the patient.

The goal is to educate and engage patients in the financial aspects of their healthcare, to couple patients with the best funding mechanisms for their situations, and to prevent downstream debt to them and the hospital.

These outcomes are very achievable, but everyone in the healthcare system is going to have to align around patient-centered financial engagement in order for it to occur. There are many different players in the healthcare arena that impact each patient's financial experience. I will talk about each of these important roles, and the critical part they play in the patient financial experience, in the next chapter.

CHAPTER 6

. . . .

THE UNUSUAL
SUSPECTS

"Patient experience" is at the forefront of a lot of initiatives in health-care today. These programs focus primarily on the clinical or customer service aspects in delivering healthcare.   Hospitals are also getting paid based on how well they can create a good "patient experience." What does not get enough attention is the patient's *financial* experience. Yet, as the share of patients-as-payers grows, the patient's financial experience is becoming a critical component of healthcare delivery.

The patient's financial experience is not the responsibility of a single person or a single department in a hospital or clinic. Each of the stake-holders in the healthcare arena plays a role in the experience. Let us take a look at some of the key players.

The Employer

Employer-sponsored health insurance is the largest source of health insurance in the United States, covering about 49 percent of the total population.[341] (On average nationally, Medicaid covers about 20 percent; Medicare covers about 14 percent; nongroup coverage represents about 7 percent; other public programs about 2 percent; and the uninsured about 9 percent of the total population).[342] This means that employers have a large sphere of influence with respect to the patient's financial experience. Employers also front most of the healthcare premium bill for the com-mercially insured, as we learned in the last chapter (figure 5.5), funding almost 70 percent of the premium for employed workers.[343]

Of course, the employer's priority is not about providing healthcare for their employees—that is just a part of their role. The employer's incentive is to have engaged, healthy employees. That is their task, from a business standpoint. Because of the way health insurance evolved in the United States, employers need to offer health insurance to attract and retain employees. And although that may have been a benefit during World War II, when it allowed employers to get around wage caps to attract employees, now, in 2017, it has come back to haunt them.

And if footing the premium bill is not enough, regulations like those in the Affordable Care Act (ACA) have put pressure on employers in terms of what types of health insurance plans they must offer and what coverage must be included, as well. Small businesses, in particular, have been feeling the brunt of the increased cost of providing health insurance as part of an employee's total compensation.

A 2016 survey by the National Federation of Independent Business (NFIB) found that "cost of health insurance" is the number one business problem across all categories of small businesses.[344] As health insurance premiums have increased, the percent of small business owners who offer health insurance has dropped (figure 6.1).[345]

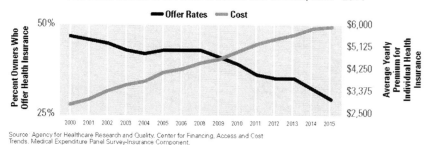

Figure 6.1 Health Insurance Offer Rates and Average Yearly Premiums for Businesses with Less Than 50 Employees, 2000–2014. Source: Wade, H., & National Federation of Independent Business (NFIB) Research Foundation. (2016, Aug.). Small business problems & priorities [PDF document]. Retrieved from http://www.nfib.com/assets/NFIB-Problems-and-Priorities-2016.pdf

Larger employers have turned to other strategies to try and control premium costs. As mentioned in previous chapters, the rapid adoption of health insurance plans with high deductibles, increased copays, and increased coinsurance percentages have been driven in large part by employers desperately seeking ways to hold down insurance premium costs. They have thrown their hands up in surrender and have shifted costs to the patient.

Some of the largest employers have the bargaining power to partner with insurers, saying, "Hey, I'm big. I want economies of scale. What can you do for me?" The insurer turns around and negotiates on the employer's behalf to get a provider network to sign something that keeps costs low. But that is still the exception, not the rule. Consolidation among insurers and among providers has certainly raised prices and decreased choices, making it a tough road for employers and their employees.

Now employers are beginning to get flak from employees that used to be directed toward insurers. Employees are asking employers about perceived health insurance plan shortcomings: "Why is this so expensive? Why isn't this covered? Why is my deductible so high?" Employers have not really stepped up in terms of educating their employees about the nitty-gritty of their health insurance coverage. They may have a health benefits education fair or something like that, but for the most part, those meetings focus on premium costs rather than the actual out-of-pocket costs the employee will incur when they use the plan. They show a comparison of plans with a high-level benefits summary, copays, deductibles, and so on, but they do not get into the granularity of consumer spend on common healthcare interventions, like we outlined in the last chapter (remember being underwater [figure 5.6]). There is an opportunity for improvement here, in the way employers engage their employees in conversations about their health insurance benefits. We will talk more about that in Chapter 10.

The Health Insurance Company (Big Brother)

Can you imagine a world without insurance? Insurers take a lot of heat for their profit margins and intrusive rules, but where would we be without health insurance companies to spread the risk around and make healthcare costs manageable? Insurers have a single goal in the patient-as-payer scenario: to provide coverage and access to care at the lowest cost.

The media often focuses on personal stories about claims that are *not* paid—outlining a treatment or medication that was excluded from coverage. What you do not hear about is the claims that *are* paid, and that number is big. For example, UnitedHealthcare, which administers more than 70 million health policies, is the largest health carrier in the United States.[346] In 2016, UnitedHealthcare collected approximately $144 billion in premium revenue and paid approximately $117 billion in healthcare claims.[347] After operating expenses, this represented a meager 3.6 percent margin.[348] Insurance companies are a big business with big expenses—medical expenses—and their margins are in the single digits. They are bearing the burden of costs with the rest of the healthcare industry. Do they make more than hospitals? Certainly. Are they making too much? Perhaps. Could the system survive without them? Never.

Consumers need health insurance coverage to manage costs, but health insurers need profits in order to continue to exist. If enrollees spend too much, premiums go up. This is what happened with many ACA individual market plans. For example, in January 2016, United-Health Group reported $720 million in losses on individual-market health plans.[349] People who signed up on the ACA health exchanges incurred higher claims risk than anticipated. Many insurers suffered losses—meaning more claims were paid out than premiums collected—because too many sick people signed up, and not enough healthy people did. That is why many insurers are either fleeing the individual exchange markets or significantly raising premium costs on health insurance exchange plans. As shown in figure 6.2, there has been a steady decline in the number of insurers represented in exchange plans offerings.[350] In 2016, 85 percent of enrollees had a choice of three or more insurers. In 2017, that number dropped by nearly a third, to 57 percent (figure 6.2).[351]

57% of exchange enrollees will have a choice of three or more insurers in 2017, down from 85% of exchange enrollees in 2016

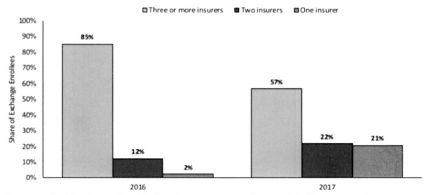

Source: Kaiser Family Foundation analysis of data from the 2017 QHP Landscape file released by healthcare.gov on October 24, 2016. Note: For states that do not use healthcare.gov in 2017, insurer participation is estimated based on information gathered from state exchange websites, insurer press releases, and media reports as of August 26, 2016. Enrollment is based on 2016 signups.

Figure 6.2 Decline in Number of Insurers Participating in ACA Exchange Plans. Source: Cox, C., Long, M., Semanskii, A., Kamal, R., Claxton, G., & Levitt, L. (2016, Nov. 1). 2017 premium changes and insurer participation in the Affordable Care Act's health insurance marketplaces. The Henry J. Kaiser Family Foundation. Retrieved from http://kff.org/health-reform/issue-brief/2017-premium-changes-and-insurer-participation-in-the-affordable-care-acts-health-insurance-marketplaces/

Likewise, if group plan premiums get too high, employers will not buy them. If employers do not buy them, insurers cannot sell insurance. If they cannot sell insurance plans, they will not exist as an insurer. Without insurance, you have an uninsured, self-pay patient population. Even with the decrease in the uninsured rate, Fitch Ratings has stated an *increase* in uncompensated care is not outside the realm of possibilities, given the rising deductibles, disruption to the ACA plans, and the fragility of the exchange plans.[352]

Insurers have to keep their costs down in order to continue to operate. Revenue and expense is a primary driver. They have shareholders they have to please, they have shares and stock prices, and if those stock prices are not performing well, things get really interesting.

So insurers have to manage costs. They have very sophisticated tools for that and there are large financial consequences if the numbers do not pan out. First, they must calculate claim risks accurately for the groups they cover. If they overestimate the risk for a particular claims pool, premium prices will have been overstated for the actual medical costs, making the insurance companies' plans less competitive in the market. If they underestimate the claims risk, as happened with the plans offered to the individual market through ACA, they suffer losses. So their actuarial calculations for the risk pool must be correct. Do not get me wrong, they are extremely good at it, but even the actuaries got thrown for a loop when the "young invincibles" did not show up for the ACA party.

I worked at an insurance company at one point, and the intricacy of actuarial calculations is pretty impressive. Group insurance benefit packages are structured around the per-member-per-month (PMPM) benefit risks or, in other words, the average estimated cost of services per individual per month. Now if you have an employee group that has 85 percent smokers, the premium is going to be higher than an employer with more nonsmokers, because the risk is higher. Same for an employer with carpenters as compared to one with desk jobs. The deductibles and benefits will be structured in a way to account for the increased risk.

Actuarial calculations are so sophisticated these days that I could literally ask one of the actuaries, "Can you tell me the number of 32-year-olds who smoke, who elected a plan with a $10 copay, and who visited the doctor six times or more in the following counties?" To compensate, perhaps the network referrals needed to be restricted to a subset of pulmonologists, or primary care physician (PCP) gatekeepers needed to be added for referrals, or a targeted smoking cessation incentive campaign needed to be included. That is a hypothetical example, but the point is, insurers have to be able to calculate risk to that level of granularity because their survival as a company depends on it. Every penny counts when addressing the healthcare benefits and behaviors of the hundreds of millions of members.

In conversations with employers, insurers can present these options. For example, they might say, "Yes, we can cover infertility treatments, but it will cost you an additional $1.25 per month per member in premiums to include that coverage. Still want to offer it?" Makes you feel a little weird, huh? It always comes down to following the money—in this case, flexing benefits up and down to hit a claims risk that hits a price point on a premium. There are winners and losers in that, but it involves allocating the resources (premium) affordably, for the maximum coverage and palatability for the employees (scope of coverage). Scope of coverage and premium affordability are inversely related, and human resources hears about it, even if premiums are low. Why is this not covered? Insurance is not free care for all—it was fundamentally designed to be an access bridge for consumers to cover unexpected costs. It has evolved into an entitled, often criticized catchall. Ignore the costs, or their impact on affordability? Cover the care? It is a tough balance.

The second tool insurers have to reduce expenses is leveraging economies of scale to negotiate discounts with providers. Individuals do not have the negotiating power to leverage economies of scale, but an insurer, representing hundreds or thousands or millions of potential patients, can bring that to the table when negotiating discounts for provider services.

At the patient level, insurers manage risk by establishing gatekeepers, such as the PCPs, who work with patients to direct access to services through a health maintenance organization (HMO). Even preferred provider organization (PPO) plans have elements of "managed care"— discounted rates with a narrow network of providers, or required authorizations and pre-certifications to access specialists or receive certain treatments or medications.

There are even plan designs with benefits that are structured at different levels depending on where you get your care, for example, no co-pay—that is, "free"—if you have a surgery in-network, but a $200 copay is required for an out-of-network surgery. Narrow networks, where there are only a few choices of places to receive care—sometimes only a single provider—are often structured this way. Some are even more restrictive, with only emergency benefits available out-of-network. Narrow networks are very much like those HMOs we all hated 20 years ago, but decreased choices equal decreased costs.

What is interesting these days is that because of high-deductible health plans (HDHPs)—at least with electively scheduled care—insurers often do not get into the mix until the third or fourth quarter of the year.

Before this, the patient is paying the provider out of pocket until they reach their deductible. So besides collecting premiums, insurers are not really coming into the picture as part of the patient financial experience until later in the year. They sit and watch that deductible grow, hoping it will curb utilization and—ultimately—cost.

The Schegistrar

Believe it or not, I did not make this word up. Google it and you will find a number of hospital job openings that use this term. Although it does not yet appear in the US Department of Labor Bureau of Labor Statistics *Occupational Outlook Handbook* (*OOH*), I have no doubt it will be appearing there soon. The schegistrar is the linchpin who connects the patient's clinical and financial experiences. There is probably no more critical position to the patient financial experience than this person. I call them the "smartest people in the hospital" (not clinically, but financially).

The schegistrar is a combination scheduler/registrar who also performs other duties as assigned. They have to know it all, and they wear many hats. They are concierges, info desk representatives, cashiers, admissions clerks, schedulers, financial navigators, insurance specialists, and receptionists, all in one. They are likely the first person the patient connects with at the hospital. They greet the patient, schedule the patient, register the patient, and may even do financial verification for coverage— be it insurance, charity, or the government—on behalf of the patient. They see every single patient, and they know the most about them, from a demographic and coverage standpoint. They have more interaction with the patient-as-payer than just about anyone else in the hospital. They serve as the bridge between the patient and the insurer, and the bridge between the patient and the hospital's billing department. And if the patient is uninsured, they wear two more hats: bill collector and/or counselor, depending on the patient's financial position.

Know this: Every hospital has (or should have) at least one schegistrar, although they may call them by different titles, such as patient access representatives, patient financial navigators, or patient financial advocates. Some hospitals have some of these roles shared across varying titles, which honestly can make it quite complex for a patient ("Oh, I don't know how to schedule, call someone else" or "I don't ask patients for money, go see the cashier").

These positions are often put into career ladders, tiered by the knowledge, skills, and abilities mastered at each level. Typically, an entry level role (Scheduler) would be someone who knows how to schedule patients; Level Two (Registrar) could be someone who knows how to schedule and admit, that is create accounts at registration. Level Three (Insurance Verification Specialist) could be someone who has Level Two skills, but who can also talk to insurance companies to get authorizations. Level Four people may have all of those skills plus the ability to provide reports to billing to appeal insurance decisions and get things covered by talking to a doctor's office to meet the plans rules. Level Five staff (Financial Counselors or Insurance Verification Specialists) know how to do all of those things plus screen patients for eligibility in health benefit exchange plans, Medicaid, or the hospital's charity program. Essentially, Level Five staff members are über-patient financial specialists.

Schegistrars are the staff who sit up front and say, "Mr. Smith, we have checked your insurance and you have a copay of $50 today. How would you like to pay that?" And they have to explain where they got that $50 figure with a presentation that is excruciating in detail, articulate, confident, accurate, polished, elegant, and with a smile-on-your-face "I love my job" attitude. You have not lived until you have asked a patient for money. These guys and gals do just that with a smile every day.

They have to say hard things like, "Insurance is a contract and it is between you and your insurer. I am sorry, but you will have to call them directly." They have to follow a "customer is always right" attitude, as patients have a higher service standard. Most patients, if not all, do not *want* to be at a clinic or hospital. They have something going on—they are ill, they are not feeling well—and as such, may not be in the best of moods. It is tough to smile at someone who does not smile back, over and over. Patients are very hard customers, and asking them for money or discussing payment options is often the straw that breaks the camel's back. It is necessary, as we talked about, so it has to be delivered in an elegant, collaborative way. Schegistrars are hired for their gift of people skills. It is a core competency.

Schegistrars have to communicate a lot of information in a short amount of time, and often defend things that they have very little control over. Patients get angry at them for things that are not their fault, saying things like, "I already told that *other* person why I'm here and my date of birth! My insurance covers this! How dare you ask me for money!" The hospital's billers accuse the schegistrars of not collecting the right information up front: "You didn't check the patient's insurance. You typed the number in wrong. You didn't collect the copay. You collected too much money. You didn't collect enough money. You didn't collect at all." If the schegistrar misses any detail, things downstream stall or reject, requiring rework. Schegistrars represent the first encounter for the patient and for data entry and as such, are the first to take the blame.

Despite the intensity of these patient conversations, in the ideal world, schegistrars would talk to 100 percent of the patients, 100 percent of the time—especially in this new patient-as-payer world. Schegistrars are the ones who introduce the conversation about the financial aspects of the patient's care. (In reality, maybe 30 percent of patients have a meaningful conversation about the financial aspects of their care at any point in their encounter with the hospital.) They genuinely want to help the patient get in for their care as fast as possible, get registered with the correct information, pay for things they can (or at least know what they are going to pay), and have them be as happy as possible. Really they do. It is why they applied for the job.

In my perfect world, I would have an army of schegistrars following each patient throughout the hospital, right by the patient's side, with a little clipboard (or tablet these days). "This procedure is going to be this much. What do you think? Let's talk about it. Let's call your insurance company." Now, this may be disruptive, and actually might annoy a patient (especially one that was admitted for a migraine or nausea), but insurance does not cover everything. In fact, as we talked about, it covers only a part. So how do you introduce that into the conversation?

I (as well as many clinicians I encountered) have struggled with identifying the best time to have these conversations. Ideally, it is before care is delivered, with a (very) accurate forecast. Short of that, then before a patient leaves. Having the conversation in real time would also certainly annoy the clinical staff, as the schegistrar would likely be in their way: "Oops, slow down, that requires a preauthorization. Pardon me, but that does not meet medical necessity requirements. Your insurance is not going to cover this. Do you still want to proceed?"

The schegistrar would be the patient's best friend—but sometimes, also, most hated, because they have to deliver the news about what is and is not covered. The schegistrar would certainly slow the process down, but they would make sure the patient was informed, every step of the way, of the financial implications of every aspect of their care. There is some benefit in that, and I would argue that it is a necessary annoyance. The key would be to do it at the right time, with the right people, with the right information. In time, patients would be grateful for the interactions as they would know what was coming from a billing standpoint. It would be one less thing to worry about. Financial conversations in parallel with clinical ones are possible. In every other industry we have pulled it off—even at the dentist. Why not in healthcare?

Hated or loved, schegistrars are indispensable to the patient financial experience. When the schegistrars are able to engage patients—often, appropriately, and upfront—it makes everybody else's job easier. And it can make the patient's life easier, by ensuring the patient is fully informed about the financial aspects of their care.

The Nurse

In any setting—whether it is a doctor's office, clinic, or hospital—if you had a stopwatch, you would find that patients spend more time with registered nurses (RNs) than any other clinician. That fact is a function of cost, resources, and working to the "top of your license." (Top of license means work as intended, or maximizing resources—RNs should do RN work, schegistrars should do patient access, phlebotomists should draw blood. If an RN performed lab tests that would not be working to the top of their license—sure they can do it, but it would not be the best use of resources.)

Nurses have a very large boundary when it comes to payment

discussions. If you even suggest that the nurse may have a role in the patient-as-payer scenario, the typical response you will get from a nurse is, "That isn't my job. My job is to treat patients." It is oil and water; the clinical and financial side shall never mix.

Now nurses generally do not need to operate in the realm of patient payment, but they are often put in that position. Nurses interact with the patient more than any other clinician, so patients ask them the most questions, and sometimes those questions have to do with cost and payment concerns. Because of that, nurses have an important role in the patient financial experience.

I have observed this working particularly well in emergency departments or discharge planning. The nurse can "hand off" the patient to a financial counselor: "We are all done with you, Mr. Wiik. We have got you stitched up and you are doing well. Here is your paperwork for your visit. By the way, on your way out, you need to stop and talk to one of our financial counselors about what you are going to owe us for the awesomeness you just experienced, okay? They accept most major credit cards. Thank you!"

The nurse is often the ideal person to make the transition between wrapping up the clinical care component of the patient experience and facilitating the patient's engagement in the financial aspects of care. This is not currently a common practice in hospitals, but it may become more common in the not-so-distant future. Again, right person, right time, and right information. I have interacted with *a lot* of patients, and most (not all), want to take care of the bill before they leave—again, one less hassle.

The Doctor

The doctor's role is patient-centered, as it should be. As important as the financial engagement conversation is for a hospital, you never, ever want to infringe upon the patient-physician relationship. I get the heebie-jeebies when I think about the idea of physicians who seriously weigh the cost of an intervention before suggesting it. It scares me, honestly. Physicians should order what will fix it, always. Cost is a factor, but physicians should remain focused on the clinical aspects of patient care: "What's going on here? What tests might I need to make a more accurate diagnosis? What treatments would be most effective for this particular diagnosis in this particular patient?" I am not suggesting that costs should be thrown out the window; they should absolutely be a consideration as things are ordered in a collaborative discussion with the patient. Having these conversations at the right time ensures the care can happen from a financing standpoint. Cost should not be a barrier to prescribing effective treatment (even though costs often can present a barrier later).

As much as they want to focus only on providing care, physicians themselves are not immune to the outside influences of the healthcare system. As we will talk about in a minute, when the physician is determining what tests to order, it is possible that part of that thought process will include, "What tests do I need to order, not only to diagnose this patient, but also to protect myself from a malpractice lawsuit down the line?" As costs come into the picture (and they are more and more), physicians have to weigh outcome, risk, and the patient-doctor relationship: "Dr. Smith, can you order something cheaper? I cannot afford that."

It puts physicians in a weird spot. Patients are the new payers and want to follow their money. More and more frequently, patients are approaching physicians and healthcare facilities from the perspective of a consumer—a consumer who wants to bargain and discuss options. Physicians want what is best for their patients, knows what that is, and now may be challenged on costs as related to the intensity of the interventions. Selecting an alternative, less-expensive treatment opens physicians up for risk. It will be an ethical dilemma for certain, and frankly, I am not sure how it will be solved without some legislative malpractice options. But I digress.

The adoption of electronic health records (EHRs) and electronic medical records (EMR) is another example of how changes in healthcare infringe on the relationship between the physician and his or her patient. The proliferation of EHRs has added a sometimes disruptive documentation obligation to the physician-patient interaction. Instead of the physician recording notes into a Dictaphone after the fact, the physician is now compelled to document the physician-patient interaction in real time on an electronic tablet. Physicians may have their backs to a monitor in an exam room as well, seemingly paying more attention to the computer than the patient.

Just as physicians have accommodated the age of EHRs, physicians may have a role to play in the new world of patient-as-payer—not as an agent of the financial interests of the hospital, but as facilitator of the patient financial engagement process that will keep the whole system running smoothly. Wanting what is best for the patient now has an affordability component. We talked about medical nonadherence a few chapters back. Just because something is ordered does not means it happens. In the last chapter, we talked about how patients delay care for fear of the costs. With a small tweak in the patient-physician interaction, magic can happen that increases the likelihood of the patient complying with the physician's orders, clinically and financially.

Let me give you an example of what I mean.

I travel a lot in my current job. One time I came home from a trip, woke up Saturday morning, and during morning cereal and cartoons I noticed a rash on my seven-year-old son's leg. I asked my wife about it, and she said it had just showed up and she was not sure what it was.

I looked more closely and saw it was about the size of a silver dollar, and it had some red striping on it, which to me indicated there might be some kind of infection. "We need to take him somewhere and get it looked at today," I said. Of course, it was off hours, on the weekend, and the pediatrician's office was closed. (You know my feelings on costs of care and emergency rooms, so that was out.)

I ended up taking him to one of those grocery store retail clinics. I like those places. You are in, you are out, and it is a copay, baby. Plus, I got a latte at the coffee place next to the bananas while we waited. It was awesome. Anyway, the clinician looked at the rash and indeed, diagnosed it as an infection. She began writing up a prescription for an antibiotic. She paused as she was writing the script, looked up, and said, "Wait, do you have insurance?"

I sat up straight in my chair. I have been working in this industry for a long time, and I have never been asked a question like that. I was intrigued. I wanted to know her intentions and have some fun, too. Hey,

I was sipping away at my coffee, it was Saturday, and we had no plans.

"Why does it matter whether I have insurance or not?" I asked.

She replied, "It is important your son get this medicine to clear up the infection. If you don't have insurance, I want to make sure you have the coverage to afford the antibiotics I'm ordering. I want to make sure you have a way of accessing these drugs so your son can get better, because if you don't have a way to fund the treatment, it's not going to happen. If you don't have insurance, or can't afford the copay, I have some vouchers I can give you for the medication."

I was floored. This is a conversation that rarely happens in health-care. I am not sure it can always happen exactly the way this did, but nonetheless it was refreshing. Typically, providers approach coverage as "verification." Is there coverage for this or not—it rarely gets into benefits or options. You get asked about insurance coverage, but the focus is gen-erally on whether you have it or not, versus the affordability of your care.

I do not know if this was because the caregiver was young, or if it was the way the clinic does things, or the caffeine from the coffee, but having the fundability conversation as part of the clinical one was remarkable. That conversation did not change the outcome—I was going to get treat-ment for my son one way or the other—the nurse practitioner (NP) and I assumed that. But the conversation accounted for the fact that there were several different possible paths to payment for the outcome the NP was aiming for, and she took the time to figure that out.

I realize this cannot happen in every situation—in an emergency department, for example, when things are happening so fast, or in a trauma situation in which there is no way to engage the patient in this type of conversation. There also are not vouchers or discounting or free care for everything.

But what about when it is not an emergency? What about when it is an elective procedure? What if the physician had information about your ability to pay, or lack of an ability to pay, and how that might deter your care? What types of options could be discussed then? What financ-ing options could be discussed that otherwise would have never been brought forward?

If the patient's financial need and funding mechanism could be coupled with the physician's clinical plan, it could enhance the delivery clinically *and* financially. Patients could understand the costs and how they were paying and would proceed with that plan, and the physicians would know the care plan would be followed without financial barriers. We are not there yet, and I understand this is a radical concept. But as affordability disrupts care, it may be an idea to look at in the near term.

Pharmaceutical Supplies (Wholesale Distributors)

In Chapter 3 we talked about the role of Big Pharma—pharmaceutical manufacturers—in US healthcare economics. In this section, I am talking about one small slice of the pharmaceutical supply chain that particularly impacts providers such as hospitals: wholesale distributers. Just like Budweiser does not typically sell directly to individual liquor stores, pharmaceutical manufacturers do not generally interact directly with healthcare providers. That role is handled by wholesale distributers, who purchase products from the manufacturers and distribute them to hospitals and other providers.

As of 2015, three companies dominated the pharmaceuticals distribution market: McKesson Corporation, AmerisourceBergen, and Cardinal Health[353] Between them, these three companies account for between 85 and 90 percent of all revenues from drug distribution in the United States, with combined revenues of $378.4 billion in 2015.[354]

For hospitals, the wholesale distributors' role is to get the drugs the hospital needs; to make sure the hospital has what they need when they need it; and presumably, to negotiate a discount for the provider. Pharmaceuticals represent a very large expense for hospitals and also can end up being a large expense to the patient as a payer.

Why, if the distributor is negotiating a discounted rate for the hospital, does an aspirin show up as costing $10 on your hospital bill? The answer to that goes back to how hospitals are paid. Say 10 patients need an aspirin that costs the hospital $5 to purchase per pill. If we have 10 patients, that is $50 in cost for the 10 pills. Two patients are self-pay, paying out of pocket, and can afford it, so they each pay the discounted price of $6. Two people have commercial insurance that is paying a discounted reimbursement rate of $7 per aspirin. Three patients have no insurance and no ability to pay, and pay nothing. Two patients have Medicare, which pays $5. The remaining three people have Medicaid, which reimburses at less than the cost (short pay or underpayment), at $1 each. Stay with me here. So, let us see, that is 12 bucks for the self-pays, 14 bucks for the insurance, none from three patients, 10 bucks from the Medicare, and three bucks from Medicaid. That is $39 total. It costs the hospital $50. See the issue? Without charging a premium for some to subsidize the others, it is a losing game.

That leaves the hospital in the red. And not only does the hospital need to recover their costs, they need to cover the cost of stocking and distributing the aspirin (paying nurses to dispense it, etcetera), as well. Basically, not everyone can pay for the aspirin, so as a hospital, they have got to offset that loss from a payer mix standpoint. That goes for any supply cost incurred in a hospital, from a gauze bandage to an IV bag to an implantable device. Aspirin, gauze, and IV bags are simple examples—imagine implants or chemo drugs.

I think it is important to explain to patients that this is what is happening behind the scenes: "You are subsidizing other people's care for the greater good of other patients in the community who otherwise could not afford the care." It does not always go over well, but hospitals need some way to equalize revenue to make a little profit to keep up with inflation or they will not be in business anymore.

Other Medical Supplies

The same economics are at work with other medical supplies. For example, take a medical device such as an implantable cardiac pacemaker, a device that detects and controls abnormal heart rhythms.

Any device you want to talk about has an average cost that fluctuates over time. Per the Modern Healthcare/ECRI Institute Technology Price Index, as of November 2016, the average cost of an implantable cardiac pacemaker was $3,820. The manufacturer has a business to run and has a profit margin to sustain their operations, as well. They have a markup that is passed along, too, but let us focus on how this translates to the costs of the hospital and how those relate to the patient.

The hospital uses the cost of the device to establish the average whole-sale price (AWP)—or "cost plus"—that forms the basis for the charge-master. Let us say the cost of the device we are talking about is $5,000. A typical calculation might be the cost of the device ($5,000) multiplied by 2.5 (the hospital mark-up) ($5,000 x 2.5 = $12,500). Then hospitals discount that back down to insurers, so insurers might pay $7,000 for that device when one of their covered patients has that procedure. That $2,000 margin helps pay for the uninsured, the underinsured, and the Medicare- and Medicaid-covered patients, none of whom reimburse the hospital the full $5,000 cost of the device.

The hospital's margin has to cover the cost to purchase the device, the cost incurred by patients who cannot pay the full price, and the cost to implant the device. The costs for the procedure (staff, labor) are more fixed. That is why hospitals have to recover costs on items like pharmaceuticals and implantable devices, which are more variable. (Hospitals will also try to get them donated or deeply discounted to production costs where they can for patients who lack the ability to pay.)

Technology (Clinical)

Technological advances, especially advances in clinical technology, represent a significant reason for the cost of healthcare in the United States. Imaging is a great example. I spent half of my career in an imaging center, and we were very proud of the technology we had. It was the best we could offer our patients.

We always got a little perturbed when a new model came out and someone had it before we did. If someone else had it, and we did not, the patients would let us know. Or another game is if you do not get it first, you miss the boat, or you are practicing medicine below the standard of care in the industry, and so on. There will always be a better, faster, more accurate, more sensitive piece of technology, and capital expenses in a hospital is a scarcely allocated resource. When the patient says, "Hey, those guys across the street have a 64-slice CT scanner and you guys only have a 16-slice CT scanner. Does that mean the other guy's scanner is four times as good?" it can put a hospital in an awkward position. The provider has to start defending themselves from those kinds of queries.

The answer to that question is that yes, the 64-slice scanner probably is better, in terms of the sensitivity of the scanner, the speed with which it can acquire images, the quality of images, and those types of things. So the question becomes: What is "good enough" from a technology standpoint? Employers and insurers are obligated to cover what the medical community says is good enough. Physicians always want the best, for good reason. Interestingly, patients can often drive the definition of good enough, as well.

Patients consistently choose top-shelf technology when it comes to their healthcare. That is how they shop for everything else, as well. I mean look, we have giant boxes of cereal, bacon double cheeseburgers, SUVs, TVs the size of a wall, mobile devices, tablets, multibillion dollar yachts, etcetera, because people buy them and want more. So there is always this technological mountain to scale: "Oh, look, here's a 128-slice scanner, and here is a 256-slice scanner, and we also have a 640-slice scanner coming soon." *Radiology Today* even wrote an article about the escalation of CT technology called, "CT: Customer expectations after the slice war."[355]

Patients are educating themselves. They are looking things up on the Internet. And that drives competition between hospitals for market share, which is sometimes impacted by patient awareness of clinical technology. "We'll see your PET and CT scanner and raise it by a hybrid PET CT scanner and a da Vinci unit for surgery." It becomes a retail discussion, and it creates fundability issues. In a highly saturated market with lots of facilities, patient choice and retention is paramount. Remember the supply and demand chapter? There is an abundance of supply and a lot of demand. Technology thrives in that environment; technology is expensive and business is good. Because of this, insurance carriers—even Medicare—make every attempt to curb new technology costs with HDHPs, plan exclusions, authorizations, and medical necessity requirements where they can to keep premiums in check. They have been somewhat successful in this area if you ask the hospitals and the vendors, but by the look of things, a lot of technology is being produced and a lot of hospitals are buying.

Could healthcare technology get to the same point as vacuum cleaners and refrigerators from a consumer standpoint, where consumers eventually have checklists to make comparisons, and differentiate between "good," "better," and "best" with respect to healthcare technologies? Healthcare technology is becoming more transparent, but it is not there yet. Litigation and physician pressures, as well as the fact that the new technology really is raising the standard of care in many cases (pacemakers, stents, calcium score CTs, artificial hearts, etcetera), puts technology in place as a major driver of healthcare costs. Will patients or the industry accept "good" over "best" for care based on cost or affordability? That is tough to ponder, but demands some attention, because as technology costs increase, funding options are diminishing.

There is no doubt, however, that technology drives costs and at some point, funding mechanisms are going to have to accommodate that. Will copays vary by the quality of the technology? It might be something we have to look at, because we cannot keep topping the scale out and driving up technology costs like we have been for the last 50 years.

Technology (Administrative)

We talked about the advent of EHR systems in Chapter 4. The Health Information Technology for Economic and Clinical Health (HITECH) Act, and subsequent implementation of the meaningful use (MU) program incentives and penalties, drove hospital adoption of EHRs to an all-time high over the past 10 years.[356] This also added a tremendous capital investment burden (aka added cost) for hospitals as billions of dollars were (and are) being spent on EHR systems.

While the adoption of EHRs has been really helpful from a clinical perspective, it has been much less helpful from a revenue cycle management perspective. As we talked about earlier, meaningful use criteria focused on improving the quality and safety of care from a clinical standpoint, but revenue cycle management got left behind.

Twenty years ago, most revenue cycle processes were manual. Human beings manually reviewed the majority of the claims forms that went out the door. Now, maybe 5 percent of those transactions are reviewed by a human being. The rest are processed automatically and electronically. The reason that is a problem is that since clinical documentation automation was not designed specifically to support revenue cycle management processes, a lot of steps can get missed. Unless electronic stopgaps are added that mirror the paper revenue cycle processes, claims can fly out the door that will not get paid. The "paper" rules have to be added and integrated into the EHR just as the MU elements were added: Is the patient eligible for care? Is the patient eligible for the benefits that were provided? Is there an authorization on file? Does it meet medical necessity? Does it meet precertification? Does it meet the additional medical necessity requirements? Was it coded correctly? Were the charges listed correctly? Was the claim sent to the right place? That is why there is such a proliferation of third-party vendors out there—the EHRs left most of these elements at the station.

From a revenue cycle standpoint, I would say that less than half of the required elements to ensure reimbursement exist within the big EHRs right now. Maybe 75 percent of the required elements are captured in some of the most evolved EHRs, like Epic, Allscripts, or Cerner. But many hospitals are still using legacy systems that were designed to generate a bill, and that is it. Even with an evolved EHR, information from an insurance clearinghouse, a plan coverage rule, patient benefit accumulators (like a deductible-met amount), or a patient's credit score (gulp) do not exist within the EHR. They have to fetch that information from elsewhere. And the architecture of the big EHR systems is often closed, or at least variable between systems. These systems were not designed to verify coverage, connect patients to funding mechanisms, or collect payments from patients, because that was not originally a significant part of the collection process.

It is becoming critically important that providers are able to use automated systems to document that claims are getting paid and reimbursed at the level they should be. Diminishing revenue from the insurance companies, the government, or the patient infringe upon the bottom line and can be detrimental to profitability. Inefficient or inaccurate billing processes can cause critical deficits in cash flow that can make the difference between being in the red or being in the black.

A large gap exists between a hospital's process to collect payments and a patient-friendly billing process. Your average grocery store has a better payment system than most hospitals do, from the patient-as-payer standpoint. Most grocery stores have self-checkout lanes, where you can run your groceries through a scanner, get your total, apply your coupons, insert your credit card, sign electronically, and pay on the spot. How many of those have you seen in a hospital?

I challenge you to find an industry that makes it more difficult to pay your bill than the healthcare industry. It is an inefficient and expensive process. The legacy processes in most hospital billing departments inflate the cost to collect. Even more concerning is the misalignment between hospital billing processes and patients' preferred payment methods. At best, mobile statements exist, but the payment and connectivity is still on the back end for the most part, at the point that is least effective for collecting from the patient.

A lot of hospitals are still generating paper invoices that get mailed to patients in paper envelopes. Who bills that way these days besides the healthcare industry? I mean really! Think about it. Who else sends you a bill in the mail without any other option to pay online? Maybe the utilities company? And while hospitals are figuring out how to collect from patients by mail, millennials are getting older. Millennials—people born between 1981 and 2005—have overtaken baby boomers as America's largest generation.[357] And millennials most decidedly do *not* use paper to pay bills. Good luck billing them through an envelope in the mail.

Millennials are the new patient payers. Most hospitals are not prepared to meet them where they are at in terms of patient-friendly, technology-enabled billing and payment processes. Healthcare billing and collections will have to innovate and automate on a grand scale. It will not be cheap, but it will be necessary. Considering this new reality, a dramatic—even revolutionary—overhaul in healthcare industry billing and payment practices is long overdue (no pun intended).

The Biller

The care has been delivered; charges have been gathered; the bill is assembled; charges and authorizations and precertifications are documented where needed; and then the claim or statement gets billed. Before the current patient-as-payer era, that bill might have gone only to a government or commercial insurance payer and they paid you back. A small copay or self-pay balance was then collected from the patient. But because of HDHPs and related developments, the insurer sends back an explanation of benefits (EOB) indicating large portions that apply to a patient, and the patient is the payer for most of the charges. Those without insurance have huge bills to contend with.

As I mentioned earlier, most hospital systems are not optimized for modern patient billing. Hospital billing processes are about as consumer-unfriendly as a billing process can be. Bills come after services have been delivered—sometimes well after services have been delivered. Google "How long does it take to get a hospital bill" and you will find patients with stories of having received a bill for hospital services months—or, in some cases, years—after services were rendered.

Healthcare bills also often come in bits and pieces—one bill from the hospital, one from the physician, one from the anesthesiologist, and so on. If you have had a surgery, you might get as many as three, or four, or six different bills. And to the consumer, none of them make any sense.

You do not find this in any industry other than healthcare. Can you imagine if your car mechanic billed like that? "Here is your bill for the parts," and then, a few weeks later, "Here is the bill for the labor." That would not fly. On an airline, you do not get separate bills from the pilot, the fuel company, the baggage handler, and the flight attendant. I do not know why healthcare billing has devolved into this. The healthcare industry has somehow accepted that billing has to be that way, even though that would not be acceptable in any other industry. (Consolidated billing offers another opportunity for healthcare providers to deliver what patients want. We will talk more about that in the last chapter.)

Now all of this, of course, is not the responsibility of the hospital biller. The biller's responsibility is to make sure the bill is accurate and the claim is clean before it goes out the door. The biller runs sweep, if you will, on the schegistrar, including collecting what the schegistrar may have neglected to collect upfront. The schegistrar may have undercollected or overcollected in terms of upfront patient payments. The biller, with the benefit of 20/20 hindsight, has a clearer view of patient responsibility and often holds the schegistrar accountable for missing collections or missing documentation. (In all fairness, the biller also checks the work of the coders and the clinicians, through various scrubbers and protocols, to make sure that bill can go out.)

Building a communication bridge between the schegistrar, on the front-end, and the billing department, on the back-end, can be an extremely helpful strategy for hospitals. If the schegistrar knows, "If I don't ask the patient this question, this bill won't fly," then the schegistrar can adjust for that. Likewise, if the billing department representative understands and communicates the message, "If the schegistrar doesn't know to ask this question, I won't have all the information I need to send out a bill," then it improves both departments' ability to streamline the billing process.

The patient generally has little interaction with the biller. Billers submit claims; collectors collect cash. That is why the hospital's internal collector is the next character in this story.

The Collector (internal)

Hospitals often have several types of collectors, including one type that specializes in collecting reimbursement from insurance and another type that works on the cash, which is the revenue coming back from the patient. We will focus on the patient side of this, as in the balance after insurance (BAI) or true self-pay (uninsured) patients.

This process is highly variable across billing offices, and I have seen it all. Some have very sophisticated protocols that age the accounts with thresholds and likelihood of payment from the insurance or the patient. There are electronic work queues and productivity and yield reports reviewed daily. Others may print off a report every morning, with a paper queue of some sort that they usually work. They may work it cradle-to-grave (age of account), or high-to-low (balance amount), or both. The thought process is something like this: "Mr. Smith came in on December 10. Mrs. Jones came in on December 11. Both claims went off to insurance. Mr. Smith still owes $50. Mrs. Jones still owes $100. I think I will start with Mrs. Jones, since she owes more."

This emphasizes the importance of an accurate, engaged conversation with the patient on the front end. How poorly or how well the hospital did at the beginning of this process will determine its fate. Studies show that traditional hospital collection processes (that is, collecting after the patient has been treated) results in a collection rate of 50 percent to 70 percent for insured patients.[358] Other studies show patients are 90 percent likely to pay prior to seeing their physician; 70 percent likely to pay when checking out; and only 40 percent likely to pay after leaving the facility.[359] And as we talked about in the last chapter, as the amount becomes higher or as time goes by, that likelihood of payment diminishes while the cost to collect it increases. That is why upfront collection conversations are critical to ensure financial engagement of the patient.

But that conversation has to be accurate. If the hospital gives the patient one estimate up front, and then the bill comes, and the collector is trying to collect a different amount, the hospital loses credibility with the patient, the patient is less likely to pay the balance, and the patient is certainly less likely to pay in advance next time. So all of the players—schegistrar, biller, collector—have to be aligned to optimize the patient financial experience.

Before the patient was the payer, these conversations happened between the biller, the internal collector, the insurance provider, and sometimes the patient. Now that the patient is more in the mix, the complications of these conversations have increased exponentially. Providers have not yet fully revamped their processes to adjust to this new reality.

"Rocco," the Collector (external)

"Rocco" is what happens when the wheels fall off the wagon. And Rocco can also be what happens when hospitals reach their capacity in terms of collections staff. It comes down to a math problem: How many humans does it take to collect this much cash in this much time? It is not complicated, and based on the answer, hospitals make a decision whether or not to outsource collections and when to pull the trigger on extraordinary collection actions. Hospitals would love to do it all for the benefit of their patients, but frankly there are not enough resources or time to accomplish this task.

Many hospitals use external collections reluctantly, as a last resort. Hospitals have an obligation to treat the community they serve, as well as a reputation to uphold. Bad debt for hospitals is not a major issue, but it is a lot of cash. Bad debt or "uncollectibles" range in the mid- to high-single digits (as a percent of net patient revenue) for typical hospitals.[360] This puts it into a couple of million dollars for most hospitals. In general, hospitals are pretty flexible: They need to get paid and they do not want to be unduly aggressive about it. Compare hospitals to an automobile dealership, for example, where the collections process can escalate fairly quickly. If you miss a car payment, you are quickly going to get a notice; soon after you default on a payment, the repo man may be coming to get your car.

Hospitals do not work that way unless they have to, and it is not as simple. For one thing, you cannot take back a kidney transplant or a knee replacement the same way you can take back a car. For another thing, hospitals are invested in the relationship they have with the community they serve. They do not want to alienate that community. This paradox is what keeps CFOs up at night. On the one hand, they are thinking, "How many dollars are out there that I'm owed but I'm not collecting?" and on the other hand, they are thinking, "Am I making anyone angry? Is my hospital going to make the evening news (and not in a good way)?" There are also regulations to consider. Under the ACA, not-for-profit healthcare providers' tax-exempt status can be at risk under 501(r), which went into effect in 2016. It states that a patient must be screened for charity according to the hospital's financial assistance policies prior to engaging in "extraordinary collection actions" (for example, liens or garnishments).

Because of this, a lot of hospitals use an early-out process (a softer way to do collections as agents working on behalf of a hospital, discussed in a later chapter) to accelerate cash prior to third-party collections. They work on behalf of the hospital as an agent behind the scenes and make one last effort to get payment before things get serious. Rocco, the external collector, does not work on behalf of the hospital. When the account reaches Rocco, there are no more options: no charity-care programs, no self-pay discounts. Rocco is out for one thing only: to collect the cash. That is why he is getting paid, and his payment is based on commission. He does not have to deal with whether the bill is right or wrong; he only has to deal with the balance and the payment. That is it.

If hospitals effectively engage patients in the financial aspects of their care on the front end, and funding mechanisms are established, Rocco will rarely—if ever—have to become a part of the patient financial experience. That is how it should work, but the reality is almost all hospitals have a third-party collections process in place, and Rocco's job security is just fine.

The Litigator

Love them or hate them, lawyers play a role in the cost of healthcare, and not just when things go horribly wrong. Studies suggest that malpractice cases and "defensive medicine" practices comprise about 3 percent of overall healthcare costs in the United States, or nearly $100 billion.[361] (We have not seen one of those "Bs" in a while—I felt like it was time). However, other folks in the business, including new US Secretary of Health and Human Services Tom Price, have gone on record as saying as much as 25 percent of all healthcare dollars are spent on the practice of defensive medicine.[362] No doubt the true figure is somewhere in between.

Malpractice costs for physicians vary by specialty, since both the frequency of malpractice claims (figure 6.3) and the amount of malpractice payments (figure 6.4) vary by specialty.[363] As shown below, neurosurgery tops the lists, getting hit with almost 20 percent of the malpractice claims, with an average settlement of $300,000.

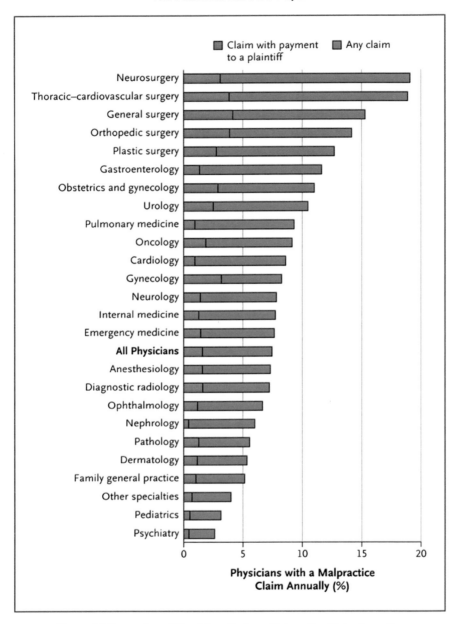

Figure 6.3 Proportion of Physicians Facing a Malpractice Claim Annually, by Specialty. Source: Jena, A. B., Seabury, S., Lakdawalla, D., & Chandra, A. (2011). Malpractice risk according to physician specialty. *New England Journal of Medicine 365*(7), 629-636. doi: 10.1056/NEJMsa1012370

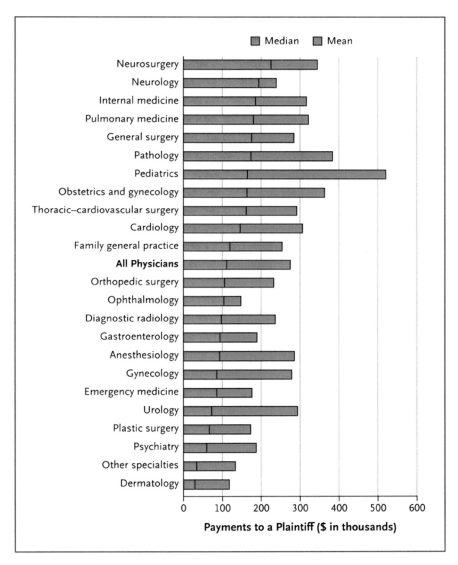

Figure 6.4 Amount of Malpractice Payments, According to Specialty.
Source: Jena, A. B., Seabury, S., Lakdawalla, D., & Chandra, A. (2011).
Malpractice risk according to physician specialty. *New England Journal
of Medicine 365*(7), 629-636. doi: 10.1056/NEJMsa1012370

The extent of the practice of "defensive medicine" is harder to quantify. Physicians implement clinical standards to ensure consistent, high-quality care is delivered to each patient. But an argument can be made that the potential for litigation has influenced the breadth and scope of the delivery of healthcare. Better to "err on the safe side," and order that extra test, than to be sued for negligence later.

Is litigation driving up overall healthcare costs unnecessarily? It depends on your perspective. Price has been a significant champion of tort reform. He believes that limits on medical malpractice awards could curb frivolous lawsuits and bring down healthcare costs.[364] Medical claims are big business, to be sure, as evidenced by TV commercials asking, "Have you been injured …" or "Did you have 'x' procedure that went bust?" Right or wrong, malpractice lawsuits drive costs that patients pay directly or indirectly.

That said, medical errors represent a significant source of injury to patients. One 2016 study, published in *The BMJ*, suggested that medical errors may be the third leading cause of death in the United States, after heart disease and cancer.[365] Critics of the research said that the study's definition of medical error was too broad, and included unavoidable complications and patient-related comorbidities.[366]

John Nance, in his book *Why Hospitals Should Fly*, gave a jaw-dropping example of the impact of medical errors.[367] He stated that the 500,000 deaths that occurred due to medical errors over a period of five years was "the equivalent of flying 1,400 fully loaded 747s into the ground."[368] Airlines represent a benchmark for safety in the United States; hospitals are still catching up.

Somewhere, there is a balance, between patient safety and excessive defensive medicine practices that add unnecessary costs. There is, after all, a difference between a negligent physician—a doctor who is drunk, or uneducated, or doing a surgery they are not credentialed to do—and a doctor who simply makes a mistake. I would argue that the threat of malpractice lawsuits and litigation has broadened the definition of medical necessity on the provider's side —but not the payer's side. Providers practice defensive medicine to offset litigation risk, and there are additional costs in this effort. That means that once again, providers are left to find creative ways to cover costs for an economic variable—litigation and the practice of defensive medicine—over which they have little control.

The Legislator

As we reviewed in Chapter 4, the government has been shaping healthcare policy for a long time. Legislators are elected to create policies that best represent the needs of Americans. They establish the "law of the land." What is the law of the land when considering healthcare policy? The Preamble to the Constitution of the United States reads as follows:

> We the People of the United States, in Order to form a more perfect Union, establish Justice, insure domestic Tranquility, provide for the common defence, promote the general Welfare, and secure the Blessings of Liberty to ourselves and our Posterity, do ordain and establish this Constitution for the United States of America.[369]

What exactly does promoting "the general welfare" include? Is access to healthcare actually a constitutional right, or not? The Constitution leaves a lot of room for interpretation. As a politician, you might interpret it as supporting a healthcare reform law, such as the ACA (as the Democrats did), or you might interpret it as prohibiting certain aspects of the ACA, such as the individual mandate (as the Republicans did).

Traditionally, healthcare reforms have ensured coverage and access, but have not adequately addressed healthcare costs. Now that the pendulum has swung the other way, I feel we will see proposed healthcare reforms that address costs and save tax dollars, possibly rolling back protections to coverage and access.

I think the United States is positioned for a reset as far as coverage. Consumers have begun to develop a sense of entitlement around insurance—an expectation that if you have a health insurance plan, you are entitled to 100 percent coverage for 100 percent of possible healthcare expenses, no matter how much they cost or how they are funded. That is not sustainable in the long term. The spend is too high, with a premium and deductible that is unaffordable for the patient and a subsidy that is too high for the government or employer.

The government is trying to structure the risk pool and benefits in a balanced way, but the bets they have been making have not been paying off. The ACA hoped to fund broader access and coverage by encouraging healthy young people to participate in the individual market health insurance pool, but that did not happen. Likewise, the Medicaid expansion granted coverage for low-income consumers, but it did not address the cost of providing those services.

Additionally, there are significant funding risks with per capita or block grant proposals for Medicaid, which as of this writing, Congress is seriously considering. The fragility of the health benefit exchange is also a rickety bridge of unknowns, with fewer members and decreased plan participation. Congress is frantically trying to stabilize the individual and exchange markets, as they realize that if those fail, Medicaid will not be able to cover the potential increases in the number of uninsured, and hospitals cannot absorb the large uncompensated care debt that could develop as a result.

As a society, we are at the point where we are going to have to make some hard choices: What should be covered under health insurance plans? What should not be covered? Who gets the coverage, and who should pay? Should it be required for all, and what if folks opt out? When health insurance was first created (Chapter 1), it was designed to provide catastrophic coverage, not to cover every person for every possible healthcare service desired.

While the stakeholders manage that, legislators at the state and federal levels continue to tinker with healthcare policy, without understanding the realities of healthcare delivery, especially from the perspective of providers like hospitals and health systems. Hospitals have to see everyone and are not in a good place to negotiate, for the most part. Without the government's help to subsidize care, they will not make it. Some legislators come to the table with a myopic perspective about the hospital's role in healthcare delivery. Some legislators view hospitals as the driving force behind healthcare costs, and their focus is more on profits than on saving costs for patients.

Are hospitals inefficient? Yes. Do hospitals have an opportunity to improve the way they do business? Absolutely. But are hospitals solely responsible for the fact that healthcare is so expensive? I would argue that they carry some of that blame, as most of our costs are from hospitals, but there are many aspects of the healthcare system over which hospitals have no control. Hospitals do not control the price of pharmaceuticals or medical devices. Hospitals do not have any control over government payer reimbursement rates, which are consistently below costs. And hospitals have unique obligations to treat—such as Emergency Medical Treatment and Labor Act (EMTALA), which we discussed in Chapter 4. There are many rules and regulations that hospitals and health systems must follow, and they are obliged to treat patients regardless of ability to pay.

Hospitals must recognize the new paradigm of the patient-as-payer, and actively deploy processes that engage patients in the financial aspects of their care. Insulating revenue losses from the patient-as-payer—regardless of the politics, costs, and expenses—must remain a long-term strategy and align with insurance (payer) strategies. Relying on payer reimbursement exclusively on the back end, and bypassing patient funding mechanisms on the front end, will result in significant bad debt risks in the long term.

It is not just *people* that impact each patient's financial experience. The *places* where those services are delivered play a role, as well. In the next chapter, we will look at the challenges associated with various types of healthcare delivery models.

CHAPTER 7

·····················

DELIVERY MODEL
CHALLENGES

Healthcare may have the most complex delivery system of just about any industry I can think of. Consider all the healthcare access points that exist in America—hospitals, freestanding emergency rooms, urgent care facilities, public health clinics, physicians' offices, retail clinics in supermarkets, specialty hospitals, long-term acute care hospitals (LTACHs), specialty clinics, ambulatory surgery centers (ASCs), rehabilitation facilities, skilled nursing facilities (SNFs)—and this is only a partial list.

No wonder patients are confused.

On top of that, add the questions, "Is this in-network for my insurance plan?" or if underinsured or uninsured, "How much does this cost?" The system is set up with the expectation that patients will self-direct their care to the appropriate access points with the appropriate costs, but very few patients are educated enough about the system and its prices to do that effectively.

Accessing Healthcare

For any particular healthcare issue, somewhere in this confusion of choices is the right place to access the system for the right care at the right price. But how is a consumer to figure that out? Most people do not know much about what services are provided at what level, or what is medically appropriate, or what their insurance plan does or does not cover, or how much it will cost. They just want to get well. So where do they go?

It depends on what is open, what is convenient, and how severe they think their situations are. We all have these scales in our heads where we weigh the possibilities: You have a fever. Maybe you choose the home remedy route first—cayenne pepper sauce or tacos and tequila—whatever your home remedy of choice might be. If that does not work, you might try some over-the-counter (OTC) meds. If your symptoms still do not improve, you might call your doctor's office—and if it is after hours, they may tell you wait, or if you cannot wait, to dial 911. If your symptoms get really bad, and you are not patient enough or not knowledgeable enough, you will go right to the highest level of care—the emergency room—and skip all the other steps.

The healthcare market has started to capitalize on that. Freestanding emergency departments are popping up on every corner, complete with billboards that blast the current waiting time. This certainly provides more access, so patients can get care faster, but is it at the appropriate level, and the appropriate cost? I would argue that in the United States, the healthcare system is set up backward. There are lots of access points for patients to come in and get care, but the easiest way to obtain care (emergency department, open 24/7) is also the most expensive. The most cost-effective way to get healthcare (see your primary care physician, first), is the hardest to get access to (open 8 a.m. to 5 p.m., Monday through Friday. Some offices attempt to have hours on weekend mornings, but it is still not enough to provide adequate access). Imagine what would happen in the scenario above if it addressed transparency—the "T-word." If prices and your out-of-pocket costs were hanging on each of the options like a big red tag on a piece of furniture—$100 for this one, $5,000 for that one—what would happen then? Here, I have stack-ranked care costs, low to high. Let us take a look.

Doctor's Office ($)

According to Healthcare Bluebook, the cost for an average doctor's office visit (new patient, 10 minutes) is $106.[370] That is pretty cost-effective, right? One of the problems with going through your doctor first is accessibility. If you are a parent, you know that your children typically do not fall off their bicycles or start vomiting uncontrollably between the hours of 8 a.m. and 5 p.m., Monday through Friday. Nope. They do that on the Fourth of July holiday, or at 9 p.m. on a Saturday night, precisely timed for the middle of the weekend when most pediatricians' offices are closed.

If you call a pediatrician's office, you may be able to connect with an on-call nurse or doctor, who will ask you to describe your child's symptoms, and attempt to triage you over the phone. Like we mentioned above, it is not unusual for these conversations to end with the caveat, "If his symptoms get worse, take him to the emergency room." Do not pass go; pay a copay of $200.

Interestingly, a national study published in 2012 found that patients with extended access (evening and weekend hours) to their "usual source of care" incurred healthcare costs that were 10.4 percent lower than patients who did not report extended access to their usual source of care.[371] The authors stated, "… those reporting access to extended hours had less use and lower related expenditures for all subcategories of use (office visits, prescription medications, emergency department visits, and hospitalizations)."[372] The authors noted the reduction in costs was related to "lower prescription drug and office visit-related (for example, testing) expenditures," suggesting that "extended office hours may be associated with more judicious use of health care resources."[373] In other words, if their doctors' offices were open later, patients would go there if they could.

Urgent Care Clinic ($$)

Urgent care clinics offer a middle ground between your primary care physician's office and the emergency department (ED) of your local hospital. They provide care for most acute—but not necessarily emergent—conditions. According to the Urgent Care Association of America (UCAOA), there are about 7,400 urgent care centers in the United States.[374] The UCAOA notes that recent growth in the number of urgent care centers "seems to be fueled by a confluence of events and awareness—primary care being somewhat hard to come by, emergency room (ER) wait times and overcrowding spreading, physicians seeing and acting on these needs in their communities, and patients driving their popularity."[375]

Urgent care clinics offer a good example of meeting consumers where they are at. The 2015 UCAOA "Benchmarking Survey" highlighted the following statistics about urgent care centers:

- Ninety-six percent of urgent care centers are open seven days a week

- About one-third of urgent care centers are located in shopping centers/strip malls (34.1 percent) and another third are located in freestanding buildings (33.2 percent), making them easy for consumers to access

- Ninety percent of urgent care patients experience wait times of 30 minutes or less before seeing a provider

- Eighty-four percent of urgent care patients complete their urgent care experience (throughput) in 60 minutes or less

- Ninety-eight percent of urgent care patients are in the appropriate care setting; only two percent are diverted to EDs[376]

Even better, UCAOA marketing materials indicate the average cost of an urgent care visit is $150.[377] From a consumer's point of view, they are überconvenient, and most patient's typical sentiment is, "urgent care clinics are awesome." You walk in, no phone call, no appointment, short wait, no line. You are in, you are out, and you can pick up a latte on the way. There is a sign on the desk: "Payment due at time of service." They collect everything upfront. I think patients-as-payers love them, because the whole experience—clinical and financial—is streamlined. They have structured their businesses just like other retail industries to ensure their consumers can easily access their services and easily pay for them, as well. Unfortunately, these streamlined processes have not been widely adopted in the acute hospital space—it has not been a priority and the bills are more complex. That said, there is opportunity for improvement here, as I feel patients-as-payers would appreciate having the same ease in access and payment at a hospital as they do in an urgent care clinic.

Emergency Departments, a.k.a. Emergency Rooms ($$$)

And then there is the ED. EDs have unfortunately devolved into a kind of "primary care physician clinic." This is true during off-hours, for reasons I have already mentioned. A 2016 report from the National Center for Health Statistics (NCHS) stated that 12 percent of adults aged 18 to 64 who visited the ER did so "because their doctor's office was not open" and 7 percent did so "because of a lack of access to other providers."[378] This results in overcrowding in the ED. The American College of Emergency Physicians (ACEP) performed a study that defined overcrowding as when the "number of patients exceeds treatment space capacity" and indicated that 90 percent of EDs have an overcrowding issue.[379] The study cited various reasons, most importantly, "'avoidable' ED visits, retrospectively identified as unnecessary or visits for conditions that could, theoretically, be addressed at the primary care/ambulatory care level."[380]

Interestingly, it also holds true that EDs serve as primary healthcare access points for patients during normal business hours. One reason is that when patients are unsure of the seriousness of their concerns, they know that the ED is a one-and-done. They do not have the knowledge (or sometimes patience) to triage themselves (Doc visit? Urgent care? ED?), but EDs have a reputation that if you go there as a patient, you are going to get whatever you need, and God bless the hospital for providing it, right? One of the reasons hospitals have this reputation is because of the Emergency Treatment and Active Labor Act (EMTALA), which we discussed in Chapter 4. EMTALA requires all hospitals that participate in Medicare to screen and stabilize anyone who presents to the hospital "campus" and requests emergency services, regardless of his or her ability to pay.[381],[382]

The ED may be the easiest place to access care, but it is also the most expensive place to deliver care. The cost is inordinate because of the fixed overhead. Healthcare Bluebook suggests that the average cost for an ER visit—for a minor problem—is $821 (compare that to our doctor's office visit of $106 or our urgent care visit of $150).[383] In spite of this, a lot of patients go to EDs for common colds, bumps and bruises, minor lacerations, and other concerns that could be treated in another setting for a much lower cost.

Let us look at a hypothetical example from a college town, where a young man was dropped off at the ED by his fraternity brothers after a night out drinking. (Note that although my example here is hypothetical, it is not far-fetched. Numerous studies have documented that a significant percentage of college student visits to the ED are precipitated by alcohol intoxication).[384] In our example, this young man had been drinking, but he also complained of breathing difficulties and chest pain. Now "chest pain" is a magic word in the ED (as it should be). You mention "chest pain" in the ED, and you will get the full wash, wax, and dry. You are going to get everything: a cardiologist, an EKG, an ED doc, a nurse, monitoring, telemetry, enzyme panels, blood drawn—because they want to make certain you are not having a heart attack or a stroke. They are going to throw everything at you, if you are presenting with the right symptoms. It is not wrong; ED staff members are trained to move quickly and save lives—that is just what happens.

This young man did not have a heart problem in this example, but he did end up with a very expensive ED bill, representing thousands of dollars. ED visits are going to be expensive, whether or not there is a chest pain involved. The same situation would have occurred if one of the frat brothers had tried a superman jump off a patio and broken his arm. The ED would have treated that, too, at a very high cost.

When mom and dad (the insurance subscribers) get the ED bill in the mail, the first thing they do is call the hospital. I speak from personal experience, as I dealt with a number of these calls myself. After the yelling and screaming about how "US healthcare expenses are ridiculous" and "How can you charge this much?" I would go into an explanation of where the costs came from. "OK, let's talk about the treatment your son received and why it costs so much." I would start by stating, "EDs are the least cost-effective way of delivering healthcare because of the intensity of the services. They are going to treat your son at the highest, most resource-intense level they can to stabilize him, because that is what EDs are designed to do.

"Now let's talk about the costs in the ED. We have at least one doctor, a nurse, a registrar, a lab tech, an imaging tech, and maybe some other folks on-call 24/7. Add that all up and that comes to, let's say, $300 an hour (or $7,200 for a 24-hour day)—just for staff. Then you add in all of the equipment: EKG machines and CT scanners and MRI scanners and X-ray machines. And then you add the cost of the facility, the labs received, the tests performed, the paperwork, the processing of the bill. Soon we are up to $15,000 a day just to operate an ED."

At this point one of two things would always happen: a "thank you" (believe it or not) for being the first person to explain why the ED costs so much, or (most of the time) more yelling and frustration about high healthcare costs. "He was there for 25 minutes! *Really*, $5,000 bucks? I'm not paying you a dime!" At that point, I would say, "It's not a matter of payment—the care happened, and the charges are accurate for the care that was provided. Your son (or his frat brothers) chose a very expensive place to go for 'drunk anxiety,' and hospitals have an obligation to ensure it is not something else." Click … dial tone … back to work. Unfortunately, it is a scenario that happens all too often.

It is similar to what we discussed in Chapter 2; patient behaviors can have a significant impact on health outcomes. In our hypothetical example, this particular patient was making choices about his health that required intense hospital resources in response. He was seeking care at the most expensive level, for something that theoretically could have been prevented. Similar types of situations happen in EDs every day; problems that could be treated much more cost-effectively in another setting end up in the ED, and are billed accordingly.

EDs have a minimum standard of response that is going to happen. They are not going to discharge a patient before they have done everything they can for him or her. They do not want to discharge patients and have them end up back in the ED. And, they do not want to get sued for not doing something that they should have done. These folks are clinically trained to specifically treat with a battery of tests, and quickly. Time is life in the ED. There is not much gray area here, but there is some opportunity for triage and for some ease in the EMTALA rules.

Maybe ED staff could say to a patient, "You know, Mr. Johnson, we think you're fine. You should go on home and call Dr. Smith tomorrow. He can order some lab work for you if he thinks it's necessary." But it rarely happens that way in an ED. Instead, it is, "Let's do everything we can while you're here to figure out what's going on, and then we'll bill you."

EDs have only three choices when a patient presents:

1. Treat and discharge

2. Treat and watch (observation)

3. Treat and watch for a long time (admit)

The most recent data available from the NCHS shows that only 9.3 percent of all ED visits actually result in hospital admission.[385] Physicians make the decision based on clinical evidence—severity of the situation, monitoring needs, and treatment needs. EMTALA makes it tricky to even have a conversation about the financial impacts of the level of care before treatment has been provided, and that is why too many patients end up with large bills for unnecessary ED visits. There seems to be a level of triage—clinical, certainly, and perhaps financial, as well—that should happen before nonemergent patients present at the ED, and that is not prevalent in hospitals.

A few hospitals are using upfront fees for nonemergent patients to encourage them to make better decisions about the level of care they require. In 2009, HCA rolled out a system-wide ED screening program in which the ED physician or nurse does an initial medical screening to classify a patient as "immediate or emergent," "urgent," or "non-emergent or non-urgent."[386] Patients in the "non-emergent or non-urgent" category can stay for treatment only if they first pay their insurance copay or deductible (if they are insured) or a $150 facility fee (if they are uninsured).[387] In 2009, Midland Memorial Hospital (Texas) implemented a free telephone triage system.[388] Potential ED patients could call the nurse to help them evaluate whether or not they truly needed an ED visit. Patients who came to the ED and were assessed as "non-emergent" were given the option of paying $150 upfront, or being referred to less expensive care, such as a nearby urgent center. The hospital reported that bad debt decreased by over $3 million in the first year the initiative was implemented.[389]

These types of programs seem to be helping patients make better decisions. Instead of walking into an ED and getting care for "free," when they are presented with required copay or facility fee upfront, they have to think about whether or not they want to stay: "Hmm, a $30 copay at my physician's office tomorrow, or a $150 facility fee right now. I think I'll wait." Hospitals are finding out that $120 delta is making a difference.[390] For-profit hospitals seem to be adopting this model more prevalently than the not-for-profits, as they have made it a priority financially. With shareholder reinforcement, for-profit hospitals have active campaigns to steer patients to the most appropriate level of care from a facility cost and patient-spend perspective—a win-win.

There is also some movement toward developing mobile apps that can help direct patients to the appropriate level of care based upon their symptoms, but that is not yet a significant factor in directing patients. This is one of the healthcare industry's many delivery model challenges that will need to be addressed in order to bend the healthcare cost curve.

Transitions of Care in the Hospital

The issue of right level of care, right treatment plan, and right reimbursement model plays out not just in access points to the healthcare system, but in the inpatient setting as well. There are many different types of hospitals, but when most people think of hospitals, they are thinking of an acute care facility (technically, this is known as a short-term acute care hospital, or STACH). I rarely hear anyone call them that, unless they work in utilization review or licensure, and in those conversations, it is typically mentioned in the context of a length-of-stay discussion. For example, "This patient has been here for weeks. This is a STACH—it is not set up to treat this type of patient for this many days."

The average length of stay (ALOS) in an acute care facility in 2016 was around five days.[391] So what? Well, given that Medicare and commercial insurance typically pay on a case rate (typically by diagnosis related group, a.k.a. DRG), the better the acute care facility can do on those days (as far as meeting ALOS), the better off it will be financially. Top-performing hospitals' ALOS hovers around 4.4 days.[392] That is still a long time—an amount equal to a short vacation for most (but not as fun and relaxing)—and no patient wants to hang out in a hospital for that long. But that is how long it takes, on average, to make you well. Hospitals are good places to have a baby and to get your life saved, but after that has been taken care of, they are pretty intense, sometimes boring, and somewhat scary places to be. Hospitals are structured to provide whatever treatment has to be done in the most efficient manner possible, and then to move patients on to their next appropriate level of care.

This is true for all levels of care in a hospital, but becomes a particularly tricky issue with patients who are in the intensive care unit (ICU). The ICU is a magical place and an awful place at the same time. ICUs are magical because they offer the best care you can get. They have a 1-1 ratio of care, specially trained docs and nurses, and accelerated treatment protocols—and they save lives every day. At the same time, they are not places you want to hang out in any longer than you have to. There is a lot of isolation; many very ill patients; and a lot of beeps, noises, alarms, and other things happening. There are a lot of staff members and there is a lot of monitoring going on. Like the ED, the ICU uses a very high, intense amount of resources. Also like the ED, the ICU is expensive because of the intensity of the care that happens there.

Transitions of Care

In an acute care hospital—whether you are in the ICU or any number of other units—there is a point at which the care transitions from intervention, to stabilization, to treatment, to recovery. The key for the hospital is to transition to the appropriate level of care at the appropriate point in time. Patient flow between levels of care is kind of an interesting dance. I am not a clinician. As the revenue-cycle management guy, I have no business talking about the appropriate level of care for a patient—there are staff members in the hospital who do that. But I did work very closely with the staff on level-of-care transitions. My job was to be the bad finance guy, to talk about what the "meter" was and when it was running.

For example: "ICU charges are $15,000 per day. The insurance company pays us for four days at $7,500 per day. After that, this patient is being treated for 'free,' or in fact, we start losing $7,500 a day. This patient has been here 10 days. That's $45,000 of free care. That's the equivalent of a medical-surgical stay for an uninsured patient." Yes, this is an awkward conversation, but there has to be awareness and balance—the better we could manage expenses on the funded patients, the more resources we had for the unfunded.

We remained diligent as active stewards of our community and the patients' dollar. Taking a pause to consider this allowed the team to move into transition or discharge planning discussions. What do we want to do? Is this the most appropriate level of care for this patient? How do we substantiate the care? What do the case manager's notes look like? Is the documentation in the medical record complete? Are the appropriate referrals and authorizations in place?" I sought clarity by asking lots of questions from the experts. Most importantly, I guided them to their plan to discharge through a financial lens, in addition to the clinical one.

When a patient is uninsured, these conversations happen in the same way, but with more emphasis on the dollars. Why? Because the whole case may be essentially "free" care with little to no funding for (or from) the patient. It is kind of like going to an expensive restaurant and all you have is 20 bucks in your pocket, and the waiter keeps bringing more food. As I mentioned, the hospital has an obligation to be a steward of every patient's resources. If the patient is incurring charges that might lead them to bankruptcy, then that patient's level of care—from a cost standpoint—might need to be discussed with the patient in more detail. The idea is always to provide the patient with the most appropriate level of services, at the right time, in the most cost-efficient manner for the patient and hospital.

There is no single correct answer regarding transitions of care. It is very challenging to balance the hospital "checkbook" across all the different payment sources and complex disease processes for patients. You do the best you can with what you have, and constantly look for opportunities to improve at every corner. You can compare your hospital's numbers to benchmark data, like the ALOS by facility type, facility size, or facility ownership (federal, nonprofit, for-profit, etcetera).[393] You can also compare your numbers to benchmark data on ALOS by chief complaint, DRG, or even by individual patient demographics. This allows you to identify opportunities, and to focus on that 5 to 20 percent of patients driving 50 to 80 percent of the costs, as we talked about in Chapter 2. You should not say, "Hey, you guys keep patients five days, and the national average is four days. What's wrong with you?" It is not about blame; it is about awareness. Healthcare is an art, not a science. There are many complicated patients who do not fit into neat diagnostic categories. They may have multiple diagnoses, comorbidities, and multiple physicians with differing opinions about their readiness to transition to another level of care.

Patients' care delivery becomes very difficult to manage when there are multiple disease processes happening and multiple resources involved in their care. Delivery mechanisms are not set up to treat highly complicated patients, and I would argue that insurance plans often are not set up to deal effectively with complex patients, either. When the clinical aspects are not in sync, or the clinical aspects are not aligned with reimbursement, things can go sideways really quickly.

When patients start to reach thresholds on length of stay—for example, they have been in the ICU for several weeks—the conversation evolves into, "Well, they are never going to come off the ventilator" or "they have to be on these monitors forever" or "they will be immobilized for eight weeks." At a certain point, it does not make sense to keep hanging out in an ICU.

But the patient's family may not understand this. In the United States, we have an attitude toward healthcare that says: "Give me everything! Forget the costs and just go full speed ahead! I will figure out how to pay for it later. Why can't they stay here for that long?" That is not necessarily wrong; it is human nature. But it presents an ethical dilemma when you have a patient who has been in the ICU for weeks, has had the same progress note for the last five days, and no prognosis for improvement. Hospitals are not designed to treat at that level, and insurance, frankly, is not designed to fund care for perpetuity.

At the hospital where I worked, we set up a utilization review committee that met once a week. This was a collaborative, multispecialty effort, which drove results that benefited the patient and the hospital outcomes—clinically and financially. We looked at anybody who had a length of stay that was longer than the benchmark for his or her diagnosis, and we would talk about the patient from a holistic perspective. Case Management 101, right? We would include anyone involved in the patient's care who needed to be there—the doctor, the nurses, the utilization review nurse, the ER nurse, the unit director, and somebody from finance—to talk about why the patient was there so long. Patients really should not overstay basic length-of-stay thresholds, unless they are really, really sick or they are "stuck."

If the patient was really, really sick, we needed to determine a long-term plan for his or her care, because a long-term plan should not involve a short-term acute care facility. Short-term acute care facilities typically treat patients for less than 30 days. Reimbursement, certainly, is not going to support long-term stays that deviate substantially from the expected length of stay. As the care becomes constant, and the funding starts to diminish, discussions were necessary to re-evaluate.

In our review meetings of long-stay patients, I would ask: "What are we really doing for this patient? What are we doing clinically for them? We talked about this patient last week, when they had already been in the ICU for five days, and now it's been 12 days. So what's happening?" These patients were stuck in the hospital, waiting for the next step. But, there would always be a reason: "Well, the infectious disease doc hasn't put a note in," or "The cancer doc hasn't done this," or "They still want to deliver these drugs intravenously instead of by mouth," or, "The family wants the patient to stay here as long as it takes." OK, how do we get to the next step? Sometimes ethics committees or the patient advocates got involved as well, as these were very difficult decisions. Neither insurance, nor the patient-as-payer, pay for being stuck. Sometimes it ended up getting really frustrating, because it is really hard to turn that battleship.

That said, good things typically came out of those conversations. It opened up a dialogue between the hospitalists, the intensivists, the infectious disease docs, the surgeons, and the other clinical staff that was not really there before, and that is the key. Utilization review nurses would drive this boat, and would say: "Hey, cardiologist and neurologist, you guys have each different opinions about when this patient will be ready to move to the next level of care. Insurance coverage is lapsed for this course of treatment, and the family is getting mixed messages. Can we talk about that?" When each clinician is off working in their own little silo, that is not very patient-centered care. But when everyone is collaborating—including the finance guy—you can start to move the needle in a way that improves clinical outcomes, quality, and cost. You can let the data speak. One of my many mantras is, "In God we trust, all others bring data." The data can get to root causes, for example, "Why do patients with these comorbidities get stuck?" or even better, "How could we discharge this patient more efficiently next time?" My favorite types of conversations.

Discharge/Transitions to Other Facilities

Everybody wants a patient to go home as early as his or her status allows. The patient, the family, the physician, the nurse, the insurance company—everybody wants the patient to go home earlier. That is often the first question you have as a patient: "When do I get to go home?" And the answer is always, "We'll see ... let's check with the doctor in the morning." So it is everybody's goal, but how are you going to get there?

Discharge planning is a conversation that has to happen from the day the patient is admitted. What is the discharge plan going to look like? What are the barriers to discharge? Are financial resources a barrier to discharge? What is the next appropriate level of care? Should the patient be discharged to an LTACH? LTACHs are set up for patients who are going to need care for weeks, rather than days. They are staffed and trained to deliver that kind of care, with protocols for things like weaning off ventilator use and regaining mobility.

Discharge planning works with the physician on the appropriate disposition (setting) for care. Should the patient be discharged to a rehabilitation facility or an SNF? Can the patient be discharged home? What clinical needs will they have after discharge?

These conversations happen between the attending physicians, hospitalists, the intensivists from the ICU, the charge nurses, and the family members. Cost is not the driver in these conversations, but it is certainly a relevant part of the level-of-care conversation. If the hospital's care plan has stalled without a clear strategy for the long term, or half of the patient's insurance-allowed inpatient days are exhausted, or both, where does that leave the patient? Where does that leave the family? As stewards in revenue cycle, we have an obligation to minimize the impact of the costs to the patient wherever we can.

Transitions are easier when funding mechanisms exist—like commercial insurance or Medicare—because you have a way to pay for different levels of care. But when you have a self-pay or Medicaid or charity care patient, transitions can become extremely difficult. Given that facilities like LTACHs and SNFs are not obligated to accept patients like short-term acute care hospitals, because they do not have an ED (and the restrictions of EMTALA), they can limit the number of Medicaid or self-pay patients. Where does that leave the patient?

Hospitals do what they can. Sometimes they have agreements in place with other facilities; sometimes they do not. At our hospital, we sometimes would have to say: "We are all in this together. We take our share of uninsured, you should take some, too. It is not fair to not accept them, and your level of care is more appropriate." For patients who were still stuck, (typically uninsured), where we could not find an accepting facility, we developed a respite care program. The respite care program provided a "bridge" between the hospital and home—we created our own mid-level care program for patients who no longer needed the services of an acute care hospital, but who, for various reasons, could not take care of themselves safely at home. They were eligible for discharge, but did not have funding or family to care for them once discharged.

We would rent hotel rooms and arrange for home health visits at those locations. Placing a patient temporarily in a hotel room at $99 dollars a night, with a home health nursing visiting twice a day at $30 an hour, is a lot less expensive than keeping a patient in the hospital for another week. And it is not just a matter of cost efficiency. Clinically, if you do not need to be in a hospital, you should not be there, and most patients do not want to be there. In spite of all the quality controls, hospitals have lots of ill patients. The risk of being confined in a hospital and other complications make it in patients' best interest to be discharged as soon as feasibly possible.

Hospitals are sometimes placed in the difficult position of making choices that are not cost-effective. They have legal obligations under their licensure, and they play an important role in the communities they serve. That is why hospitals exist—they are the last line, the safety net. If a patient comes in with an injury that leaves him paralyzed, and he has no insurance, what do you do? Do you keep him in the hospital, at a cost of thousands of dollars a day, because he has nowhere else to go? For how long? Hospitals are not set up financially or clinically for these types of patients. Yet they come into the hospital through the ED, and can present significant challenges to hospitals trying to discharge them to more appropriate facilities.

These kinds of discussions and trade-offs happen at every level of care. Whether you are deciding if the patient is going to be discharged to home, an LTACH or a SNF, or you are deciding if orthopedic follow-up would be better in a rehab facility or at a gym, the conversation is the same. What level of care will provide the best outcome for the patient, with the most appropriate level of resources?

Focused Factories

"Focused factories" is a concept borrowed from manufacturing. Under the focused factory concept, a factory can increase its competitiveness, productivity, and efficiency by "learning to focus on a limited, concise, manageable set of products, technologies, volumes, and markets."[394] They do one, or two, or three things exclusively, and they do them very, very well.

Healthcare has delivery models that mimic the focused factory concept. One example is specialty hospitals that focus on one disease process or continuum, such as cardiology or oncology, or women's health centers. Another example is ASCs that focus on a limited number of outpatient procedures (orthopedics, ophthalmology, gastrointestinal). These places have optimized and streamlined their patient services from a clinical delivery, capacity, throughput, and financial standpoint. They are well-oiled machines.

This kind of specialization came about for a few reasons. First: capitalism at its finest. Demand exists for healthcare organizations that are indisputably the "best" at what they do. If you build it, they will come. This kind of specialization also serves clinicians. For physicians who want to specialize in one disease process or one treatment area, specialty hospitals offer a distraction-free environment for that kind of practice. They also typically focus on high-volume, revenue-generating procedures, which makes them extremely profitable, and which is attractive to physicians.

I visited a dedicated cardiovascular care center, and it was one of the most amazing places I had ever seen. Everything was set up to optimize heart care. They had an ED specifically focused on cardiac emergencies. If you came into the ED and did not have a cardiovascular issue, they would stabilize you and transfer you somewhere else. The ED was set up to accommodate open-heart surgery, if necessary. Every aspect of the hospital—the ED, the diagnostic and imaging equipment, the ICU, the physician providers, the operating room suites—was optimized for treating cardiac cases. I did not speak with the clinical staff, because that is out of my scope, but I did speak without the finance and compliance staff. I asked them, "What is it like billing for this place?" They said: "It's glorious. Most of our claims look the same. We know what the charge description master looks like; we know what kind of plan benefits most of our patients are coming in with; our contracts are pretty simple; and we know what we're getting paid. We're able to have really holistic, patient-centered conversations, because the fact that we're specialized takes a lot of the unknowns and variability out of the equation."

Specialty hospitals may still see patients with multiple disease processes, but the majority of the patients that present fit into their area of focus. The bandwidth of information you are dealing with in a specialty hospital is an inch wide and a mile deep, unlike the bandwidth you are dealing with in a general, community hospital, which is a mile wide.

The same is true for facilities such as ASCs. By specializing exclusively in particular procedures, they are able to keep overhead costs low. Facilities, technology, supplies, staff, workflow processes—all are optimized to support very specific procedures. Most of them use data analytics to provide insight as to capacity, turn-around-time, revenue yield per patient, infections or complications per procedure, and others issues. Business intelligence is used to ensure they function like a Swiss clock.

This theory is borne out in the outcomes specialized healthcare services facilities are able to achieve. ASCs have become very efficient at doing knees, hips, elbows, and backs in an orthopedic setting, and have demonstrated they can do more of them, safely, and at a lower cost than a general hospital. A study published in *Health Affairs* indicated that procedures performed in ASCs are up to 25 percent more efficient and cost-effective than the same procedures performed in a hospital.[395]

Maybe it is because specialty hospitals and ASCs have a more predictable patient load and workflow, but regardless, they have figured out how to effectively manage that patient clinically, and how to do it at a lower cost. Insurance companies are starting to pay attention to this, and are setting their plans' designs up and establishing reimbursement policies to steer patients toward these types of facilities. Right or wrong, that is how the market is moving.

Besides the cost-efficiencies of specialization, ASCs and other specialty facilities benefit from the fact that they can turn away patients who do not fit their delivery model. They have the flexibility to turn away sicker patients, with multiple comorbidities, who need a broader scope of support than a specialized facility can provide. They also may have more flexibility than EMTALA-obligated facilities to turn away patients who do not have funding mechanisms in place. This will be a paradigm shift for hospitals performing a lot of ambulatory procedures. The variability in delivery of care, the types of patients treated, and the various funding mechanisms will make it very challenging for hospitals to continue to compete in this market with ASCs.

The Challenge for Hospitals

The majority of community hospitals may never have the opportunity to develop into focused factories. It is not typically feasible in their cost structure or design. General, community hospitals exist to treat anything and everything. They serve as a giant funnel; they will treat any patient who presents in the ED, or who is referred by a physician. Without the narrow focus of specialty hospitals and ASCs, it becomes very challenging for hospitals to deliver services, and to get reimbursed for everything they are obligated to deliver, because the scope is so random, variable, and complicated.

In this context, care delivery—including levels of care and service intensity—represents a complex process for hospitals to navigate. How does the patient transition from admission to diagnoses, to treatment, to intervention, to discharge, to outpatient care? Right now, that is a highly inefficient process in most hospitals. Level of care is not being managed effectively at the hospital level (and I mean that with love). There is a lot of "marinating" at the wrong level of care.

In 2016, the Healthcare Financial Management Association (HFMA) published an article entitled, "Using Data and Analytics to Improve Clinical and Financial Performance."[396] The authors stated, "… unwarranted variation in care is a significant source of suboptimal patient outcomes and unnecessarily high costs."[397] The authors further elaborated on this unwarranted variation, citing suboptimal clinical practices, overuse of interventions, and not following evidence-based protocols, among others.[398] The authors pointed out that some of the challenges to reducing unwarranted variability include, "gaps in clinicians' knowledge, lack of economic incentives to drive desired clinical behaviors, concerns about malpractice risk, physicians' desire for the ability to go with personal preferences, and inadequate decision-support tools."[399] They summate:

> Hospitals and physicians typically have been compensated for the care they provide even if such care creates unwarranted variation in quality or cost. The value mandate from both private and public purchasers and payers is rapidly changing this situation, putting a high-intensity spotlight on unwarranted variation in care and providing incentives to reduce such variation.[400]

As the HFMA article points out, reimbursement is a contributing factor to this problem. The current system is set up backward, because it reimburses each of the individual components, not the overall outcome. It makes it a kind of a shell game for patients and providers. (In Chapter

9 we will talk about value-based care programs like accountable care organizations [ACOs], which are trying to address the weaknesses of the silo-based healthcare delivery model.)

Until reimbursement mechanisms become more aligned with outcomes-based care, what can hospitals do? I think that one area where hospitals struggle is with the utilization review component. Appropriate utilization review can help hospitals begin to align the three different universes of right level of care or intervention, at the right time, and with the right outcome. It is Utilization Review 101. The definition of insanity—doing the same things over and over again, and expecting a different result—applies here. Having standard protocols with no metrics on use as they relate to impact or outcome is a quick way to drive up costs in an insane manner.

Insurance companies are big on utilization review, in a way that hospitals have not yet taken advantage of. Insurance companies, and to some extent, for-profit hospitals, are doing utilization review all day long. Productivity analysts are looking at nurse-to-bed ratios, how many patients have been admitted, how many patients are being seen by a particular doctor, what drugs are being administered, how many X-rays are being done, what the length of stay is, and other benchmarks and variables. Looking at these data sets and understanding the variances, and managing those variances to reduce variability in the delivery of care, is key to bending the cost curve.

In fact, it can make a huge impact on cost: Show me all of the admissions you did last year by physician, add in the diagnoses codes, weight them by DRGs, and start looking for variances. Is there a doctor who admits the patient every time a patient says, "I have a headache"? Is there a doctor who orders an MRI instead? What are the outcomes of those interventions? This is a grossly simple example, but you get the point. Manage what you measure, and hold yourselves accountable to the care provided—clinically and financially.

Hospitals are just beginning to use business intelligence, that is, taking all of their data—all of their claims data, all of their diagnostic data, all of their productivity data, all of their labor data—and their spend, and making comparisons. "When our patient has this diagnosis, he stays six days and has three MRIs and uses this much medication, but when a patient with the same diagnosis goes to this place across town, he uses half of those resources, and has the same outcome. Why is that? What are they doing differently?"

How do we leverage that data? The big academic medical centers are beginning to do that, to take that data and use it in ways that make the art of medicine more of a science. If we can collect that data and use it to make better predictions of outcomes and reduce variability in delivery, costs will certainly come down. As we gain insights though analytics and closely evaluate the level of care provided, the healthcare cost curve can begin to bend. Insights as to *why* and *how* the patient sought that level of care, how well the patient got better (or not), and at what cost, will enable care to be better directed by the provider for the patient-as-payer.

WHAT HAPPENS NEXT

CHAPTER 8

. . . .

OTHER
BUSINESS MODELS

Many other industries have successfully adapted their business models to be consumer-centric. Why haven't hospitals and the healthcare industry in general adopted care-delivery models that meet the patient as a consumer? Healthcare can gain a lot of insight from other industries. Airlines, Amazon, auto mechanics, dentists, supermarkets, restaurants, and veterinarians have all figured consumers out. What can healthcare learn from other industries' customer service successes?

In particular, because the patient is the new payer, healthcare needs to understand how to make the patient's financial experience friendlier by asking the right questions. How do we make the healthcare financial experience more like a retail experience? Patients should be able to shop for their healthcare plans and find plans that align with their healthcare needs and their pocketbook. Patients need access to information about out-of-pocket costs and quality of care in order to intelligently shop for physicians, treatments, and facilities. Patients need lots of options to navigate financial aspects of their care from the very beginning of their healthcare experience. Other industries have met consumers where they are, making the buying process seamless, as they know that the customer is valuable and can be lost. Healthcare has a reactive mindset to some extent—when a patient wants x, the hospital scrambles to provide y. Planning for the financial elements of the care is often an afterthought.

I am not the first to say that healthcare has a lot to learn from other industries. In the book *Why Hospitals Should Fly: The Ultimate Plan to*

Patient Safety and Quality Care, author John Nance explained what the healthcare industry can learn about safety from the airline industry.[401] I would suggest that the healthcare industry could also learn a lot about patient financial engagement from the airline industry, and from other lines of business as well.

What Can We Learn from the Airline Industry?

When was the last time you talked to an airline employee prior to boarding a flight? Remember picking up the phone, waiting on hold, deciding if you were in the smoking or nonsmoking section, and talking prices? When you actually arrived at the airport, you waited for your ticket and then checked bags with an attendant—in other words, there was lots of face-to-face interaction. Nowadays, only a few people talk to anyone at the airlines, because technology has advanced to the point where you can make your own arrangements for almost everything. You can see what flights are available right on your mobile phone; all the prices are there, and you pay online and get an e-receipt. You can update your reservation online too, if you want. You can decide whether or not you want to check your luggage, or upgrade to a seat with extra leg room. You can sign up to receive notifications via text message so you can learn if anything about your flight changes—if there's a delay due to weather, for instance. You don't even have to print your boarding pass anymore—you can download an app and use your smartphone as a mobile boarding pass. The only conversation I have with an airline employee now is when I order a drink once I'm on board. It's a completely seamless experience for the customer.

Over the last 20 years, the way people travel has evolved to meet consumer demand. A hospital certainly isn't an airline, but I think the healthcare industry could take some examples from the airline industry. For one thing, airlines flex their prices based on demand, needs, and destination. Imagine having "boarding passes" at the hospital. You laugh, but why not? Think about scheduling your visits, paying for them like you would pay for a flight, and arriving there with your barcoded pass, prepaid and ready to fly.

I have seen some of these models in healthcare—and they work. Appointments are scheduled and paid for from the comfort of your own home, and the "boarding pass" is printed or pushed to your mobile device. Your "boarding pass" can be scanned at the parking lot, and that alerts the receptionists to get ready, giving them all the information they need about where you live, what insurance you have, how you prefer to pay, what is new in your life, and so on. The receptionist has the information she needs to greet you like you were boarding a plane: "Welcome to Memorial Airlines—er, I mean, Memorial Hospital. Nice of you to come see us today. Any issues checking in? What would you like to drink? The doctor will be right with you." A new model of customer service in healthcare is emerging.

Prepayment with Predictable Costs

Airline billing is perhaps a little easier (OK, a *lot* easier) than healthcare billing, but we could learn a few things from the flyboys. Think about the example I gave of buying a plane ticket. Think about some of the things the airlines do. For one thing, you prepay for the flight. You do not even get a bill; it's just done. OK, I hear you: "It's a plane ticket, not a healthcare claim!" Well, airlines have variable charges and costs, too. Pilots, baggage handlers, airport fees, taxes, fuel—all these costs change with airlines. Sometimes a flight gets delayed, or it may use more or less fuel because of the wind—but the airlines have managed to figure out how to amortize their costs to cover the risk.

Ticket prices also flex on demand. 3 a.m. flight? Cheaper. 3 a.m. MRI? Same price as every other MRI—if you can even get one scheduled at that hour. And good luck paying for it in advance and not seeing any other bills.

Admittedly, health care billing is not as simple as airline billing. In the airline industry, there is no third-party insurance, which is what makes healthcare so confounding. But conceptually, there are some things that airlines do with consumers that healthcare could easily adapt: flex pricing on demand, prepay, single bill, online scheduling and payment, kiosk check-in, appointment updates—and that's just naming just a few.

Airlines also have gotten very savvy about how they meet demand with price points and affordability. Ever been on an empty airplane? Or had trouble finding one within a few hours of when and where you wanted to go?

In healthcare, at least for electively scheduled or planned visits, costs should be predictable to some extent. There shouldn't be a lot of price variability. Take obstetrics, for example. Imagine that several months before a normal vaginal birth, the hospital or the OB/GYN's office sends out a welcome email to the patient. "Hello, Mrs. Smith. Congratulations on your pregnancy! Here are some choices you have for your birth experience, and here are the costs associated with each of those choices. Here is your 'boarding pass' for your 'flight' in a few months." Just imagine...

Of course, with an airline flight, the consumer is focused on a price point, whereas with a birth, the consumer is probably focused on safety first. "I'm going to have a baby delivered, so I want it to be safe." I would argue that the safety issue is pretty comparable across most facilities—unless you are talking about a particularly high-risk birth, an anticipated need for a neonatal intensive care unit (NICU) or something like that—so price point might be the next consideration for a birth, after safety. Most hospitals deliver babies, and most are pretty darn good at it. They do it a lot, and are very safe, just like the airlines.

If the OB/GYN and/or the affiliated hospital reached out to the expectant mother prior to the delivery, the patient's financial experience could go a lot more smoothly, too. Just as in our airport example (checked luggage? or no checked luggage? extra leg room? or not?), hospitals could work with expectant moms to identify coverage and costs prior to the delivery. Is the hospital you plan to go to in-network for your plan? Are you planning on having an epidural or not? If you are, is the anesthesiologist who will deliver the epidural in-network or not? What impact will these options have on the portion of your bill for which you are responsible? We also may have a "weather delay" and you may have to take another flight if we need to do a C-section.

Talking through costs ahead of time can help ensure that the delivery aligns with the patient's wishes, and also allows the hospital to develop a reasonably accurate cost estimate. Most expectant families would welcome the opportunity to prepay for services, rather than dealing with a big bill on the backend at the same time that they are struggling with the sleep deprivation and schedule disruption that goes along with bringing a newborn home.

There are some hospitals that do this. At five months out, they say, "This is our estimate of what your total bill will be." As we have discussed elsewhere in this book, another advantage of addressing the funding issue early is that it provides time to find funding mechanisms that meet a particular family's needs. If patients are going to have trouble paying the bill, now is the time to identify appropriate funding mechanisms, such as charity care or Medicaid. Discovering ways to help a patient navigate funding challenges *before* the baby comes is an added bonus.

Imagine if you took an airline flight and didn't get the bill until after you got off the plane. Or imagine that you got three separate bills: one for the fuel (drugs), one for the pilot (physician), and one from the airline (hospital). That would never happen—but that is exactly what happens in healthcare. Again, delivering a baby is not the same as taking a plane ride, but the financial experience of delivering a baby could be improved by taking some cues from the airlines and addressing financing issues in advance.

The healthcare industry's payment and financing model is still stuck in 1985. And one of the reasons why is that the consumer has always been the payer in the airline industry, but has only recently become the payer in the healthcare industry. The healthcare industry is just not responding quickly enough to that change. Fasten your seatbelt: millennials will be "flying" your healthcare "airline" soon. Put your tray tables up and move your seat into the full upright position. There is going to be a little turbulence (payment), folks.

What Can We Learn from Amazon?

Amazon launched in 1995 as a company that just sold books.[402] It's way beyond that now, as everyone knows. Amazon's relentless customer-centric focus shows in the explosive growth the company has seen. Does anyone do digital better than Amazon? You can buy almost ANYTHING on Amazon, fairly easily, and it comes to your door. Doesn't fit? Send it back and get another one, with everything handled online.

Digital Customer Engagement

When the government's health insurance exchange opened, then-President Barack Obama famously said, "Just visit healthcare.gov, and there you can compare insurance plans, side by side, the same way you'd shop for a plane ticket on Kayak or a TV on Amazon..."[403]

It didn't turn out to be that simple. Purchasing healthcare is a little more complex than buying a TV, but why did we make it hard? TVs have lots of sizes, bells, and whistles too, but we understand those. Why? Because they met us all as a consumer. We pay for them and they want our business. It has to be easy and somewhat pleasant to buy a TV or you'll shop somewhere else. Healthcare.gov does not yet deliver the same customer experience that Amazon.com does, and it likely never will. But that doesn't mean that the healthcare industry can't aspire to an Amazon-like digital consumer experience.

Healthcare could do a few things—just addressing the T-word and adding a payment method and financing options could go a long way. Amazon even has its own credit card! Imagine if hospitals did that? News flash: some do. The customer experience in healthcare is focused on your care and health, as it should be. There is not much about your buying experience. Every other industry, even Amazon, cares about how the purchase went. Was it easy to purchase this item? Would you write a review of it? Would you tell a friend? Shoppers who bought that also tended to buy this—do you want this too? How was your experience? Healthcare does have the Hospital Consumer Assessment of Healthcare Providers and Systems (HCAHPS), as required by the Centers for Medicare and Medicaid Services (CMS), but the questions in that assessment don't address how your billing and payment experience went. The consumer experience is key. Amazon figured that out, and hospitals are still scratching their heads a little.

In 2014, Strategy& (PwC's strategy consulting group) conducted a survey of 2,339 US residents to get a clearer picture of the customer experience in healthcare. Their conclusion was, "There's a new boss in U.S. healthcare: the consumer."[404] One of the many conclusions of the survey was that "respondents under the age of 45 identify digital as their preferred means of engagement to manage their health, outranking traditional facility visits or phone calls."[405] The younger the respondent, the more pronounced their preference for digital engagement (figure 8.1).[406]

Preferred forms of engagement for managing health, by age

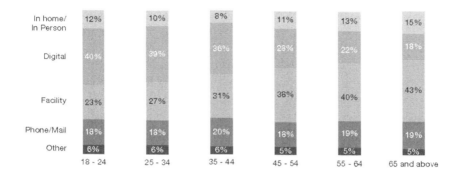

Figure 8.1 Preferred Forms of Engagement for Managing Health, by Age. Source: Esupiñán, J., Fengler, K., & Kaura, A. (2014), The birth of the healthcare consumer: growing demands for choice, engagement and experience. Strategy&. Retrieved from https://www.strategyand. pwc.com/media/file/The-birth-of-the-healthcare-consumer.pdf

Hospitals tiptoed into digital engagement with patients with the implementation of patient portals (secure online websites) as part of the Medicare and Medicaid EHR Incentive Programs.[407] This was a patient electronic access measure, and it applied to both eligible professionals (physicians) and eligible hospitals. The goal of the measure was to make it easy and quick for patients to access their personal health information.

In order for hospitals to meet the benchmark to achieve Meaningful Use (MU) Stage 2 federal incentives in the 2017 reporting period, "more than 5 percent of unique patients discharged from the inpatient or emergency department of an eligible hospital or [Critical Access

Hospital] CAH (or patient authorized representative) view, download or transmit to a third party their health information during the EHR reporting period."[408]

That is easier said than done. This is one of the tasks that often falls to the schegistrar, who we talked about in Chapter 6. One of the 800 things schegistrars have to keep track of is collecting patient email addresses in order to meet Meaningful Use Patient Electronic Access criteria. Health information management (HIM, a.k.a. medical records) actually enrolls patients in the portal program, but without an email collected by the schegistrar, it is hard to get patients enrolled.

At my previous hospital, we instituted an incentive program where we paid staff to collect email addresses from patients. The juice was worth the squeeze to reach the MU Stage 2 incentive payments. The MU incentives were a good carrot to get the emails, but adding *more* things to a schegistrar's list of things to do is a quick path to them walking out the door to find another job.

Meeting the patient electronic access criteria is a numbers game. To achieve the required portal access rate, you have to have x number of patients ping the portal. Well, to have x number of patients ping the portal, you have to capture y number of emails. And to capture y number of emails, you have to ask z number of patients for their email addresses. It made sense to pay my team per email collected because so many EHR Incentive Program dollars were at stake through the MU program.

Meeting MU criteria is a start, but isn't enough to put the healthcare industry in competition with Amazon.com for digital customer service. Healthcare needs to find a way to create a positive, engaged consumer experience for their patients.

Patient engagement continues to be an important focus at CMS. But that's certainly not the only reason healthcare providers need to focus on enhancing digital access and digital patient engagement.

Better patient engagement *and* better patient pay yield? What's not to like? Get those patients enrolled on a portal and have them pay those bills there—ideally, in advance. Then watch the cash flow. That's why the healthcare industry needs to continue to aspire to Amazon.com-like digital customer service.

What Can We Learn from Auto Mechanics?

In Chapter 5, we talked about pre-service estimates. One thing that auto mechanics have on healthcare is that they give consumers an estimate up-front. And if they don't know that estimate right away, they will do some diagnostics and then call the consumer with an estimate when they have figured out what is going on.

Options with Prices Attached

Often, mechanics call not only with an estimate, but options. "Based on your car's mileage, we should do a 30,000 mile inspection and service. You seem to have a small oil leak, but we can keep an eye on that and address it down the road. Your transmission, however, is shot. To replace it, we can use a remanufactured transmission with a three-year, unlimited-mile warranty for $2,500, or we can use a rebuilt transmission with a 12-month, 12,000-mile warranty for $1,750. What would you like us to do?"

Not only do auto mechanics give pre-service estimates, they also generally let you know which repairs are urgent, and which can be delayed if affordability is a problem. When you have choices (rebuilt vs. remanufactured transmission, for instance), they will also tell you the costs associated with those different options.

I don't think that is very often the case in healthcare.

"Mrs. Smith, your LDL cholesterol is well above the normal range. You could treat that with lifestyle changes—lose some weight, and increase the amount of exercise you are getting each week—or I could just go ahead and write you a prescription for a statin to treat your high cholesterol. I could put you on Statin A, which will run you about $10 a month. Generic Statin A is covered by most Medicare and insurance plans. Or I could put you on Statin B. Some patients who develop muscle pain (myalgia) in response to other statins are able to better tolerate Statin B. However, Statin B is not covered by most Medicare and insurance plans, so it will run you about $256 a month for the prescription. How would you like to proceed?"

Can you imagine if that type of conversation were a part of every clinical interaction? That would really give patients the clinical and financial information they need to make consumer-directed choices.

One more aspect of the auto mechanic business that the healthcare industry could learn from is the billing process. Your bill is consolidated. You don't get one bill for parts and a separate bill for labor, although these costs are likely itemized on the single bill you do receive. And you pay for repairs up-front—or you don't get your car back. There is no "legalized shoplifting" in the auto repair industry like there is in healthcare.

What Can We Learn from Dentists?

The patient-as-payer trend is relatively new for hospitals and physicians. Dentists, on the other hand, have had a lot more time in the seat collecting money directly from patients. Dental insurance didn't get its start until the mid-1950s. Prior to that, dentistry was conducted on a strictly cash pay-for-services basis.[409] Even though dental insurance has since become more widely available, by 2016, only 66 percent of Americans had dental benefits.[410]

Even when patients do have dental insurance benefits, coverage is often limited. Though monthly premiums vary, the average is around $50 per month, and many plans have annual limits as low as $1,000.[411] This means that even patients with dental benefits often pay a significant sum out of pocket.

Medicare doesn't cover dental benefits, either.[412] CMS regulations drive a lot of hospital policies precisely because hospitals rely on revenue from Medicare patients. That is not a factor for dentists.

Payment at Time of Service

All of this is to say that dental practices have been dealing with the patient-as-payer reality for a long time. They had to, or they would go out business. Because of the large out-of-pocket expenses for dental procedures, patients often presented a significant bad debt risk. That is why the patient financial experience in a dentist's office is pretty streamlined. It starts with that little plaque (no pun intended) that you usually see on the receptionist's desk that says, "Payment due at time of service." Whether they collect it before treatment, or at that little desk afterwards, it is an embedded process for every patient. It does not matter if a patient is there for a routine cleaning or an aching tooth; the expectation for payment has been set from the start.

Because payment is due at the time of service, clarity about costs is an expectation. Generally, individual patients are given precise estimates of costs, including the impact of insurance benefits, at the time a particular procedure is scheduled. For example, if you have just had your cleaning and the dentist's exam indicates you need a filling, you are handed off to the appointment scheduler, who will schedule the appointment for your filling and also give you the cost of the procedure. If the office needs to check with insurance before giving you an accurate cost, they will generally call you back before your appointment to let you know what your final out-of-pocket cost will be. In this sense, dental practices are more consumer-friendly than most hospitals, because dentists are essentially giving pre-service estimates to 100 percent of their patients.

Consumers who want to shop dentists by procedure costs have a more difficult time of it. That T-word (transparency) has been identified as an issue for dentists. Dental costs vary widely depending on geographic area, on whether the patient has insurance coverage or not, and on individual dental practice charges (sound familiar?). A 2013 study of dental price variation and transparency in nine major US markets found that 27 percent of dentists "did not disclose prices over the phone to potential new patients, even when directly asked for price information regarding common procedures."[413] The same study found that the costs of common dental procedures vary widely, even within the same neighborhood. Prices varied by an average of 384 percent across six common procedures.[414] The report concluded that the "opaque" nature of dental pricing made it difficult for consumers to effectively "shop" for dental services.[415]

This problem has given rise to sites like FAIR Health (fairhealthconsumer.org) and WhyPayMore Dental (whypaymoredental.com), which work with consumers and dentists to make dental care easier to shop. Granted, there are fewer insurance rules and procedures in dentistry, but the costs are much more readily available than in healthcare. Dentistry is continuing to work toward building a business model that is very consumer-focused. They have to, or they would find themselves underwater pretty quickly.

What Can We Learn from Supermarkets?

In Chapter 5, I compared the current patient experience in healthcare to shopping in a dark grocery store, where you can't see the prices and your doctor is picking up items and throwing them into the cart. But the reality is that supermarkets have the customer service experience nailed down. In the Temkin Group's Q1 2016 Consumer Benchmark Survey of 10,000 US consumers, supermarkets dominated the list of the 20 highest rated companies, while health plans dominated the lower end of the scale (figure 8.2).[416]

What have supermarkets figured out that the healthcare industry has not? I can think of a few things.

Flexible, Responsive Pricing

Supermarkets have prices on every single item in the store, and they update them frequently. Almost every item (even produce) has a Universal Product Code (UPC) affixed to it somewhere, which includes a machine-readable barcode and a human-readable number. The barcode identifies the item, not the price, but when the cash register scans the barcode, it pulls the price associated with that barcode from the store's central computer. This makes it easy for stores to change prices as needed—when they are running a sale, for instance, or when the cost of oranges goes up because of a cold snap in Florida. It makes supermarkets very flexible in terms of raising or lowering prices in response to market conditions.

Hospitals, as we've mentioned, do not have prices displayed for anything, and they update their prices annually at best if they are a not-for-profit institution, or maybe quarterly if they are for-profit. And the charge description master (CDM) is anything but a supercomputer. What if hospitals had the pricing infrastructure that supermarkets have,

2016 Temkin Experience Ratings (TxR), Highest & Lowest Rated

Highest Rated Companies

Rank	Company	Industry	TxR
1	Publix	Supermarkets	81%
2	H-E-B	Supermarkets	79%
3	Chick-fil-A	Fast Food	78%
3	True Value	Retailers	78%
3	Save-a-Lot	Supermarkets	78%
3	Kroger	Supermarkets	78%
7	Wegmans	Supermarkets	77%
7	A credit union	Banks	77%
9	Aldi	Supermarkets	76%
9	Amazon.com	Retailers	76%
9	O'Reilly Auto Parts	Retailers	76%
12	Subway	Fast Food	75%
12	Food Lion	Supermarkets	75%
12	ShopRite	Supermarkets	75%
12	Regions	Banks	75%
12	Dollar Tree	Retailers	75%
12	QVC	Retailers	75%
12	Giant Eagle	Supermarkets	75%
12	USAA	Banks	75%
20	Trader Joe's	Supermarkets	74%
20	Sam's Club	Retailers	74%
20	Wawa Food Markets	Supermarkets	74%
20	Little Caesar's	Fast Food	74%
20	Winn-Dixie	Supermarkets	74%
20	Hy-Vee	Supermarkets	74%

Lowest Rated Companies

Rank	Company	Industry	TxR
294	Fujitsu	Appliances	29%
293	Health Net	Health Plans	32%
292	Dollar	Rental Cars	36%
289	Comcast	TV Service	37%
289	CareFirst (BCBS)	Health Plans	37%
289	Highmark (BCBS)	Health Plans	37%
288	Empire (BCBS)	Health Plans	38%
284	Spirit Airlines	Airlines	40%
284	Comcast	ISP	40%
284	Blue Shield of California	Health Plans	40%
284	Medicaid	Health Plans	40%
283	Motel 6	Hotels	41%
282	AT&T	TV Service	43%
278	Columbia Natural Gas	Utilities	44%
278	eMachines	Computers & Tablets	44%
278	Volkswagen	Auto Dealers	44%
278	Compaq	Computers & Tablets	44%
274	Hitachi	Appliances	45%
274	Chrysler	Auto Dealers	45%
274	Thrifty	Rental Cars	45%
274	HSBC	Credit Cards	45%
270	Time Warner Cable	TV Service	46%
270	Blackboard	Software	46%
270	Haier	Appliances	46%
270	Days Inn	Hotels	46%

Figure 8.2 Temkin Experience Ratings. Source: Temkin Group. (2016, March). 2016 Temkin Experience Ratings. Retrieved from http://temkingroup.com/research-reports/2016-temkin-experience-ratings/

one where they could easily track and adjust prices as needed? Could that help hospitals manage costs more efficiently?

Barcodes are being used for clinical applications in hospitals. Specifically, they are being used for medication administration to improve workflow efficiency and patient safety.[417] There are also hospitals using barcoding for patient safety with blood banks, implantable devices, and other uses. These, in turn, drop a charge to the bill when scanned. As innovative as that is, to my knowledge no one is yet exploring how bar codes might be used to enhance the financial process or the patient financial experience in a hospital. Imagine if hospitals had a patient checkout area, just like at a supermarket, with a receipt, a credit-card processing terminal, and a smiling receptionist saying, "And how will we be paying today?" What might the possibilities be?

Loyalty Programs

Raise your hand if you have a supermarket loyalty card in your wallet or a tag on your keychain. Loyalty cards are advertised as providing product discounts to valued customers. Safeway advertises a "Club Price" on grocery items, available only to holders of the Safeway Club Card. King Soopers periodically mails out coupons for discounted and free items, based on loyalty card holders' individual shopping habits. In this way, they are able to use individual customer data to personalize the customer experience.

Could loyalty cards have an application in healthcare? Thankfully, most people do not visit the hospital as frequently as they visit the grocery store, but encouraging customer loyalty is not actually the most important aspect of those cards for supermarkets. Supermarkets are after the data—individual and aggregate—they gain from the customers using those cards. Imagine how much useful information a supermarket can learn by analyzing your shopping habits over time:[418]

- What time did you come shopping?

- What are you buying?

- What are you buying that is new?

- What did you stop buying?

- How much are you willing to spend on eggs?

- How much are you willing to spend on milk?

- How much are you willing to spend on dog food?

This type of information can be analyzed and used to help supermarkets make all kinds of decisions, such whether they need to increase or decrease the inventory of specific products, or whether they should hike or lower prices on specific items based on shopping patterns in specific ZIP codes.[419] They can use the aggregate data to more efficiently respond to geographic and socioeconomic variations in the market.

Hospitals have a lot of data on individual patients. So far, this data has been used primarily for clinical applications, and, of course, to verify the patient's identity to determine insurance coverage eligibility. If we analyzed that data from a customer financial experience perspective, I wonder what we might be able to improve. Imagine the application of that level of analytics to the payment experience in healthcare. How long do patients typically take to pay a bill? Does it vary by balance amount? Does it vary by socioeconomic status? Does it vary by procedure? Does it vary by season? Does it vary by day of the week? The goal of this analysis is not to be Big Brother, but to understand payment behaviors and tailor your billing experience to meet patients as consumers. Supermarkets have done that, and they are marvelous at it.

Like supermarkets, hospitals also might be able to use individual patient data to personalize the patient financial experience. A recent article in Forbes suggested that personalization is one of the top trends in customer service and customer experience:[420]

> Personalization creates a better customer experience. Technology has made it easier than ever to track customer preferences and history. Big data gives us trends and insights with uncanny accuracy. There is no reason to not create a more personalized experience that caters to a customer's individual needs.

Convenience

Supermarkets are designed with customer convenience and customer access in mind. Remember when supermarkets *weren't* open 24/7? If supermarkets can figure out how to operate 24/7 and still make money, why can't a hospital figure that out, at least on an outpatient basis? I admit, it is weird going to a supermarket at night. There are maybe three people there, and the staff is restocking the inventory, but you are able to get what you need when you need it. Hospitals do not even give you that choice (other than in the prohibitively expensive emergency room).

Supermarkets have designed the payment experience to be easy as well. Most stores are designed so you have to walk through (or at least past) the cashier lanes to exit the store. Just a friendly reminder that you *do* have to pay for your purchases before you leave. And if you do not want to stand in line, you can go through the self-checkout. Thanks to those UPC barcodes on everything, checkout is fast and easy. Regular credit card, chip card, coupons, you name it—those self-service lanes can handle it all. Supermarkets, unlike hospitals, make it easy for customers to pay. Studies show that consumers continue to be dissatisfied with hospital payment and billing processes.[421]

US consumers were asked survey questions designed to measure their opinions on various aspects of the payment and billing processes for hospitals, pharmacies and health insurers.

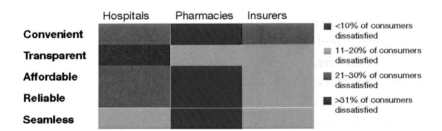

Figure 8.3 Consumers Are Dissatisfied with Healthcare Payment and Billing Processes. Source: Health Research Institute. (2015, May). Money matters: Billing and payment for a new health economy [PDF document]. PricewaterhouseCoopers. Retrieved from http:// www.pwc.com/us/en/health-industries/health-research-institute/ publications/pdf/pwc-hri-healthcare-billing-and-payments.pdf

What Can We Learn from Restaurants?

Restaurants are right up there with supermarkets in terms of meeting customers where they are. Restaurants are a tough business. The quickest way to lose lots of money is to open a restaurant. Variable food costs, ridiculous competition, and a highly saturated market with diverse options make it hard to start, and stay, in business. Restaurants measure how much food is consumed and what time customers come and go, and flex their prices and hours accordingly. They are constantly adapting to meet consumers with happy hours, early bird dinners, specials, and now even loyalty cards (taking a clue from supermarkets). "Fill out this survey and tell us about your experience and get a free appetizer next time," they might tell customers. Restaurants constantly measure and analyze data to inform the way they deliver food and service to the consumer to keep them coming back.

Predictive Analytics

Restaurants, like supermarkets, are benefiting from the effective use of data and analytics. In 2012, an article in *The New Yorker* spelled out the lessons the healthcare industry could learn from the Cheesecake Factory.[422]

The article pointed out how important forecasting models are used in the restaurant industry. The Cheesecake Factory uses historical data to predict and control food costs.[423] Using analytics, the restaurant chain can predict consumption, down to the number of chicken breasts ordered each week, and make adjustments for things like bad weather or scheduled sports events that impact the restaurant's guest count.[424] The company is able to attain an extreme degree of efficiency, and minimize waste, using these analytics.

Healthcare has begun using predictive analytics for clinical applications in population health. Kaiser Permanente is using predictive analytics in Southern California to identify the 1 percent of members likely to generate 29 percent of total healthcare costs.[425] Identifying this population helps Kaiser reach out proactively to manage care and improve patient outcomes (and lower costs) for these patients. I believe predictive analytics is healthcare's future—clinically and financially. If it's possible to use predictive analytics to project, and improve, clinical outcomes for individual patients, might it also be possible to use them to project, and improve, the financial experience for individual patients? Companies like Optum, Wellspring, McKesson, and others are betting on it. They are taking enormous sets of data from claims, payments, EMRs, and anything else they can find to identify and analyze the 20 percent of patients generating 80 percent of the costs. Moving that needle just a little can save costs and create capacity. You cannot manage what you don't measure.

Standardization

In the section about supermarkets, we talked about how supermarkets can use loyalty cards to personalize the individual customer experience. In some contexts, standardization can improve the customer experience as well. Think about the typical chain restaurant. If you go to a McDonald's or an Olive Garden or a Chili's, you have an expectation of what the restaurant will look like, what the atmosphere will be like, what will be on the menu, and how much it will cost. Standardization drives efficiency in chain operations. I travel a lot, and am always amazed how each restaurant in a chain looks, cooks, talks, and serves the same. If Big Macs always come with two pickle slices, the chain knows how many pickle slices to order and the customer knows how many pickle slices to expect. Costs, staffing, physical plant expenses, and everything else are all narrowed in these models —they are "focused factories." It's a way to control outcomes, and to deliver a consistent customer experience.

The healthcare experience is not necessarily personalized (customer-centric), but it is not standardized, either. In knee replacement surgeries, it is often physician preference that dictates what brand or type of implant the patient will receive.[426] This lack of consistency can drive significant differences in hospital costs and in patient outcomes. (Remember the "focused factories" discussion in Chapter 7?)

Are patient financial experiences consistent across most hospitals? I don't think so. Are patient financial experiences consistent within the same hospital? That is not common, either. Reporting relationships, different markets and payer models, as well as different patient demographics make it hard to standardize payment processes and intake. You make impacts where you can in the revenue cycle, but it is a constantly moving target.

During my hospital tenure, my team and I were able to drive efficiency among the schegistrars by standardizing the questions asked during the registration process. We were a lean shop, so we would measure the amount of time it took for a patient to go from a scheduled appointment through registration. A scheduled appointment included the name, date of birth, the time the patient was coming in, and maybe the procedure they had scheduled and the reason for it. Then we had registration pages to fill out: What's your address? What's your email? What's your insurance? Does this procedure require a pre-authorization?

When I started, it was taking us up to 25 minute to get through each registration. We got it down to 10 minutes. We started by removing waste. We took inventory of every single item of data we captured, who was using it, how long it took to register a patient, and how many patients we saw. We noticed that some of the registration screens were stuffed with questions for data sets that weren't actually being used down the line. "Hey, what's this field for?" "I don't know, oncology wanted it." "Well, oncology can collect it down the line, if they need it." We had criteria: What is required to create an account clinically, one that you could document and charge on? What's required to deliver care? What's required to submit a claim? We had "have-to-have" categories and "nice-to-have" categories.

We went through a formal process failure mode effects analysis (PFMEA). It's a checklist you go through to estimate the likelihood of something happening, the severity of it happening, and the frequency of it happening; you then develop a risk priority number (RPN) score for each potential outcome. Then we stack ranked them by importance.

The most important pieces of data in a hospital are the name and date of birth. These are identifiers to make sure you have the right patient in front of you—primarily for safety, and then, of course, for payment. Believe it or not, a patient's personal cell phone number has become more important than their Social Security number (SSN), as their cell number is familiar, stays current, and does not involve fraud. Most insurance providers are moving away from SSNs as a patient identifier because of fraud concerns and HIPAA worries.

We measured all of the data collection that was going on because in a hospital, your resources are very finite and you have to use them effectively. You only have time to capture what is critically essential to document, treat, and bill a patient. Anything else is noise, and only serves to delay the next patient who is waiting to pay you. Using PFMEA, we were able to cut the time it took to register patients in half. By evaluating and standardizing the registration process, we were able to make the process more efficient for the patients and for the schegistrars. You always have to ask, "What is a way to do this more efficiently with what I have?" Often, standardizing processes is the best way to get to improvements like increasing throughput and decreasing denials. Restaurants standardize menus, how they order food for their kitchen, what time they will be open, and how many servers will be there, and they can also predict when folks will come in to eat. Being hungry is different than being ill, but nonetheless, there are some pearls of wisdom that healthcare can learn from restaurants.

What Can We Learn from Veterinarians?

Pet ownership is big in the United States. According to the American Pet Products Association (APPA), 68 percent of US households own a pet.[427] The APPA estimates that US pet owners will spend $69.36 billion on pets in 2017, with $16.62 billion going to veterinary care.[428] As of this writing, my household has five pets—two dogs, one lizard, one guinea pig, and one fish. Two of those pets have health insurance.

Healthcare is much more highly regulated than veterinary services, but veterinary service delivery is beginning to mimic human healthcare delivery. Magnetic resonance imaging (MRI) is now an option for dogs, to help diagnose problems such as brain and spinal cord injuries.[429] Costs can run upwards of $2,500, including the scan, anesthesia (to keep the animal still during the MRI) and monitoring.[430]

I appreciate having veterinary care available, and I bring my furry family to the vet, often. I do have concerns about costs—as do many other pet-friendly families. Veterinary costs are traveling the same path as human healthcare costs, and without any bridling mechanisms. For example, who established the price of $2,500 for an MRI for a dog? I love my dogs. I had a great one leave me recently, but I would never, ever drop $2,500 on an MRI. Nope.

But that price is there because someone is paying it. We have all been there. We give that look when we hear how much it is going to cost to get the golf ball extracted from Fido. It's often ten to twenty times more than what we "paid" for Fido, and we start doing the math in our head. Is Fido worth that? Sometimes he is, sometimes he isn't. Prices have stayed pretty high for veterinarian treatments—they are not cheap. Hundreds of millions of dollars are spent on Fido every year, and those costs keep increasing (figure 8.4).[431]

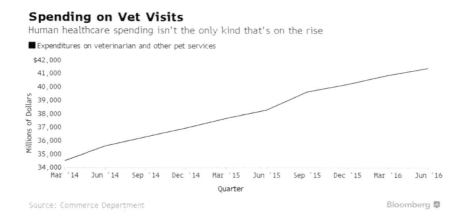

Figure 8.4 Increased Spending on Vet Visits. Source: Smialek, J. (2016, Sept. 27). Your pet's vet bill offers insight into rising U.S. healthcare costs: Climbing vet bills suggest it's not just regulation and insurance behind health care cost inflation. Bloomberg. Retrieved from https://www.bloomberg.com/news/articles/2016-09-27/your-pet-s-vet-bill-offers-insight-into-rising-u-s-healthcare-costs

And now there is insurance to pay for vet bills too. Here we go again, but along the furry route? Not quite. Although veterinary pet insurance has been available in North America since at least 1980, less than 1 percent of pet owners are estimated to have purchased a pet health insurance policy.[432],[433] (Although, on an interesting note, a study by the North American Pet Health Insurance Association (NAPHIA) found that clients with pet insurance spend more on veterinary care than clients who don't have pet insurance.[434] Moral hazard for pets, anyone?)

A 2016 paper on the parallels between American human healthcare and American pet care noted four interesting similarities between the two industries:[435]

- Rapid growth in spending as a share of GDP over the last two decades

- Strong income-spending gradient

- Rapid growth in the employment of healthcare providers

- Similar propensity for high spending at the end of life

The authors state that from an economic perspective, human healthcare parallels pet healthcare because "treatment decisions are triggered by health episodes that are often difficult to forecast, they are channeled by expert intermediaries who may not fully internalize the financial cost associated with treatment, and they often involve emotional and financial tradeoffs."[436]

The authors point out that unlike human healthcare, veterinary care involves much less government regulation and involvement, and insurance is still a negligible factor.[437] The authors add:[438]

> The fact that despite these differences [government involvement, insurance]—often mentioned as potential explanations for the large and rapidly growing healthcare sector in the US—some pet health care patterns appear qualitatively quite similar to the analogous human health care pattern, strikes us as noteworthy. It should give us pause before attributing the large and rising healthcare costs in the US solely to the prevalence of insurance and government involvement.

Proactively Offering Alternative Payment Methods

Where veterinarian practices are ahead of human healthcare practices is in proactively discussing costs and payment options with consumers. As far back as 2009, as many as 57 percent of veterinary practices were offering third-party payment plans as an option for consumers, and 55 percent were offering internal payment plans (figure 8.5).[439]

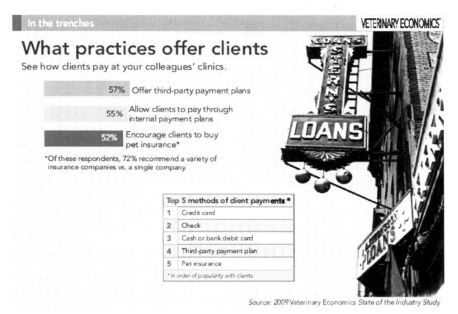

Figure 8.5 Alternative Payment Methods for Veterinary Practices, 2009. Source: dvm360.com. (2009, Aug. 1) Veterinarians offer alternative payment methods to cash-strapped clients. Retrieved from http://veterinarybusiness.dvm360.com/ veterinarians-offer-alternative-payment-methods-cash-strapped-clients#

A 2014 update on preferred client payment options showed third-party payment providers, in-house payment plans, and "wellness" or monthly plans were the top options for veterinary practices.[440] For whatever reason, veterinary practices have no hesitation when it comes to discussing treatment costs—and payment options—up-front, before services are delivered. Fido is worth it, and financing is provided in advance. That's something the human healthcare industry could learn from.

CHAPTER 9

FUTURE FUNDING MECHANISMS

Since patients are the new payers, they need to be connected to funding mechanisms as early in the process as possible. Verifying whether the patient has insurance coverage, whether that insurance covers the services that the patient is accessing, and, finally, whether the patient can pay their portion of the costs are all critical elements of the financial clearance process. That process can be more effective if providers have developed methods to prioritize patients and to differentiate between *ability* to pay and *willingness* to pay from the start.

Some hospitals have built-in screening workflows that help them put patients in the correct funding bucket—a preflight checklist, if you will. "Do you have insurance? Yes/No. If not, then you are self-pay; here is how much that is going to be. Can't afford it? Then maybe you qualify for needs-based discounting? Yes/No. Here is the discounted amount. Still can't pay? Perhaps you are eligible for charity care? Yes/No."

If the patient is uninsured or underinsured and does not qualify for any secondary financial assistance, what is the funding mechanism going to be? Cash, check, charge, loan, goat, chicken? This is where providers can help patients navigate the various financing options that may be available to them.

Once upon a time, providers didn't worry too much about patient-as-payer revenue losses. They worked on it when they could, and the rest was an acceptable loss. But that was when patient-as-payer revenue made up only 10 percent of all patient revenue. Now that number has reached 30 percent—and is still climbing—so what once seemed like an acceptable loss is suddenly going to mean the difference between profitability or cutting back. Providers need to think about the types of funding mechanisms that patients need in this new patient-as-payer world, and they need to operationalize ways of connecting patients to funding mechanisms.

Internal Funding Mechanisms

Payment plans, loans, charity care, and segmentation of accounts are all options that providers can use to match individual patients to funding mechanisms.

Payment Plans

Payment plans have been a part of hospital revenue cycle management for a long time, but provider adoption has not kept pace with the increasing patient out-of-pocket spend and uninsured and underinsured trends that have been developing. Hospitals have a lot of catching up to do.

Traditionally, hospitals haven't introduced payment plans until an account has aged 60 to 90 days. When you wait that long, you have already assumed the risk. Your chance of collecting has already gone down by at least a third. And if the bill isn't something the patient can afford, it's just a scenic route to bad debt.

The best practice is to agree on a payment plan pre-service for electively scheduled encounters. "Mrs. Jones, I see you are coming in for a hip surgery, and when I look at your benefits, I see you will have a balance of $2,400 after insurance pays. We can set up a payment plan for you. How will you be paying the first payment of $200? We accept cash, check, and most major credit cards." (No goats or chickens).

Hospitals can do the same thing for self-pay patients when the patient's balance is high. "We realize this is a large amount to pay all at once. What if we spread this across three payments? The first one is $150. How will you be paying for that today?"

Sometimes, if a provider offers a patient a short-term payment plan up front, they will receive payment from the patient almost faster than they would from the insurance company. Some hospitals fall into the trap of extremely long terms, where patients are paying $10 a month on a $10,000 bill. Aging that amount of cash over that amount of time is not efficient. The collection costs outweigh the revenue. Hospitals are not banks, although they often behave just like them. Hospitals with more mature policies might limit payment plans to no more than 12 months. If the patient can't afford that, they pay what they can, and then are referred to the charity policy or offered a needs-based discount, followed by debt forgiveness. There are sophisticated ways of managing patient balances, and hospitals need to have strategies in place to manage that patient debt.

Loans

There is no other industry with the level of consumer expense that healthcare now has that does not have loan mechanisms in place. Consumers use loans to cover other large expenses, like mortgages and cars. What about loans to cover healthcare expenses? As I said, most hospitals are operating like banks already, but they are doing so indirectly. They "float" a healthcare service. That service has some level of cost to provide, but hospitals don't collect up front. They bill downstream. "Hey, you were provided this service. This is how much you owe." And they expect payment back. That is an indirect, unqualified loan by all other business standards—except that providers are the party responsible for the expense, not the person taking out the loan (a.k.a. "legalized shoplifting").

HealthFirst Financial (www.healthfirstfinancial.com), ClearBalance (www.clearbalance.org), and CareCredit (www.carecredit.com) are examples of organizations set up to offer medical expense payment options. According to HealthFirst Financial's website, it is a "patient financing company" that offers "affordable monthly payments for medical bills."[441] ClearBalance offers "affordable healthcare financing" in the form of "a consumer-friendly loan program," according to its website.[442] CareCredit, on the other hand, "is one of the largest and most popular health, wellness and beauty credit cards in the nation," according to its website.[443] CareCredit offers "shorter term financing options of 6, 12, 18 or 24 months" with no interest charged "on purchases of $200 or more when you make the minimum monthly payments and pay the full amount due by the end of the promotional period. If you do not, interest is charged from the original purchase date."[444] As of this printing, CareCredit's published APR for new accounts was 26.99 percent.[445]

Companies such as these may not help patients with overall affordability issues, but they can help providers get out of the banking (indirect loan) business by giving patients another option. Healthcare, for whatever reason, hasn't been proactive about offering patients financing options, but that is starting to change. Hospitals need that cash, and fast. If someone can front it and assume some or all of the risk, that's a win-win.

In the future, I see more conversations like this happening between the hospital's financial counselor and the patient: "Hello, Mrs. Jones. You are on the schedule for a hip replacement surgery here in six months. We see that your insurance plan has a $5,000 deductible. We have calculated what your estimate is going to be, and this procedure is going to exhaust your deductible. So you will have a patient responsibility of $7,128 that is unfunded. What are your plans for paying that?"

Mrs. Jones: "Well, I, uh, guess you could bill me."

Financial counselor: "That's great, but rather than sending that bill to you in the mail, and dealing with that headache, we have some payment options for you. We can establish financing options that would provide you with a 12-month interest-free loan. The first payment is $594. We accept cash, check, and most major credit cards."

For patients who have the capacity to take on loans, this kind of proactive approach would be a nice alternative to sending an uncollectable invoice for seven grand in an envelope. It is still $594 a month, which is rent or a nice car payment for some, but that may not necessarily be resolved anytime soon. The point is that the loan is still an option. It provides the patient with awareness of the costs, a discussion about how the patient's share of the costs is going to be paid, and how the hospital can help. This is not prevalent in hospitals, but there is momentum with these increased patient balances. I believe that these kinds of healthcare financing options will really take off over the next decade. They have to, unless deductibles and coinsurance die or get significantly lower. (Death to the deductible!)

Charity Care

Most hospitals have a charity care program, offering discounted or no-cost services to patients who meet specific financial criteria. Not-for-profit hospitals are required by law to do so under Section 501(r). Eligibility for charity services is often based on the patient's income in relationship to specified federal poverty levels (FPL; see figure 5.10 in Chapter 5). For example, for 2017, 200 percent of the FPL for a family of four is $49,200. So a hospital might have a charity policy in place that specifies that patients earning up to 200 percent of the FPL are eligible for free care.

However, documenting whether or not patients qualify for charity care is sometimes easier said than done. Some patients are unable to provide income information. Some patients withhold information about income or insurance coverage. Sometimes the information provided will not hold up to an audit or government review. Because of these challenges, a few hospitals are beginning to use more sophisticated methods to distinguish between patients who really cannot afford treatment and those who can pay but do not want to.

One possible means to that end would be to run pre-service credit checks on patients. This is a reasonable approach, but for whatever reason, hospitals are lagging. Hospitals are very, very reluctant to run credit on patients, whether on the front end or the back end. (I do see hospitals more willing to do it on the back end, when they are trying to deal with a large amount of aging bad debt.) Having a patient ask about why their hospital needed to check their credit score spooks hospitals a little. As noted, hospitals are starting to function like banks, at least indirectly. The paradigm of billing through an envelope is going to have to shift. Hospitals are de facto creditors, unless they want to allow the status quo of "legalized shoplifting" to continue.

Hospitals need an accurate way to differentiate between ability to pay and willingness to pay, and running credit checks on patient accounts is one way to do that. I get that hospitals are concerned about their relationship with the patient and their role in the community. But as the payer mix shifts more toward the patient, hospitals are going to have to consider evaluating credit as part of their process of collecting revenue from patients. Individual patient balances are beginning to run into the tens of thousands or hundreds of thousands of dollars. Every other industry dealing with those kinds of accounts receivables balances is checking credit scores. Why aren't hospitals?

I am not suggesting that hospitals should run credit on every single patient. But there are patients (on the front end) and patient accounts (on the back end) where it is very important to be able to differentiate between ability and willingness to pay. Having that information empowers hospitals to help those patients who need it, and to collect from those who have an ability to pay. That kind of data analytics can actually help hospitals implement their charity care policies more equitably, and that is huge.

Matching Patients with Funding Mechanisms

Throughout this book, I have alluded to tools and processes that can help hospitals differentiate between a patient's ability to pay and a patient's willingness to pay. This differentiation or sorting or segmentation, if you will, is becoming increasingly critical as costs continue to shift from traditional insurers to patients.

One tool, as I mentioned above, would be to conduct pre-service credit checks on patients. The advantage of a pre-service credit check is that it helps hospitals match patients with appropriate funding mechanisms *from the start*. (And you know my favorite saying by now. Say it together with me: "The least expensive time to collect is *right now*."). This prevents collection hassles and headaches for both the patient and the hospital down the road. If this is well communicated and understood, and framed by the fact that "that's how every other industry approaches credit for large balances," patients should get on board, but they are a finicky lot, so I'm not promising anything.

However, sometimes it is not possible to play that patient/funding matching game up-front. In that case, the hospital would find itself in the position of having large account receivables balances tied up in aging patient debt. Traditionally, hospitals pull these debt reports and have their internal collects staff start "smiling and dialing," either in order of cradle to grave (i.e., working from the newest debt to the oldest) or by high/low balances, or some combination of the two. I have also seen hospitals rely on third parties to sort out who will pay. Hospitals have paid 18 to 25 points in commissions to early outs (who work on behalf of the hospital for a soft collection) or third-party collection agencies (where debt is actually assigned) and those guys absolutely score those accounts by credit ratings or the like when that debt is written off and brought over to them. That is twenty cents or more on the dollar for a relatively low yield. It's a math problem, and headcount is tough, but that is a wasted expense in these times.

What if there were a better way for hospitals to sort this debt out themselves? There actually is: using data analytics or business intelligence tools to sort patient debt in a way that helps providers maximize their collection efforts. Hospital collections teams can do this in-house with the right people, processes, and technology. Instead of relying on the oldest/newest or highest/lowest paradigms, hospitals can use data analytics to sort patient accounts by ability to pay. This enables hospitals to efficiently delegate patient accounts to the appropriate staff for follow-up. Less than 200 of FPL? Forget smiling and dialing—send them an application for the hospital's charity program. Between 200 and 400 percent of FPL? Consider a needs-based discount, and talk to them about a payment plan. Above 400 percent of FPL? Start smiling and dialing, with the confidence of knowing these patients can pay their full bill. Access to business intelligence about each patient's ability to pay can make a big difference. Without this information, collections staff are shooting in the dark. With it, collections staff can be deployed effectively and efficiently in a way that is aligned with the patient's ability to pay—and that ends up yielding the greatest return for the hospital.

External Funding Mechanisms

Other funding mechanisms are outside of the provider's control. High-risk pools, alternative "insurance," value-based care, vouchers, single-payer healthcare, and universal health coverage are a few of the options either in existence already, or being debated today.

High-Risk Pools

One approach to containing claims risk is to create state-level high-risk pools to absorb the costs of the claims from those patients who are un-insurable due to pre-existing conditions. As I noted in Chapter 2 (figure 2.2), healthcare spending in the United States is concentrated in a small percentage of the population. According to the Kaiser Family Founda-tion, "in any given year, the healthiest 50 percent of the population ac-counts for less than 3 percent of total healthcare expenditures, while the sickest 10 percent account for nearly two-thirds of population health spending."[446]

The theory behind establishing and funding high-risk pools is that if you establish a feasible way to pay for the sickest members of the population, you prevent adverse selection from tanking the rest of the health insurance system.

Prior to the passage of the ACA, state high-risk pools covered more than 200,000 people.[447] The catch was that when the state high-risk pools implemented controls—high premiums, pre-existing condition exclu-sions, lifetime and/or annual limits, or high deductibles—they reduced access for the sickest patients. It's a trade-off either way—controls reduce access, but without controls, the costs high-risk pools incur would make them unsustainable.

Because the ACA prohibited insurers from implementing pre-existing condition exclusions, state high-risk pools became less relevant. Now that pre-existing condition exclusions are on the table again in discussions of ACA repeal, replace, or reform, state high-risk pools are being discussed again. Funding them consistently and equitably is a magic trick, though. There has to be enough source funding and engagement from a large population for them to work. With a balanced risk pool, they have their benefits in providing a very needy population access to care.

Unfortunately, this concentration of costs and provision of access to benefits via state high-risk pools also has an Achilles heel. A 2015 article published by the Commonwealth Fund stated that high-risk pools are not a realistic alternative to coverage under the ACA for the following reasons:[448]

"In a nutshell, high-risk pools:

1. are prohibitively expensive to administer,

2. are prohibitively expensive for consumers to purchase, and

3. offer much less than optimal coverage, often with annual and lifetime limits, coverage gaps, and very high premiums and deductibles."

Dang it. I thought we may have had an answer there. You'll just have to wait until Chapter 10 for some potential solutions.

Alternative "Insurance"

When is an insurance plan not an insurance plan? Some folks struggling with the affordability of premiums and benefits offered by traditional insurers have taken an alternative route: they participate in nonprofit health care sharing ministries (HCSM) instead. Examples of healthcare sharing ministries include Christian Healthcare Ministries (CHM; www. chministries.org), Liberty HealthShare (www.libertyhealthshare.org), Medi-Share (mychristiancare.org/medi-share), and Samaritan Ministries (samaritanministries.org).

HCSMs offer a nonprofit alternative to for-profit, private health insurance plans. Because HCSMs are not actually insurance plans, they are not required to comply with ACA-specified minimum essential coverages or other ACA insurance regulations. Participation in a qualified HCSM does, however, exempt the participant from the tax penalty the ACA imposes on the uninsured.[449] Per the ACA, to qualify as an HCSM, the organization must be tax-exempt; must have been in existence and sharing medical expenses continuously since December 31, 1999; and must have members who:[450]

- Share a common set of ethical or religious beliefs

- Share medical expenses in accordance with those beliefs, even after a member develops a medical condition.

Program details vary, but most request that members contribute a voluntary monthly donation, which is often scaled to reflect family size and age of participants. Program eligibility is based upon shared beliefs. For example, CHM guidelines specify that all members must abstain from the use of tobacco and the illegal use of drugs; follow Biblical principles regarding the use of alcohol; and attend group worship regularly as health permits.[451] Covered benefits are also tied to shared religious beliefs. For example, CHM excludes bills for "abortions or births from unwed mothers" and also excludes "bills incurred as the result of the abuse of drugs or alcohol [and] costs incurred from self-inflicted, non-accidental incidents."[452]

Payment of costs incurred is not guaranteed. Most HCSM programs require members to accept an annual personal responsibility amount (similar to a deductible); most programs have exclusions related to pre-existing conditions; and most programs have per-incident caps on the amount of expenses that can be shared. Most HCSM programs will negotiate with providers on behalf of members to secure discounts for services.[453]

Membership in HCSMs more than doubled, from about 200,000 to about 530,000, after the passage of the ACA.[454] HCSMs present a unique challenge for providers, as they may present as self-pay/cash-pay in the initial encounter. That means no contract with the provider, so discounts are negotiated on a case-by-case basis. The patient presents as if a third party is paying, but it's a non-contractual relationship, so there is no guarantee of payment. It can be very complicated for a hospital to navigate these types of payment situations.

These types of programs can drive hospitals nuts, and are usually treated as self-pay. They lack the reserves and plan rules to afford patient cost sharing—at any level. Pre-payment is unheard of from the patient perspective. It can be very difficult to navigate these plans. I like the concept—they just need to be called (and follow) insurance rules where it makes sense. (Yes, I too, cannot believe I am actually *asking* for insurance rules, but in this case I think it makes sense.)

Value-Based Care

The Centers for Medicare and Medicaid Services (CMS) is driving a movement toward value-based care (VBC). VBC pays providers for the *quality* of care they provide (based on quality measures related to specific outcomes), rather than for the *quantity* of care they provide (the traditional fee-for-service model).[455] In a commercial context, VBC is expressed in pay-for-performance agreements.

How does this impact funding mechanisms for the patient? Well, patients are relatively insulated from the impacts of VBC for now, as it has more to do with getting at provider outcomes and maximizing reimbursement from the insurance carrier. Care delivery should produce improved clinical outcomes with less cost, hence the name. Healthcare is not new to quality initiatives—they have been in CMS's wheelhouse for some time. These initiatives are all typically structured under the same philosophy: measure what you do, improve what you measure, reap the benefits of being more efficient. They have elements of provider coordination, interoperability, and data analytics—so they should all have improved care delivery, resulting in less cost, lower taxes, and more affordable care, right? We'll see.

Providers are scrambling to get "value ready," as this is a big shift for them. There are lots of dollars at risk, and healthcare is a highly dynamic market. The Healthcare Financial Management Association (HFMA) conducted a study in 2015 to see how prepared providers are for "value-based payment readiness" (figure 9.1).[456] The percentage of responding organizations who rate themselves highly or extremely capable in various areas related to value-based payment ranged from in the mid-teens to just over 50, translating to lots of work still to undertake to meet the standard. These numbers are a little troubling, but it is a journey, not a destination. Fundamentally changing how providers get paid is one step to a new funding mechanism for cost reform and patients paying less for their care.

Figure 9.1 Value-Based Payment Readiness. Source: Healthcare Financial Management Association (HFMA). (2015). Value-based payment readiness. Retrieved from https://www.hfma.org/value-basedpaymentreadiness/##

VBC is a very complex concept, and with it comes a plethora of regulation. Several pieces of legislation pertaining to VBC have passed in the last 10 years, including 2008's Medicare Improvements for Patients and Providers Act (MIPPA), 2010's Patient Protection and Affordable Care Act (PPACA), 2014's Protecting Access to Medicare Act (PAMA), and 2015's Medicare Access and CHIP Reauthorization Act (MACRA).[457] VBC programs based on these pieces of legislation have been implemented by CMS over the past several years (figure 9.2).[458]

The Hospital Readmissions Reduction Program (HRRP), implemented in 2012, was one of the initial programs to emerge from CMS's emphasis on value-based care.[459] The ACA provided the legislative foundation for the HRRP.[460] Readmissions to the hospital are costly for patients and for the Medicare program. Medicare designed the HRRP to incentivize hospitals to prioritize better coordination of transitions of care; to improve discharge planning, including education and follow-up for discharged patients; and to improve continuity of care.[461] HRRP

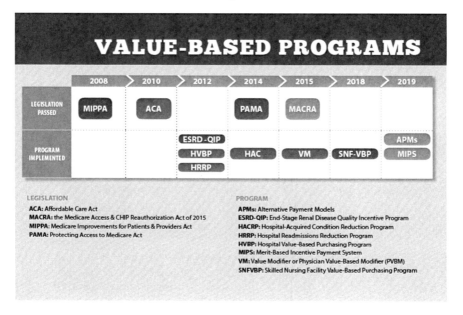

Figure 9.2 CMS Value-Based Program Timeline. Source: Centers for Medicare & Medicaid Services (CMS). (n.d.). What are the value-based programs? Retrieved from https://www.cms.gov/Medicare/Quality-Initiatives-Patient-Assessment-Instruments/Value-Based-Programs/Value-Based-Programs.html

requires CMS to reduce payments to hospitals with excessive readmissions, defined as readmissions within 30 days of discharge.[462] In 2016, a total of 2,597 hospitals (more than half of the nation's hospitals) incurred readmission penalties.[463] As a result of these penalties, Medicare is withholding $528 million in payments from hospitals over the 2017 fiscal year.

HRRP is moving the needle on national discharge rates (figure 9.3).[464] Hospitals are modifying transition of care practices to bend the curve on readmissions. Although hospitals are taking a big hit in penalties, changes in discharge practices that result in decreasing readmissions have the potential to generate significant cost savings for CMS and patients. Paying for how *well* you do something, versus how *many times* you do it—imagine that.

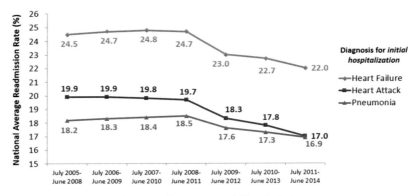

Figure 2
National Medicare Readmission Rates Started to Fall in 2012

Notes: National readmission rates include unplanned hospitalizations for any cause within 30 days of discharge from an initial hospitalization for either heart failure, heart attack, or pneumonia. Readmission rates are risk-adjusted for certain patient characteristics, such as age and other medical conditions.
Source: Kaiser Family Foundation analysis of CMS Hospital Compare data files.

Figure 9.3 National Medicare Readmission Rates Started To Fall in 2012. Source: Boccuti, C., & Casillas, G. (2017, March 10). Aiming for fewer hospital U-turns: The Medicare Hospital Readmission Reduction Program. The Henry J. Kaiser Family Foundation. Retrieved from http://kff.org/medicare/issue-brief/aiming-for-fewer-hospital-u-turns-the-medicare-hospital-readmission-reduction-program/

Accountable care organizations (ACOs) are another value-based care initiative that came out of the ACA legislation.[465] ACOs are formal networks of providers, including doctors, hospitals, and other healthcare providers, who voluntarily work together to provide coordinated care to their Medicare patients.[466] The purpose of ACOs is to make sure patients "get the right care at the right time, while avoiding unnecessary duplication of services and preventing medical errors."[467] Some critics describe ACOs as HMOs in disguise. Others argue that ACO models have addressed some of the shortcomings of HMOs, and may offer the potential of an improved model of care.[468] In a 2012 article in *Health Affairs*, Austin B. Frakt and Rick Mayes state:[469]

> The United States remains in the same situation it has been in for decades: unsure of how to bend the cost curve while maintaining or improving the quality of care. With accountable care

organizations, the search for the sweet spot between provider and payer risk continues.

The authors envision the balance between provider and payer risk—the sweet spot—as existing somewhere between fee-for-service reimbursement models on the one hand and capitation on the other (figure 9.4).[470]

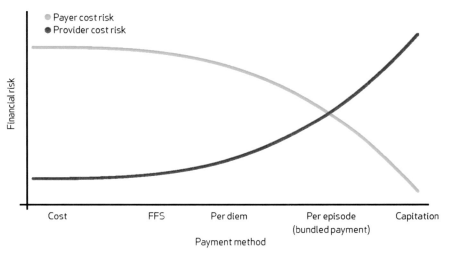

Figure 9.4 Financial Risk of Care for Provider and Payer, by Payment Method. Source: Frakt, A. B., & Mayes, R. (2012). Beyond capitation: How new payment experiments seek to find the 'sweet spot' in amount of risk providers and payers bear. *Health Affairs, 31*(9), 1951-1958. Retrieved from http://content.healthaffairs.org/content/31/9/1951.full

Had enough of acronyms? Well, we aren't done yet. CMS excels at generating acronym-worthy programs, and with VBC, CMS has created many more. MACRA provided the legislative authority for additional CMS value-based programs that impact eligible professionals, under the heading of CMS's Quality Payment Program (QPP).[471] MACRA ended the Sustainable Growth Rate (SGR) formula.[472] SGR was Medicare's attempt to "counter the tendency toward spending growth driven by the fee-for-service model that rewards volume and intensity. The SGR formula automatically reduced Medicare physician fees if physician spending exceeded a target based on overall economic growth."[473] The SGR was a mechanism to ensure inflationary spend was kept in check, and quality outcomes were measured, rewarded, or penalized, depending on performance.

Under the QPP, eligible professionals and groups that include eligible professionals will be included in one of two new payment tracks, when the program is implemented beginning in 2019: the Merit-Based Incentive Payment System (MIPS) and the Alternate Payment Models (APMs; figure 9.5).[474] Both models are designed to link physician payment to performance and health outcomes instead of volume.

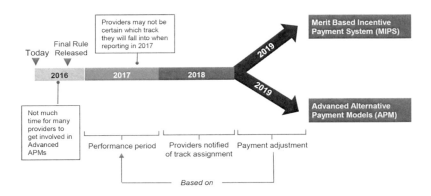

Figure 9.5 Quality Payment Program Implementation Timeline. Source: Teske, K. (2017, Jan. 13). Your questions about the 2017 MACRA final rule—answered. Advisory Board. Retrieved from https://www.advisory. com/research/physician-practice-roundtable/members/expert-insights/2016/nine-faqs-on-provider-payment-under-macra

A deeper dive into the QPP takes us to even more acronyms. The CMS Innovation Center (https://innovation.cms.gov/About) is tasked with testing healthcare payment and service delivery models that have the potential to "improve care, lower costs, and better align payment systems to support patient-centered practices."[475] One of the models the CMS Innovation Center has put forth is called Comprehensive Primary Care Plus (CPC+), which is an advanced primary care medical home model.[476] The 2017 MACRA final rule qualifies CPC+ as an Advanced Alternative Payment Model (APM).[477] APMs are focused on care management, transitions, and population health management (PHM).

All right. Enough with the alphabet soup! What will be the ultimate impact of all these VBC programs? Well, this is expensive soup, and if providers are not prepared, they could stand to lose a lot of money. ACOs put up some guardrails and an infrastructure, but the ACOs still need to report on MACRA for their physicians. Most providers will not seek the complex APMs—they ran out of time after MACRA passed in 2015. Medicare reimbursement is established for these programs and depending on how you do, by 2022 reimbursement ranges from minus 9 percent on the downside to plus 27 percent on the upside.[478]

CMS calls the downside a "negative payment adjustment," but in all honesty, it's a penalty. CMS says the penalties and bonuses (I'm going to call them what they mean to a clinic) will be neutral. Other observers are questioning whether or not MACRA will actually have a revenue-neutral impact on providers, or if the consequences will be more serious:[479]

> Like all well-intentioned laws, The Medicare Access and CHIP Reauthorization Act of 2015 (MACRA) will have unintended consequences. Some providers in small independent practices will either opt-out of Medicare entirely, or decline to accept new Medicare patients if they currently fall below the threshold for exemption (less than $30,000 in Part B billings or 100 Part B patients). To ease small practices into MACRA, the Final Rule issued by the Centers of Medicare & Medicaid Services (CMS) relaxed many of the requirements for 2017. By 2018, however, MACRA starts to impose more financial risk and stricter reporting requirements with less clarity around the return on investment. Small practices might just drop Medicare altogether and transition to a direct-care practice based on cash, membership, or a hybrid.

Note that the CMS's value-based programs will probably not get much disruption from the Trump healthcare reform legislation. Why? Because VBC addresses costs. Bending the cost curve for Medicare is something everybody wants, as all are in agreement that costs are too high. VBC programs have complex funding mechanisms that will require providers to get their ducks in a row fast to ensure they at least stay revenue neutral and are paid what they are entitled to be paid. *Maybe* patients will pay less under VBC funding mechanisms. It's still too early to tell.

Vouchers

One option for funding healthcare that has been kicked around quite a bit is the idea of vouchers. In a voucher system, consumers are given a voucher that they can use to buy health insurance from the private health insurance market.

Speaker of the House Paul Ryan has suggested in the past that vouchers could be used in place of the existing Medicare program.[480] In 2012, Ryan proposed a "premium support" model, which would limit government contributions based on the premium costs of participating health plans.[481] Although some people differentiate between premium support and voucher plans, they are essentially the same: the government would cut a voucher and say, "Go forth and purchase your health plan."

Boston University Economics Professor (and 2016 presidential candidate) Laurence Kotlikoff has articulated a detailed, national voucher plan at www.thepurplehealthplan.org. Under Kotlikoff's plan, all Americans would receive a voucher each year to purchase a basic health insurance plan from the private provider of their choice.[482] Vouchers would be individually risk-adjusted; supplemental plans would also be available. The sum total of the government's spend on the vouchers would equal, but not exceed, 10 percent of the GDP.[483] You might recall from Chapter 2 that in 2015, healthcare spending in the United States reached $3.2 trillion, or 17.8 percent of the GDP.[484] This is projected to reach over 20 percent by 2025, per *HealthAffairs*.[485] Funding for the vouchers would come from the elimination of the programs the voucher system would replace, including Medicare, Medicaid, CHIP, ACA subsidies, and tax breaks for employer-based healthcare.[486] At this time, the Purple Health Plan is only a proposal. No one has picked up the Purple voucher flag and run with it—yet.

A smaller-scale version of the voucher system would be an employer voucher system for employees. In this scenario, employers contain their health insurance premium costs by setting up a defined-contribution health plan and issuing employees a voucher, or monthly healthcare allowance. Employees then choose a health plan through the ACA exchanges or in the private insurance market.[487]

I think vouchers have potential. If the consumer has a voucher and is paying for their premiums out of that, they are going to start shopping—not only for their health plan, but also for their providers. Insurers would have to administer and price plans that met the spend for the voucher, and they would have to aggressively market to retain their members. Providers would have to manage their costs and outcomes a lot better, or they would not be able to play ball long. If consumers are savvy, they are going to spend the least they can against that voucher. That would really be a consumer-directed plan.

What?! A consumer plan that afforded choice on cost, had aligned goals, and stabilized the market? Too good to be true? Perhaps. Critics of the voucher system say it is too expensive and inefficient.[488] Because vouchers do nothing to contain rising healthcare costs, fixed voucher amounts will cover fewer and fewer benefits over time as healthcare costs continue to increase.[489] Proponents of single-payer systems (see the next section) characterize voucher systems as too expensive, because they rely on the private health insurance market to deliver coverage.[490] These critics point out that overhead costs for private insurance are significantly more expensive than overhead costs for programs such as Medicare. After all, private plans include expenses (stockholder profits, marketing expenses) that Medicare does not incur.[491]

Voucher-type systems are not a silver bullet that will cure the healthcare system. Like so many of the solutions we have touched on in this book, solutions that address only one aspect of healthcare's affordability problem (choice) sometimes end up creating other problems (affordability). Something has to give with these mechanisms, and I'll say it again—you cannot have affordable coverage for an unaffordable product.

Single-Payer Healthcare

A single-payer healthcare system is one in which there is one payer for all citizens. In this scenario, private insurers would disappear. A single payer—the government—would provide health insurance for everyone. Single payer is *not* synonymous with socialized medicine, because in a single-payer system, the *delivery* of care can still be privatized. Single payer refers to a means of financing healthcare, not a means of delivering it.

An example of a single-payer system is Medicare. Through the Medicare program, the government provides coverage for the elderly, but patients choose their own providers. As of this writing, the single payer movement in the United States is focused on the concept of "Medicare for All"—in other words, expanding Medicare coverage to all US citizens, not just the elderly. H.R. 676, the Expanded & Improved Medicare for All Act, was introduced by Representative John Conyers in January of 2017. As of April 2017, 104 House Democrats were listed as cosponsors of the bill.[492]

> Note that this is far from the first time this bill has been introduced to Congress. Representative Conyers introduced various versions of the Expanded and Improved Medicare for All Act previously in 2003-2004, 2005-2006, 2007-2008, 2009-2010, 2011-2012, 2013-2014, and 2015-2016.[493] That's worthy of note: it was introduced in seven congressional sessions and failed every time. At least they are persistent. This year marks the largest number of cosponsors the bill has ever received.[494] Thirty-two representatives joined as cosponsors after the American Healthcare Act failed to garner enough support to come to a vote in March 2017 (see Ryancare in Chapter 4).

Despite H.R. 676 and other legislations' bumpy road in Congress, physicians are still rallying. In June 2016, Physicians for a National Health Program (PNHP) published a physician-developed single-payer proposal in the *American Journal of Public Health*.[495] In January 2017, the PNHP announced their support for Conyers's Medicare for All bill.[496]

Interestingly, the public's support of single-payer healthcare varies a lot, depending upon what you call it. A 2016 Kaiser Family Foundation Health Tracking Poll found that 63 percent of respondents felt "very positive" or "somewhat positive" about "Medicare for All," while only 44 percent of respondents felt "very positive" or "somewhat positive" about a "single-payer health insurance system" (Figure 9.6).[497] The poll results do not indicate how the respondents defined the difference between these terms. We do know this: it makes for great conversation at dinner, as *everyone's* got an opinion. (Remember though, no spaghetti! That could get messy.)

Figure 7

Reactions Vary Depending on What You Call It

Please tell me if you have a positive or negative reaction to each term.

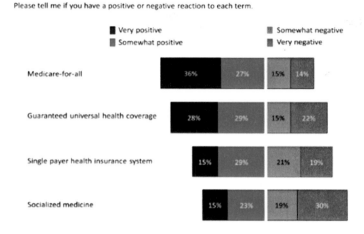

NOTE: Neutral/Neither positive or negative (Vol.) and Don't know/Refused responses not shown.
SOURCE: Kaiser Family Foundation Health Tracking Poll (conducted February 10-18, 2016)

Figure 9.6 Reactions Vary Depending on What You Call It. Source: DiJulio, B., Firth, J., Kirzinger, A., & Brodie, M. (2016, Feb. 25). Kaiser health tracking poll, Figure 7 Reactions vary depending on what you call it. Retrieved from http://kff.org/global-health-policy/poll-finding/kaiser-health-tracking-poll-february-2016/

Universal Health Coverage

Universal health coverage (UHC) is sometimes used interchangeably with single payer, but they are not necessarily synonyms. Universal coverage can be obtained in a variety of ways. A single-payer system is one way—but not the only way—to achieve universal coverage.

Could something like this work in the United States? It's hard to say. The ACA's individual mandate was not effective in achieving universal coverage. The insignificant tax penalties for the uninsured did not provide enough incentive for the young invincibles to participate; and the adverse selection that developed as a consequence is tanking the plans on the ACA health exchanges. That doesn't mean universal coverage could never work in the United States; it just means it didn't work this time.

The funding mechanisms I have outlined here are not all of the possible options. They are just a few examples of what has been tried or is being debated today. I am not suggesting that any particular one of these solutions is the best solution. What I am saying is that the cocktail of private commercial insurance, CMS offerings, and uninsured people that we are all currently sipping from is a stiff drink. It is not sustainable over time.

As we look to the future, I believe that what we will see is some type of hybrid model. The government will have to play a role, with subsidies or rules or both. All of us will have to share in the costs, and any workable solution will certainly require a sacrifice of some of our choices. We will need to address spend and affordability and get a funding mechanism that pays on outcomes. Value-based care is a start, but costs and utilization at the hospital level are in their infancy. A patients-as-a-payer future trending towards $10,000 deductibles and 50 percent coinsurance is alarming. That is debt shifting, not insurance. If we do not come up with something, the government will decide something for us. I know this—in America, we have the freedom to vote for what we want. But sometimes we vote for something and then suffer buyer's (or voter's) remorse afterwards. What kind of healthcare solution would you vote for?

CHAPTER 10

. . . .

WOULDN'T IT
BE NICE

I like the Beach Boys. Remember them? One of their songs, "Wouldn't It Be Nice" includes the lyric, "Wouldn't it be nice if we were older? Then we wouldn't have to wait so long…"[498] I know that dates me, and yes, I'm getting more gray hair—working in healthcare finance while raising eight-year- and twelve-year-old boys is a path to accelerated aging. When I encounter a challenge, I often sing my own version of "wouldn't it be nice…" in my head. For example, "Wouldn't it be nice if healthcare were stable, and we did not have to pay so much…" (It's OK to sing along if you would like). Or, "Wouldn't it be nice if patients were empowered to pay their bills and hospitals did not have to wait so long to get paid…" (OK, I'll stop).

My point is that for the foreseeable future—as you now understand from traveling with me through this book—the patient IS the new payer in healthcare. Providers are only slowly beginning to recognize this new reality and adapt to it. For the well-being of both patients and providers, the industry must design and implement new revenue cycle management processes that engage patients in the financial aspects of their care. Everybody wins in this scenario: patients are given support in understanding and accessing funding mechanisms to pay for their care, and providers stand to increase revenue and decrease debt by engaging patients in financial discussions before treatment is delivered.

Over the course of this book we have touched on a number of ways that hospitals and health systems can deliver a more patient-friendly

237

financial experience. Some providers are already experimenting with a variety of these approaches. Others are continuing to operate in the dark ages of revenue cycle management, with legacy processes still based on the presumption that commercial and government payers are the way we will always get paid.

Below are a few "wouldn't it be nice" ideas about how to engage patients in the financial aspects of their care. Some of these ideas can only be implemented outside the scope of the hospital or health system operations, but are worth considering nonetheless. Many of these ideas can be implemented directly by hospitals and healthcare systems.

Feel free to reach out to me if you would like more information about how to implement some of these ideas within your own healthcare system. My philosophy is that the more of us who know and do something about the current state of affairs, the better our healthcare system will be— for the patient, the provider, the insurer, and the employer. Those four stakeholders have to collaborate, get along, and focus on better health at a lower cost. Most will agree that value-based healthcare is the way to get there, but we are facing a long journey, not just a destination. Keep in mind that deductibles are not going anywhere or fixing anything. So, "Wouldn't it be nice if the four stakeholders could get together, and not have to wait so long?" (Caught you singing again!)

As I stated earlier, I am a revenue cycle management guy, and nothing gives me greater pleasure than working with hospitals and health systems to help their patients. I get goosebumps when I see them achieve long-term sustainability by adapting their revenue cycle management processes to accommodate this new patient-is-the-new-payer reality. Some organizations really excel at this change. Patient financial experience is at the forefront for them, and their patient satisfaction surveys (Hospital Consumer Assessment of Healthcare Providers and Systems (HCAHPS)), financials, volumes, and benchmark key performance indicators (KPIs) prove it. I am not going to name them, but I bet you can. If not, send me a note and I will fill you in on some of my favorites. Patient-friendly revenue cycle management is achievable. The time to start implementing it is now.

If I could wave a magic wand and re-orient the healthcare system to contain costs, become more patient-friendly, and empower patients to engage in more self-directed care, these are a few of the things I would change…

Wouldn't It Be Nice If…
Employees Actively Engaged in Healthcare Coverage Conversations with Their Employers about How Their Health Plans Work?

As I noted in Chapter 6, employer-sponsored health insurance is the largest source of health insurance in the United States, covering about 49 percent of the total population.499 If patients engaged more with their employers about the plans they chose, they would be taking a huge step in the right direction. While plans are brokered and evaluated, benefits literacy is often an issue for the patient, who is left with questions. What are the benefits? What is not covered? What is the likely out-of-pocket spend per plan? Which plan as the lowest premium? Will I need these options? I'm not sure if familiarity with the benefits is just not a priority for the employer or their employee, or if it is an afterthought, where people push off certain issues until after they have already made a decision. I am sure that most employees do not understand the benefits they have purchased from their employer.

The Kaiser Family Foundation (KFF) and the Robert Wood Johnson Foundation (RWJF) convened a national roundtable in 2014 on the topic of consumer assistance after the Affordable Care Act (ACA) was implemented. Roundtable participants agreed that insurance literacy was a significant barrier that affected "how well consumers can make plan choices and use coverage effectively."[500] Roundtable participants indicated that many consumers still did not understand the importance of getting coverage, how it worked, or even what a deductible was.[501]

The Society for Human Resource Management (SHRM) speaks of "financial wellness" as a confounding topic for human resources and employees.[502] They expand on that idea and state:

For instance, employers may not understand how voluntary benefits such as supplemental life insurance might work with retirement savings to provide for beneficiaries under a worst-case scenario, or how health savings accounts can help with high deductibles in consumer-directed health plans.[503]

The same article quotes Betsy Dill—a Los Angeles-based senior partner and US financial wellness leader at the consulting firm Mercer—as saying, "Employers need to look at how they integrate these solutions into a more employee-first experience."[504]

A town-hall type meeting for employees might be an option. Consider the idea of a three-way meeting between the employer, the hospital, and the employees. Include the company's human resources department along with a representative from a local hospital—perhaps a financial counselor—who can explain, "Here are the plans you have chosen. And here is how coverage plays out in some typical scenarios, such as childbirth, a visit to the emergency department, or a knee replacement surgery." Walk employees through these scenarios and explain what the typical costs are, along with what the out-of-pocket patient responsibility would be with their particular coverage.

Educate employees about the specific details of the plans they have selected. Make attendance mandatory, or provide an incentive or discount if an employee attends. A variety of benefit questions could be addressed, including: What is a deductible? How does it work? What is a copay? What is coinsurance? If the employer plan includes a health savings account (HSA) option, educate employees about that as well. Is the employer contributing to the HSA? How much? Is the employee contributing to the HSA? Is an automatic contribution an option? Why is that a good idea?

Employers can also point employees toward resources such as <u>healthcarebluebook.com</u>, where they can find fair market prices for the procedures, tests, services or medications they are considering. Why not encourage employees to use these resources to shop for their care? Employees really should approach buying healthcare in the same way they shop for anything else because employees will own that premium dollar. They will own that deductible.

Address levels of care from a clinical and cost perspective by answering questions such as these: When is it appropriate to go to the emergency room (ER)? When is it appropriate to go to the primary care physician (PCP)? When is it appropriate to go to urgent care? What are your urgent care options with your coverage in your community? Employers can outline costs for each option and the type of care they provide with answers such as, "Emergency departments (EDs) do it all and are open all the time, but are expensive… PCPs that have evening hours might be better in some cases," and so on.

Without a determined, collaborative effort from the employer and employees to uncover the realities of the coverage, we are left with a situation where employees must self-navigate a healthcare system, which is very difficult to understand and use. As a result, when employees access their employer-provided health benefits without fully understanding what the benefits are or how they work, they are unable to make choices that address the patient financial responsibility aspects of their healthcare.

A well-executed employee education effort would benefit employees *and* employers. If more employees are able to make educated decisions about their healthcare, their employers' claims risks are more likely to go down, which may be reflected in lower premiums down the road. Bottom line: We have a heightened sense of urgency as patients are themselves rapidly becoming payers. Some feel that employers need to change from *optional* benefits education sessions to *mandatory* sessions so that patients have to educate themselves about the coverage (and costs) of their care. I have heard a lot of talk about patient engagement. Imagine complete employee engagement surrounding the financial implications of their benefit plan choices. Wouldn't that be nice?

Wouldn't It Be Nice If...
Patients Had the Information They Needed at Their Fingertips to Actually Engage in Self-Directed Care?

Cost-shifting to patients, through designs such as high-deductible health plans (HDHPs), is supposed to help patients become more self-directed in their care. That is not happening, in part because patients don't have access to user-friendly, complete information about costs and coverage that would help them make wise use of their healthcare dollar. While some employers and companies have tools that calculate costs by procedure, they are not yet pushing for widespread adoption.

What if these tools went mobile and you could use an app on your phone designed to help you make your healthcare decisions? You could type in "headache" and get a list of all the facilities near your location that could treat a headache along with what the average charge would be for that care. You could enter your plan information and see in-network providers for your specific plan along with a breakdown of your out-of-pocket costs. And then you could link to the appointment schedule for the provider you chose, based on all of the previous information.

Wouldn't it be nice if the healthcare experience mirrored more retail purchases, like what our example describes? That would truly be self-directed care. A number of developers, including Stride Health (stride-health.com), are working on apps that deliver parts of this puzzle. Stride Health leads the pack with a healthcare app that works like Uber. They just need a few more pieces before consumers can set up a profile, enroll in insurance, and start shopping (and requesting) their care—virtually.

In the United States consumers will have 947 million mobile-connected devices (phones, tablets, etc.) by 2020, nearly 2.8 devices per person.[505] This number will represent a two-fold increase from 2015.[506] By 2020, the number of cell phones worldwide will outnumber people who have water and electricity.[507] And who will be using those devices? We talked about the millennials in earlier chapters—they will most certainly want to access, pay for, and experience their healthcare as they do everything else. Wouldn't it be nice if healthcare were ready?

Wouldn't It Be Nice If...
Consumers Had More Choices for Benefit Plan Designs?

Insurance has become unaffordable because of all of the factors that we have discussed—high costs, consolidation, legislation, and oversupply. Again, you cannot have affordable insurance for an unaffordable product. This is another one of those tricky areas where you have to find balance. As costs were hidden from patients, the scope of benefits grew, along with premiums and deductibles. The ACA was intended to fill a gap for access to care, and mandated minimum essential coverage (MEC) that spelled out what ACA-compliant plans had to cover. Remember that increased scope of coverage resulted in higher premiums. With those premiums also came unaffordable deductibles. The ACA did not address utilization or costs, and it did not encourage bare-bones catastrophic plans with low monthly premiums and minimal benefits. Although catastrophic health plans are available to people under the age of 30, and to people of any age who qualify for a hardship or affordability exemption, they are not available to the general public.[508] The ACA plans were neither attractive nor sustainable to the young invincibles. Unless they stabilize soon, these plans are becoming bad business for insurance carriers.

Catastrophic plans take us back to what health insurance was originally designed for: to protect people from catastrophic illness or injury, rather than to cover everything under the sun (or penalize you if you fail to offer it as an employer or purchase it as an employee). Providing coverage that is flexible enough to meet the individual needs of every consumer—that they can afford and understand, and that everyone can support—is a daunting task. I have heard insanity defined as doing the same thing over and over and expecting a different result. We will have to do something different. The current path and coverage models are not working to control costs. Perhaps value-based care will help with this, along with population health management, but the plan benefit designs we have are not sustainable. With healthcare premiums and deductibles skyrocketing quickly, and exceeding the limits of affordability, it might be time to have a broad band of coverage levels that are tailored (and priced) for each patient's clinical needs AND affordability. Wouldn't that be nice?

Wouldn't It Be Nice If...
Health Insurance Plans Included Incentives or Penalties to Reduce Unhealthy Behaviors (Besides Smoking) That Contribute to Chronic Diseases?

As I talked about in Chapter 2, one of the growing problems we face in the United States is the increasing prevalence of chronic disease related to behavior choices. Insurers have long recognized the increased health claims risks associated with cigarette smoking. In fact, many employers and insurers implement tobacco surcharges on premiums for smokers. The ACA allows insurance companies to charge tobacco users up to 50 percent more than enrollees who don't use tobacco.[509] The ACA also included smoking cessation interventions as one of the mandatory preventive benefits covered by ACA-compliant plans.[510] What about obesity? The ACA also addressed our country's appetite for fast food by mandating that calories be displayed on menus so that folks know what is going in as they eat.[511] As of this writing, the US Food and Drug Administration (FDA) has delayed implementation of the rule until May 2018, but some eating establishments are already making calorie information available.

As far as I know, we do not yet have premium incentives based on how many cheeseburgers or beers a person consumes. Group health plans spread this risk—if you are an individual, the ACA has you covered, for now. But what if similar "carrot-and-stick" incentives and penalties were implemented for other types of behaviors that contribute to chronic disease, such as alcohol abuse? Obesity? And lack of exercise? Some health plans are beginning to implement programs that reward enrollees for participating in specific wellness programs.

The Employment Retirement Income Security Act (ERISA), which sets minimum standards for voluntarily established pension and health plans in private industry, "prohibits discrimination by group health plans based on an individual's health status. ERISA makes exceptions for wellness programs to offer premium or cost-sharing discounts based on an individual's health status in certain circumstances."[512] ACA regulations clarified that "health-contingent" wellness programs could use premium rewards to provide incentives for specific health outcomes, such as attaining normal weight or blood pressure.[513]

I think the magic wand here is getting the patient engaging patients in their own wellness is to offer a premium price differential as an incentive. We need creative ways to motivate patients. For example, employers could tell employees, "If you go get your cholesterol measured once a quarter, we will take $50 off of your premium that month… or give you a Walmart gift card… or enter you in a raffle for a trip to Hawaii…" or "If you see your primary care doc for your annual physical, your premiums will be 5 percent lower next year." Anything that will create an incentive for patients to proactively engage with their own wellness should be considered.

Incentive plans like these are out there, and they work. WellSteps (wellsteps.com), a service provider for employers, published a white paper on the impacts of their programs.[514] According to the authors, employees enrolled in (and given an incentive by) WellSteps programs learn to lead healthier lifestyles. The authors outline double-digit percentage improvements in healthy behaviors, such as the ones your mom used to tell you to do: go outside and exercise, eat your vegetables, make sure to get your rest, and others. After employees "learn" to be healthier, their risk for chronic disease decreases significantly—we are talking 35–66 percent reductions.[515] Does this really work? WellSteps thinks so. According to their website, as of this writing, WellSteps offers a 150 percent guarantee their solutions will work.[516]

I have also heard the "glass half empty people" talk about how wellness programs are ineffective and a waste of money, or that employees will not enroll. The effectiveness of these programs may be debatable. Books have been written on how to engage patients clinically and financially, and we will leave the rationale to them. My point is that these programs certainly cannot hurt, and lots of them are around. I have no affiliation with WellSteps, but their programs seem to be making a difference.[517] Wouldn't it be nice if we as patients all had an incentive to make healthier choices and could reap the benefits of lower healthcare costs?

Wouldn't It Be Nice If...
Millennials Wanted to Buy Health Insurance?

Insurance risk pools do not work the way they are supposed to when only the elderly and/or the sick buy health insurance. You need to "chlorinate" the pool with young, healthy enrollees to spread out the claims risk over a larger, healthier population. That reasoning was supposed to hold the cost of premiums down in the ACA implementation, but—as I have mentioned before—the young invincibles didn't show up for the ACA party. How do we get them to want to buy health insurance?

A 2016 survey of millennials, conducted by the Transamerica Center for Health Studies (TCHS), found that lack of knowledge was the biggest barrier to enrollment in ACA exchange plans.[518] In fact, millennials' most common reason for not obtaining coverage was, "I did not know how to apply."[519] The second most common reason was, "Paying my health expenses and the tax penalty is less expensive than the options available to me."[520] Clearly, the premiums for the benefit-rich plans on the ACA did not meet the definition of affordability for most millennials. The same TCHS survey found that one in three millennials said that any premium over $100 per month was unaffordable, a finding that has been consistent over the past three years.[521] Wow. A hundred bucks a month is "unaffordable." I wonder how much they pay per month for their mobile phone or their lattes. We have to figure out a way to entice millennials to the party and make them want to stay.

Is there a feasible sweet spot for millennials? Can insurers design a plan that meets millennial standards for affordability while providing enough value that millennials will seek out and purchase that insurance? Perhaps a catastrophic plan that was more affordable and catered to a millennial's tastes would work. Wouldn't it be nice if we had a java insurance café with lattes, free Wi-Fi, smooth jazz, and a physician that did well visits for only $50 a month? (OK, I'll stop...)

Wouldn't It Be Nice If...
Health Insurance Premiums Spread Risk
but Also Reflected Actuarial Realities?

I'm not eligible for AARP yet. And, once they read this, they might reject me from membership. Still, I have to ask: Should health insurance premiums reflect actuarial realities? The "silver tsunami" is real. America's population is aging. Increased age = increased healthcare costs. Should healthcare premiums reflect this reality?

ACA provisions limit age-related premium differences to a ratio of 3–1. That is, premiums for the oldest insured (a 64-year-old, for example) cannot exceed three times the cost of the premiums for the younger insured (a 21-year-old, for example). Prior to the passage of the ACA, age-rating ratios averaged 5–1 or higher.[522] As of this writing, legislation is under consideration by Congress to roll back age-banding to a 5–1 ratio. In other words, insurers would be able to charge older enrollees as much as five times the premium cost of younger enrollees. This change would presumably drop premium costs for younger enrollees and increase premium costs for older enrollees. Estimates for the size of these impacts vary, depending upon your modeling scenario. AARP has estimated that changing the age-rating limit to 5–1 would "increase yearly premiums for an average 64-year-old on a silver plan by $2,100 (from $8,500 to $10,600), while reducing premiums for a 21-year-old by only $700 (from $2,800 to $2,100)."[523] AARP further states that relaxing age-banding to 5–1 would disproportionately impact adults ages 50-64, who are not yet eligible for Medicare.[524]

While I understand AARP's arguments, the reality is that older people have a higher claims risk than younger people. Older people may also have a fixed income, so we have a double-edged sword, as affordability comes into play once again. This discussion reminds me of a saying: "the monkey will dance, but at the end of the day, who is paying the monkey?" This hails from the days of organ grinders and buskers who performed in New York and other cities in the late 1800s and early 1900s. The organ grinders' performance often included a monkey, who would dance or do tricks and help the organ grinder collect money (or not) in a hat or cup. In healthcare, who is paying the monkey?

My point is that we have lots of monkeys at the disco doing the healthcare hustle, we have a hat (the employers, employees, and patients as payer), and we have an organ grinder (government), but the funding does not match the dance. It's out of balance. Some folks pay very little and get a lot, while others pay a lot and get very little. This situation does not work with taxes and it does not work with healthcare. Someone has to pay for that claims risk. Should younger people subsidize the claims risk of the older population? Or should older Americans pay premiums that more closely reflect the costs of their claims? This is a difficult societal question that we need to address. It affects Medicare spending as well. Remember when we noted that 20 percent of the population incurs 80 percent of healthcare costs? Cost increases correlate with age increases. If 65-year-old Medicare recipients pay the same premium as 85-year-old Medicare recipients, and if the average age of Medicare beneficiaries continues to increase over time due to the aging of the American population, where does that leave us? Whether we are talking about the government, the employers, or the patient-as-payer, the people watching this monkey dance are going to have empty pockets after a few more rounds.

Other types of insurance closely reflect actuarial realities. Have you tried to buy auto insurance for a teenage boy lately, especially for a new driver? Let me tell you—that will make your wallet sigh. If we had an AARP counterpart for teenage boys, I am sure they would voice concerns about reverse age discrimination. The fact is, teenage boys—particularly new drivers—are involved in more accidents than mature, experienced drivers. Auto insurance premiums reflect that. The difference is that people have a choice about wanting to drive a car, but not about being ill. That said, health insurance premiums cannot ignore actuarial realities unless someone or something with very deep pockets is willing to fund the difference. Who will that be? Taxpayers? The monkey? At some point, the health insurance philosophy of "having your cake and eating it, too" will have to stop. It is not sustainable.

Wouldn't It Be Nice If...
the Government Implemented Mandatory Contributions
to HSAs and Other Types of Health Savings Accounts?

HSAs only work if you fund them. What if a percentage (5–10 percent) of the funds you contributed to your 401(k) or 403(b) was earmarked to fund your HSA account? I think that is a better solution than a tax penalty for not having health insurance. Tax penalties have proven to be an ineffective way to mandate that people get coverage. Just as we have seen with the young invincibles, people are neither staying at the party nor paying to play.

An analysis of 400,000 HSA accounts by HelloWallet (a subsidiary of Morningstar) found that only 5 percent of the sample studied had contributed the maximum allowable amount to their HSA accounts.[525] Wow. The analysis suggested that "behavioral barriers" were preventing workers from maximizing HSA benefits.[526] These barriers include a lack of importance placed on saving for healthcare and a lack of familiarity with projecting out-of-pocket healthcare expenses.[527]

Remember that point I made a few pages back about benefits literacy? Here we are. The HelloWallet article also mentioned that healthcare plan benefits might be better funded if they were structured and explained more like retirement accounts. Can you imagine if there were as many commercials for HSAs as there are for Morgan Stanley, Prudential, and Fidelity retirement accounts? I can. "Fund your future knee surgery after skiing with 'PlanAheadHealth,' the new HSA plan. Call this number now and find out how to start saving today."

Legislators are exploring ways to make HSAs easier to fund as well as looking at changes in definitions that would allow more people to use them. Some critics have pointed out that, as they are now structured, HSAs primarily benefit those with salaries in the six figures because that is the point at which the tax benefits start to make sense.[528] We have an opportunity here to try to make them more attractive as a tax benefit to those in the lower tax brackets, so that the large administrative fees can be offset. While HSAs might offer an effective approach, they fail to help the people who need them the most. Wouldn't it be nice if we all understood what an HSA was? If it provided a wicked awesome tax benefit no matter what your income was? And if it was funded appropriately enough to pay the monkey?

Wouldn't It Be Nice If...
Most Patients Received an Estimate of Their Cost of Care and Out-Of-Pocket Expenses Before Care Was Delivered?

As I have made clear throughout this book, I do not believe that the T-word (transparency) is helpful on its own. When you consider price alone—uncoupled from information about the individual patient's benefits, coverage available, funding mechanisms, and affordability—this makes the T-word problem worse. Patients need to know what their unique out-of-pocket costs will be, given their benefits and coverage, and what funding options are available to them. We need to meet the patient-as-payer as a consumer, not as a number with a disease.

Only 35 percent of hospitals are doing pre-service estimates, according to a 2015 Availity report.[529] Come on! Really? Only a little better than one in three? We have to engage those other two patients every time, all the time. This book and those patients are telling you they want it, so let's do it! Every patient should have an upfront conversation about their cost of care, including an estimate of charges as well as information about the patient's plan coverage and expected out-of-pocket contribution. This discussion will help patients plan for their cost of care and understand funding options, and will also give providers a starting point for point of service collection. As I have mentioned before, the least expensive time to collect is *right now*... it gets really expensive to collect money tomorrow. Let's pay that monkey! Wouldn't that be nice?

Wouldn't It Be Nice If...
Hospitals Were Set Up to Collect Up Front?

The corollary to "always give patients a preservice estimate" is to collect up front. Consumers are used to making a down payment for large purchases such as a house or a car. Why not healthcare? Most people are willing to pay when you ask them. So why don't hospitals ask up front? It just hasn't been part of the healthcare provider culture. But with patients assuming more and more of first-dollar coverage, it is time to change that culture.

This shift means that when providers ask for payment up front, they should make it easy for patients to do so by providing an accurate estimate of costs and a means to pay—whether by mobile app or credit card machine right at the front desk. Look at grocery stores, auto shops, gas stations, airlines, Amazon, Home Depot, Lowes, Walmart, and nearly every other business. They ALL allow you to pay easily either before, during, or immediately after service. These businesses are set up with e-signature pads, self-checkout lanes, pre-payment options, pay-at-the-pump options—all consumer-centric models.

Most hospitals now at least have an ATM on site (hint: why not place it next to your registration desk, where the staff that collects payment sits?) Most hospitals make it HARD to pay them, and I get it—medicine is an art, not a science, with several variables in delivery and coverage that ultimately affect payment. We can find a solution here, though, that is not as far off as you might think. Patients want to pay, and hospitals need to provide an easy way of doing that. Wouldn't it be nice if patients could pay providers easily and up front, as they pay for everything else?

Wouldn't It Be Nice If...
Hospitals Employed an Army of Schegistrars to Keep the Conversation about the Patient's Financial Experience Going?

As I described in Chapter 6, schegistrars are a kind of uber-patient financial specialist. They are essential staff at any hospital. Schegistrars can do everything from registering a patient and verifying insurance eligibility to screening for health benefit exchange plans, Medicaid, or the hospital's charity program.

In my ideal world, each hospital would have an army of schegistrars. They would help each patient navigate their clinical experience by providing relevant information about their financial experience. "Your insurance covers this, but it does not cover that. How would you like to proceed?"

Physicians guide patients through the clinical experience of healthcare. "Go here, take this test, now go there, and get this treatment." And yet patients are largely left to their own devices when navigating the financial aspects of healthcare. Schegistrars could change that by addressing the financial information gaps in the patient's experience. Few hospitals have a large staff of schegistrars at their disposal. Why? Resources. Turnover, staffing constraints, delivery costs, and priorities have all deterred the schegistrar army from their mission. I'm not suggesting that hospitals need one for every single patient. While that would be nice, it's not feasible. Schegistrar-to-patient ratios are easily into the 1–100 range at most hospitals, which only leaves time to say, "Hello" with a smile, gather a little info, collect some cash, and thank them for their choice. After that, the patient is left to figure out the costs and charges on their own.

I am seeing more investment in people, processes, and technology to help patient access at the front end of the revenue cycle. While progress is slow, it is doable with the hospitals' expense package—we just need people with tenacity. As patient access evolves to meet the patient as a paying consumer, the revenue cycle will also evolve from a cost center to a revenue center that insulates millions of dollars for each hospital. Billing impacts patient experience. Patient bad debt is a function of funding options and assuming risk. Those are facts. Wouldn't it be nice to have a schegistrar who can serve patients and hospitals by acting as a financial navigator insulating those dollars now?

Wouldn't It Be Nice If...
Clinicians Were Able to Participate in the Conversation about Patient Financial Engagement?

I admit it: mixing up patient finances and physicians is like trying to mix oil and water. Having said that, I have no doubt that the affordability of treatment options affects clinical outcomes. If a patient cannot afford to follow through with the physician's orders—for a procedure or a pharmaceutical regimen—then the patient's clinical outcome will be negatively impacted.

Physicians are clinical specialists, not health insurance specialists. Nonetheless, physicians can play a role in handing patients off to specialized financial counselors who can work with the patients within the constraints of their individual health plans to determine the best funding mechanisms going forward. Holding financial conversations before, during, and after you consider treatment options could have an enormous effect. Dentists—as well as most primary care clinics (for the interventions done there)—have taken this approach for some time. Once the patient needs to go somewhere else, the burden of explaining treatment or financial options is no longer the caregiver's problem. I'm not suggesting that it needs to be their problem exclusively, either. Wouldn't it be nice to have costs explained to each patient in tandem with every encounter (at scheduling, prescription fill, office visit, discharge, imaging exam, etc.?)

Wouldn't It Be Nice If...
Hospitals and Health Systems Could More Efficiently Sort Patient-Payer Accounts Receivables by Ability to Pay and Likelihood of Payment?

Many hospitals and healthcare systems have extremely inefficient systems for prioritizing and following up on patient-as-payer accounts receivables. They use cradle-to-grave (oldest amount due to newest amount due); high-to-low (largest amount due to smallest amount due); or a combination of the two types of reports to figure out who to collect cash from on the back end. Providers routinely pay a premium for someone else to collect their payments, and carry on.

What if providers were able to use data analytics to separate patient accounts into buckets that made more sense from a collection standpoint? These tools could generate reports that tell a provider, "This third of patients has a high likelihood of payment. They are at or above 1,000 percent of the Federal Poverty Level (FPL) and are worth following up on. This third has no money. They are below 200 percent of the FPL. It is not even worth making a phone call to them. Give them a charity care application instead. This third is in the middle and would benefit from a payment plan." This is mind blowing: Why are so few providers applying this approach to all those scheduled patients coming in this week, at least to the ones who are self-paying or have a high balance-after-insurance (BAI) of $500 or more? Someone must have a collections conversation at some point with almost every patient. Why has our industry accepted that delaying that conversation until very late in the billing process is the norm? It is time to work smarter, not harder. Providers can put workflow data to good use by adopting operating tools such as account scoring and segmentation to make hospital patient collections more productive. Wouldn't it be nice if patients were financed and analyzed like a consumer?

Wouldn't It Be Nice If...
Healthcare Providers Implemented Patient-Friendly Billing?

As I have discussed in previous chapters, nothing about healthcare bills is patient friendly. You usually don't get an estimate up front. Bills will come in the mail, weeks, months or years after your treatment. Your bills may not always be consolidated—one may come from the hospital, another from the doctor or from the anesthesiologist—and none of them may relate to the other. In addition, you might get an Explanation of Benefits (EOB) separately from your insurer. EOBs do not always align with the bills you are getting from your healthcare provider, either. Eventually once you receive a paper bill in the mail, you might have the option to pay online, but often, you have to pay by check. These practices do not accommodate the patient at all; they are frustrating, and a hassle, at best.

Consolidated Billing

Consolidated billing is achievable if you have the "political will" and technology support needed to implement it. The ideal consolidated bill would include ALL of the charges incurred by the patient in a single statement, regardless of whether the source of those charges was the hospital facility, the physician, the anesthesiologist, or anyone else involved in care delivery. The ideal consolidated bill would also include insurance benefit information as it applied to that particular bill: It would answer these questions: Was the procedure or service covered? Was a copay required? Was it collected? Where is the patient in terms of their deductible? Does coinsurance apply?

More than one study has identified confusion about healthcare bills as a reason why patients don't pay them. Reducing that confusion by generating a single, consolidated statement would help both patients and providers. Traction is there to make statements one all-encompassing bill that is easy to receive, understand, and pay. What would this look like? The ideal solution would generate a consolidated bill that can be sent electronically, is written in simple, clear language, and can be paid by mobile. Hospitals still have a long way to go on most of these practices. Wouldn't it be nice if these methods were considered standard, rather than innovative?

Digital Options

As I mentioned in Chapter 6, more than one-fifth of all millennials have never written a paper check to pay a bill.[530] There's a big disconnect between how hospitals bill patients and how patients pay bills. Online payment options are becoming more prevalent, but have not yet been adopted by all providers. Phone-based apps for online payment are even rarer. If providers want to increase their collection rates from patient payers, they need to meet patients where they are. Where are they? These days, patients—especially millennials—are on their smartphones.

Millennials pay for many things on their phones, including hotels, airline tickets, rental cars, and groceries. They even monitor their checking accounts by phone. Millennials prefer to purchase most of their consumer goods and manage their banking through their phones. The healthcare industry will need to meet them there and offer a mobile pay option.

Millennials, as a group, are inquisitive. They want things at their fingertips, delivered quickly. They will expect healthcare to deliver the same retail experience they have with any other industry. Millennials will be a big force in the new patient-as-payer world, and they will demand things that are, frankly, outside of the industry's ability to deliver right now. This gap between where we are and where we need to be almost concerns me more than HDHPs and healthcare costs. If we were to fast-forward this generation by five–ten years, they would bring the healthcare industry to its knees from a payment standpoint. Given the lag the healthcare industry typically displays in adopting, affording, and implementing complex technology, the future increase in numbers of millennial patients is a run-away train. The healthcare industry will need to pivot—quickly—to meet them, or we will have to "buckle up, buttercup" for the complaints and payment refusals.

Wouldn't It Be Nice If...
There Were Cost Controls on Litigation?

Wouldn't it be nice if you couldn't arbitrarily sue a provider for millions of dollars for just making a mistake? In the United States, malpractice insurance and defensive medicine affect a lot of healthcare costs, especially at the specialist level. Many other countries don't afford that level of litigation. People make mistakes, and the United States is a very litigious society. While the current system certainly has its pros and cons, I would argue that the costs far outweigh the benefits.

The new US Secretary of Health and Human Services, Tom Price, has suggested that "lawsuit abuse reform" is an important component of reducing the nation's total healthcare spend.[531] Price and others have recommended that a California law capping noneconomic damages in malpractice cases at $250,000 could be used as a national model.[532] Wouldn't it be nice if we funded healthcare access, payment, and funding instead of such a large number of medical lawsuits?

Wouldn't It Be Nice If...
There Were Cost Controls on Medical Devices and Pharmaceuticals?

The ACA included national standards for insurers for medical loss ratios (MLRs), which are the proportion of insurance premium revenues that must be spent on clinical services and quality improvement.[533] Would it be feasible to implement a similar kind of cost containment strategy on medical device manufacturers and pharmaceuticals? Pharmaceutical and device costs are significant drivers of healthcare costs. Could you put cost containment measures in place without stifling innovation? The medical device tax, the Cadillac tax, and any number of bills aimed at the pharmaceutical industry are all examples of the "popularity" of reforming healthcare with legislation. The problem is that there is often little—if any—alignment across all of the stakeholders. In fact, it is a full-on "goat rodeo." Manufacturers expect a large premium for investments in innovation over an extended period of time; patients demand the intervention regardless of cost; physicians are consistently held to a higher standard of care; and costs and utilization escalate exponentially. Innovations can improve healthcare delivery, but there is no backstop to costs.

Remember what happened with EpiPens? When the price increased from $100 per two-pack to $608 per two-pack in less than 10 years, the company CEO was summoned to a Congressional hearing to explain the price increase.[534] I'm not a big government guy, but we need some alignment, right? If we do not figure it out, the government is going to figure it out for us. Wouldn't it be nice if pricing and affordability were a consideration along with healthcare innovation?

Wouldn't It Be Nice If...
All of the Healthcare Stakeholders—Patients, Providers, Suppliers, Insurers, the Government, and Others— Could Work Together to Find New Solutions for America's Healthcare Crisis?

It may sound trite, but it's true: we are all in this together. Each stakeholder plays an essential role in the US healthcare system.

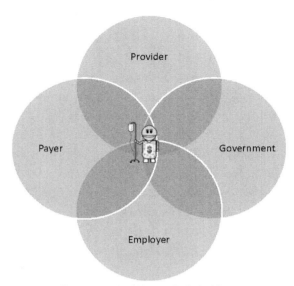

Figure 10.1 Healthcare Stakeholders.

If employers or the government continue to be obligated to offer plans without any regard for cost, they will not be able to offer them anymore. They can only shift so much cost to the patient. And if patients cannot afford premiums or deductibles, insurers and providers lose. The ranks of the uninsured will rise, and the providers' uncompensated care costs will rise along with them. If insurers cannot make enough in premium revenue to cover claims costs, health insurance will cease to exist. If providers such as hospitals and health systems are not reimbursed at a fair rate for their services, they will go bankrupt, and patient care will suffer. You already see this happening in rural communities.

When the system becomes unbalanced, and one or another stakeholder is disproportionately enriched or penalized, the stability of the whole system is destroyed. The current US healthcare system is not sustainable for the long term. In order to create a sustainable system, all stakeholders need to come to the table and develop a system together, with checks, balances, and compromise that will be effective for the long haul.

Compromise is a key word. In 1994, Dr. William L. Kissick published a book aptly titled, "Medicine's Dilemmas: Infinite needs versus finite resources." In his book, Kissick described the "Iron Triangle" of healthcare, comprising access, cost, and quality. Kissick suggested that you could improve one or two of these healthcare components, but not all three at once. Because resources are finite, improving one or two components would come with a trade-off—likely at the expense of the third component. [535]

It's a point well taken. Commercial payers do not have infinite resources; the government certainly does not have limitless resources; and patients-as-payers do not have limitless resources. Costs cannot keep escalating without breaking the system in some way. Physician Aaron Carroll, speaking in the JAMA Forum, framed it this way:[536]

> Anyone who tells you that he or she can make the health care system more universal, improve quality, and also reduce costs is in denial or misleading you. When it comes to election season, those people are often politicians. The lesson of the iron triangle is that there are inherent trade-offs in health policy. If we wanted to conduct the debates honestly, we would acknowledge these and allow the public to decide what they really want—and what they are willing to sacrifice to get it.

No one in this country would say that healthcare is in a great place now. That's being Captain Obvious—I get that. Patients are the new payer, and this is healthcare's new reality. Patients are purchasers of healthcare, and they are savvy consumers. They have expectations that the market is not currently meeting from a financial standpoint. Patients-as-payers represent a third of the collectable revenue now, and providers will need to adapt their processes, culture, and mindset to the patient-as-payer reality to survive—until the system changes again. If it does not change, we are about to experience a healthcare revolution in this new paradigm.

We all need to come together, find common ground, and center everything on our citizens' health and welfare so that we can work toward healthcare access, coverage, interoperability, affordability, literacy, profitability, equality, and, yes, transparency— in every meaning of the word. Now wouldn't *that* be nice?

About the Author

Jonathan Wiik is an accomplished public speaker and consultant with more than 20 years' experience in healthcare, including both the acute care and insurance settings. In his career Wiik has served in various roles across the hospital and payer markets, including hospital transporter, Manager of Operations, Senior Regulatory Analyst, Product Development, Director, and Chief Revenue Officer (CRO). Wiik has been actively involved in shaping legislation impacting the healthcare industry. He currently serves as an officer on the Colorado Healthcare Financial Management Association (HFMA) Board and is President of the Board of Directors at an assisted living facility in Boulder, Colorado.

In his former role as CRO at an acute-care hospital, his responsibilities covered the entire revenue cycle, including operations in admissions, scheduling, financial clearance, utilization review, clinical case management, billing, reimbursement, and collections. He is Silver Certified in Lean and served as value-stream owner for revenue cycle, implementing improvements that led to multi-million dollar improvements in expenses and revenues at an acute-care facility. Wiik developed several nationally-recognized programs in Point-of-Service (POS) collections, financial clearance, and best practices in hospital operations. Wiik currently serves as a Principal at TransUnion, in the Healthcare Solutions Division. He holds a Bachelor's Degree in Sports Medicine, a Master's Degree in Healthcare Administration, and an MBA.

He enjoys spending time with his wonderful wife and two very energetic red-headed boys. He likes doing anything in outdoors and is a certified whitewater rafting guide instructor. He also enjoys traveling and has visited several continents, including a six-month stay in Antarctica and the South Pole.

To contact Jonathan for a speaking engagement or business consultation, please reach out via email jwiik@patientisthenewpayer.com on LinkedIn: linkedin.com/in/jonathan-wiik-283228, or send a tweet to @ JonathanWiik1.

Glossary

················

Accountable Care Organization (ACO): An ACO is a voluntary network of healthcare providers (physician groups, hospitals, and other health providers) who work together to provide high-quality, coordinated care to Medicare patients. Centers for Medicare & Medicaid Services (CMS) offers several ACO programs that allow successful ACOs to share in cost savings achieved for the Medicare program.[537]

Ambulatory surgery center (ASC): An ASC is a specialized surgery center that provides surgical care for ambulatory patients. ASCs may focus on any number of surgical specialties, including ophthalmology, orthopedics, gastrointestinal, pain management, plastic surgery, urology, and others.

American Health Care Act (AHCA): The AHCA (H.R. 1628) was passed by the House of Representatives on May 4, 2017. The intent of the AHCA is to repeal and replace the Patient Protection and Affordable Care Act (PPACA), which is also known as the ACA or Obamacare.

American College of Emergency Physicians (ACEP): The ACEP is a professional organization for emergency physicians. For more information, visit acep.org.

Americas Health Insurance Plans (AHIP): AHIP is a trade association and political advocacy group formed in 2003 by the merger of two other trade associations: the Health Insurance Association of America (HIAA) the American Association of Health Plans (AAHP). For more information, visit ahip.org.

American Hospital Association (AHA): The AHA is a national organization founded in 1898 that represents and serves hospitals and healthcare networks. Membership now includes nearly 5,000 hospitals, healthcare systems, networks, other care providers, and 43,000 individual members.[538] For more information, visit.aha.org.

American Medical Association (AMA): The AMA is a national, professional association of physicians, established in 1847. The original goals of the organization were to support scientific advancement, create standards for medical education, launch a program of medical ethics, and improve public health.[539] The AMA has published the *Journal of the American Medical Association* (*JAMA*) since 1883. The AMA currently includes approximately 234,000 members[540] representing about 25 percent of all practicing physicians in the United States.[541] For more information, visit ama-assn.org.

Ambulatory Payment Classification (APC): APC is CMS' methodology for paying facilities for hospital outpatient services for Medicare patients under the Outpatient Prospective Payment System (OPPS).[542]

Average length of stay (ALOS): ALOS refers to the average number of days a patient spends in the hospital.

Average wholesale price (AWP): AWP is a benchmark for pricing and reimbursement generally used for prescription drugs. AWP is an estimate of the price retail pharmacies pay for drugs from a wholesale distributor, and is comparable to a "list" or "sticker" price. AWP also is used as a method to set pricing for implants or medical devices.

Balance after insurance (BAI): BAI refers to the patient responsibility portion of hospital charges after insurance has been applied.

Centers for Medicare & Medicaid Services (CMS): CMS is one of 11 agencies operating in the US Department of Health and Human Services (HHS). CMS provides oversight for Medicare, the federal share of Medicaid and the State Children's Health Insurance Program, the Health Insurance Marketplace, and related quality-assurance activities. See more information at cms.gov.

Chargemaster or charge description master (CDM): The CDM is a hospital-specific pricing document that includes the itemized list price for each of the goods and services the hospital bills for. The charges on the chargemaster include not only the cost of the good or service, but also overhead costs and markups.

Children's Health Insurance Program (CHIP): CHIP is a federal-state partnership that provides health insurance coverage to low-income families who earn too much money to qualify for Medicaid. In some states, CHIP also covers pregnant women. CHIP was created as part of the Balanced Budget Act of 1997.[543]

Diagnosis-Related Group (DRG): DRG is CMS' methodology for paying facilities for hospital inpatient services for Medicare patients under the OPPS.[544]

Emergency Medical Treatment and Active Labor Act of 1986 (EMTALA):
EMTALA is a federal law that ensures public access to emergency
services regardless of an individual's ability to pay. EMTALA applies to
all Medicare-participating hospitals that offer emergency services.[545]

Employee Retirement Income Security Act of 1974 (ERISA): ERISA
is a federal law that "sets minimum standards for most voluntarily
established pension and health plans in private industry to provide
protection for individuals in these plans."[546]

Explanation of benefits (EOB): Insurance companies send EOB forms
to insured individuals to explain which treatments or services were
paid for, and how much patient payment responsibility remains after
insurance has paid.

Fee-for-service (FFS): In the FFS reimbursement model, healthcare
providers, including physicians and hospitals, are paid for each service
performed. Bills might be paid by the patient and then submitted to
the insurance company, or submitted by the provider to the patient's
insurance carrier for reimbursement.[547] An FFS model incentivizes
greater use of services on the part of providers.

Health care sharing ministry (HCSM): An HCSM offers a nonprofit
alternative to purchasing health insurance from private, for-profit
insurers. Under the ACA, people who enroll in qualifying, tax-exempt
HCSMs that meet ACA criteria qualify for a health coverage exemption
and do not have to pay a tax penalty for lack of qualified coverage.[548]

Healthcare Financial Management Association (HFMA): HFMA is a
membership organization for healthcare finance executives and
leaders. For more information, visit hfma.org.

Health Insurance Association of America (HIAA): HIAA is a trade
association for health insurance companies. HIAA played a key role in
defeating President Bill Clinton's health reform act (the Health Security
Act, a.k.a. "Hillarycare" in the early 1990s. In 2003 HIAA merged with the
American AAHP. The combined trade association is now called AHIP.

Health Insurance Portability and Accountability Act of 1996 (HIPAA):
HIPAA establishes standards and rules to protect the privacy and
security of individuals' health information, as well as outlining
methods for transactions between covered entities for documentation,
billing, and reimbursement. The purpose of HIPAA was "to amend the

Internal Revenue Code of 1986 to improve portability and continuity of health insurance coverage in the group and individual markets, to combat waste, fraud, and abuse in health insurance and healthcare delivery, to promote the use of medical savings accounts, to improve access to long-term care services and coverage, to simplify the administration of health insurance, and for other purposes."[549]

Health savings account (HSA): An HSA is a tax-exempt account that eligible individuals (individuals with qualifying insurance plans) can set up to pay and/or reimburse qualified medical expenses.[550]

Health reimbursement arrangement (HRA): An HRA is an account funded by an individual's employer that is used to reimburse employees, tax-free, for qualified medical expenses.[551]

High-deductible health plan (HDHP): In lay terms, an HDHP is any health insurance policy with a high deductible. Internal Revenue Service (IRS) procedures specify that only individuals enrolled in qualifying HDHPs are eligible for the tax benefits associated with establishing an HSA. For 2017, qualifying HDHPs are those with a minimum annual deductible of $1,300 for self-only coverage and a minimum annual deductible of $2,600 for family coverage.[552]

Hillarycare: A derisive nickname for the Health Security Act, which was introduced to Congress by President Bill Clinton in 1993. The legislation did not pass.

Hospital Consumer Assessment of Healthcare Providers and Systems (HCAHPS): HCAHPS is a national, standardized survey designed to collect and measure patient perceptions of their hospital experiences. All hospitals subject to the CMS Inpatient Prospective Payment System (IPPS) must collect and report HCAHPS data annually. HCAHPS results are available to the public on the Hospital Compare website, medicare. gov/hospitalcompare. Summary analysis is available at hcahpsonline.org.

Hospital Readmissions Reduction Program (HRRP): HRRP is a value-based care program launched by CMS in 2012. HRRP is designed to incentivize hospitals to prioritize better coordination of transitions of care; improved discharge planning, including education and follow-up for discharged patients; and improved continuity of care.[553] HRRP requires CMS to reduce payments to hospitals with excessive readmissions, defined as readmissions within 30 days of discharge.[554]

International Classification of Diseases (ICD): The ICD is an international diagnostic classification standard that defines diseases, disorders, injuries, and other health conditions using standardized codes. The ICD has undergone multiple revisions since it was first adopted by the World Health Organization (WHO) in 1948. ICD-10 was endorsed by WHO in 1990, and implemented in the United States, per CMS, in 2015.[555],[556]

Long-term acute care hospital (LTACH or LTCH): An LTACH is a hospital designed to provide medical and rehabilitative support for patients who require acute care support for longer than 25 days.[557]

Meaningful use (MU): The American Recovery and Reinvestment Act of 2009 (ARRA) authorized CMS to create an incentive program to encourage healthcare providers to adopt and use electronic health record (EHR) technology.[558] The MU program was designed to improve the quality, safety, and efficiency of healthcare delivery through the use of electronic medical record (EMR) technology.[559]

Medicare Access and CHIP Reauthorization Act of 2015 (MACRA): MACRA is one of several pieces of legislation that support CMS' focus on value-based programs/value-based payment models.[560]

Medical loss ratio (MLR): In health insurance, the MLR refers to the proportion of premium revenues spent on clinical services and quality improvement, as opposed to other costs, such as administrative overhead and marketing. The ACA requires health insurance companies to issue rebates to consumers if their MLR percentage does not meet minimum standards.

Medical savings account (MSA): Like HSAs and HRAs, the MSA is yet another way to set up a tax-exempt trust or custodial account to save money for medical expenses. MSAs were designed specifically for self-employed individuals with HDHPs and for small employers with HDHPs. There is also a Medicare Advantage MSA designed specifically for Medicare enrollees with HDHPs.[561]

Minimum essential coverage (MEC): Per the ACA, for a health insurance plan to be designated as a "qualifying" health insurance plan, thereby protecting individuals from the fee assessed on the uninsured, the plan must cover specified "essential health benefits" including specified preventive care for adults, women, and children.[562]

National Center for Health Statistics (NCHS): NCHS, part of the Centers for Disease Control and Prevention (CDC), is the principal health statistics agency in the United States. For more information see: cdc.gov/nchs.

Patient Protection and Affordable Care Act of 2010 (PPACA): Commonly referred to as the ACA or "Obamacare," the act was signed into law on March 23, 2010. The law expanded requirements for health insurance coverage; established subsidies to reduce the cost of health insurance premiums for low-income families; and expanded the Medicaid program. For more information, see healthcare.gov/glossary/patient-protection-and-affordable-care-act.

Pharmaceutical Research and Manufacturers of America (PhRMA): PhRMA is a trade group representing the country's biopharmaceutical research companies. For more information, see phrma.org.

Physician Quality Reporting System (PQRS): The PQRS is a quality-reporting program for individual eligible physicians and group practices that was created and managed by CMS. The last program year for PQRS was 2016. PQRS has been replaced by the Merit-based Incentive Program (MIPS).[563]

Population health management (PHM): PHM is the compilation and analysis of data sets across multiple sources to deliver insights for providers to improve both clinical and financial outcomes in populations.

Process failure mode effects analysis (PFMEA): PFMEA is a step-by-step approach to identifying possible failures in a process, product, or service.

Protected health information (PHI), also ePHI for electronic protected health information: Per 45 CFR Subtitle A, § 160.103, PHI is defined as "individually identifiable health information." HIPAA rules protect the privacy and security of information that meets the definition of PHI and ePHI.[564]

***Provider Reimbursement Manual* (PRM):** Published by CMS, the PRM includes two parts: 15-1 and 15-2. This manual provides the day-to-day operating instructions, policies, and procedures used to administer CMS programs. The information in the manual is based upon statues and regulations, guidelines, models, and directives. The manual is available online at cms.gov/Regulations-and-Guidance/Guidance/Manuals/Paper-Based-Manuals.html.

Reasonable and customary charges (also called usual, customary and reasonable, or UCR): Per healthcare.gov, UCR is "the amount paid for a medical service in a geographic area based on what providers in the area usually charge for the same or similar medical service. The UCR amount sometimes is used to determine the allowed amount."[565] In practice, reimbursement for out-of-network providers is often set at a percentage of the UCR charge, which may differ from what the provider actually charges for a service. When an insurer disallows a portion of a charge as being in excess of the usual and customary allowance, it means that the charge is in excess of the standard the company used to determine usual and customary, or UCR. Providers are free to charge whatever fee for service they choose. Insurance coverage is designed to provide benefits up to the plan's usual and customary percentile and is priced accordingly.[566]

Short-term acute care hospital (STACH): A STACH is a type of medical facility designed to provide short-term (less than 25 days), acute care for patients. The vast majority of hospitals in the United States are STACHs.

Sin tax: A sin tax is applied to products or services that are considered harmful to society, such tobacco, alcohol, and gambling.

Tobacco rating: Tobacco rating is a practice of charging a higher health insurance premium to smokers than to nonsmokers. The ACA allows insurance companies to charge up to 50 percent more to smokers than nonsmokers for health insurance premiums.

US Department of Health and Human Services (HHS): HHS is the federal department charged with enhancing and protecting the health and well-being of all Americans.[567] CMS is one of 11 operating divisions in HHS.

Urgent Care Association of America (UCAOA): Founded in 2004, the UCAOA is an association for all professionals working in urgent care. For more information, see ucaoa.org.

Value-based care: Value-based care programs were established to promote appropriate care delivery at a reasonable cost. They are representative of a movement from fee-for-volume to fee-for-value. CMS value-based programs tie reimbursement to patient outcomes with the goal of rewarding the quality of healthcare services provided. The traditional CMS reimbursement model—fee-for-service—incentivized service volume, as opposed to service quality.

Women's Health and Cancer Rights Act of 1998 (WHCRA): WHCRA is a federal law that ties health insurance coverage for cancer-related mastectomies to coverage for breast reconstruction.

Endnotes

1   Cohen, K. (2006). *Honoring the Medicine: The Essential Guide to Native American Healing*. New York: Ballantine Books.

2   White, J. (1913). Handbook of Indians of Canada: An Appendix to the Tenth Report of the Geographic Board of Canada, Ottawa. Retrieved from http://faculty.marianopolis.edu/c.belanger/quebechistory/encyclopedia/ MedicineandMedicinemenamongIndians.htm

3   Cohen, K. (2006). *Honoring the Medicine: The Essential Guide to Native American Healing*. New York: Ballantine Books.

4   Negus, S.S. (1957). Physicians at early Jamestown. *The Virginia Journal of Science, 8*(1). http://www.vacadsci.org/vjsArchives/v8/8-1/Physicians.pdf

5   Brown, J. (2011, Feb. 9). New Hampshire Glossary: Chirugeon [Blog post]. Retrieved from http://www.cowhampshireblog.com/2011/02/09/new-hampshire-glossary-chirugeon/

6   Negus, S.S. (1957). Physicians at early Jamestown. *The Virginia Journal of Science, 8*(1). http://www.vacadsci.org/vjsArchives/v8/8-1/Physicians.pdf

7   In the beginning: The story of the creation of the nation's first hospital. (n.d.). Retrieved from http://www.uphs.upenn.edu/paharc/features/creation.html

8   Patient admission and regulation. (n.d.). Retrieved from http://www.uphs.upenn.edu/ paharc/features/admission.html

9   Miller, J. (2016, April 28). Paying the doctor in 18th-century Philadelphia [Blog post]. Retrieved from https://blogs.loc.gov/loc/2016/04/paying-the-doctor-in-18th-century-philadelphia/

10 Miller, J. (2016, April 28). Paying the doctor in 18th-century Philadelphia [Blog post]. Retrieved from https://blogs.loc.gov/loc/2016/04/paying-the-doctor-in-18th-century-philadelphia/

11 Miller, J. (2016, April 28). Paying the doctor in 18th-century Philadelphia [Blog post]. Retrieved from https://blogs.loc.gov/loc/2016/04/paying-the-doctor-in-18th-century-philadelphia/

12 Miller, J. (2016, April 28). Paying the doctor in 18th-century Philadelphia [Blog post]. Retrieved from https://blogs.loc.gov/loc/2016/04/paying-the-doctor-in-18th-century-philadelphia/

13 Physician price fixing in 19th century Virginia. (n.d.) Retrieved from http://blog.hsl. virginia.edu/feebill/

14 Mangan, D. (2016, June 30). Costs of delivering babies vary widely in U.S., California cities most expensive. *CNBC*. Retrieved from http://www.cnbc.com/2016/06/30/costs-of-delivering-babies-vary-widely-in-us-california-cities-most-expensive.html

15 Breslaw, E.G. (2012, Dec. 10). What was healthcare like in the 1800s? *History News Network*. Retrieved from http://historynewsnetwork.org/article/149661

16 Nix, E. (2014, June 25). Why are barber poles red, white and blue? *Ask History*. Retrieved from http://www.history.com/news/ask-history/why-are-barber-poles-red-white-and-blue

17 Blumberg, A., & Davidson, A. (Hosts). (2009, Oct. 22). Accidents of history created U.S. health system [Radio broadcast episode]. Retrieved from http://www.npr.org/templates/story/story.php?storyId=114045132

18 Thomasson, M.A. (n.d.) Health insurance in the United States. *Economic History Association*. Retrieved from https://eh.net/encyclopedia/health-insurance-in-the-united-states/

19 Mosley, G.B. (2008, May). The U.S. health care non-system. *AMA Journal of Ethics,* *10*(5), 324-331. Retrieved from http://journalofethics.ama-assn.org/2008/05/mhst1-0805.html

20 Emergence of public hospitals: 1860 – 1930. (n.d.). Retrieved from https://essentialhospitals.org/about-americas-essential-hospitals/history-of-public-hospitals-in-the-united-states/emergence-of-public-hospitals-1860-1930/

21 Ballard, D. J., & Hopkins, R. S. (2009, Aug. 18). Kimball, Justin Ford. In R. M. Mullner (Eds.), Encyclopedia of health services research (pp. 678) [Online]. doi: http://dx.doi.org/10.4135/9781412971942

22 Ballard, D. J., & Hopkins, R. S. (2009, Aug. 18). Kimball, Justin Ford. In R. M. Mullner (Eds.), Encyclopedia of health services research (pp. 678) [Online]. doi: http://dx.doi.org/10.4135/9781412971942

23 About Baylor Scott & White: Baylor Health Care System history. (n.d.). Retrieved from http://www.baylorhealth.com/About/Pages/Timeline.aspx

24 Cleverly, W.O. (1989). Handbook of healthcare accounting and finance: Volume 1. Aspen Publication.

25 Lesparre, M., Lovinger, G. & Poole, K. (1998, Jan.20). A century of the AHA [PDF document]. *Hospitals & Health Networks*. Retrieved from http://www.aha.org/content/00-10/centuryAHA.pdf

26 Thomasson, M.A. (2002, July). From sickness to health: The twentieth-century development of U.S. health insurance. *Explorations in Economic History, 39*(3), 233-253. doi: http://dx.doi.org/10.1006/exeh.2002.0788

27 Mosley, G.B. (2008, May). The U.S. health care non-system. *AMA Journal of Ethics,* *10*(5), 324-331. Retrieved from http://journalofethics.ama-assn.org/2008/05/mhst1-0805.html

28 Timeline: History of health reform in the U.S. [PDF document]. (n.d.) The Henry J. Kaiser Family Foundation. Retrieved from https://kaiserfamilyfoundation.files.wordpress.com/2011/03/5-02-13-history-of-health-reform.pdf

29 Cleverly, W.O. (1989). Handbook of healthcare accounting and finance: Volume 1. Aspen Publication.

30 Cleverly, W.O. (1989). Handbook of healthcare accounting and finance: Volume 1. Aspen Publication.

31 Mosley, G.B. (2008, May). The U.S. health care non-system. *AMA Journal of Ethics,* *10*(5), 324-331. Retrieved from http://journalofethics.ama-assn.org/2008/05/mhst1-0805.html

32 Thomasson, M.A. (2002, July). From sickness to health: The twentieth-century development of U.S. health insurance. *Explorations in Economic History, 39*(3), 233-253. doi: http://dx.doi.org/10.1006/exeh.2002.0788

33 Thomasson, M.A. (2002, July). From sickness to health: The twentieth-century development of U.S. health insurance. *Explorations in Economic History, 39*(3), 233-253. doi: http://dx.doi.org/10.1006/exeh.2002.0788

34 Rappleye, E. (2015, June 10). 25 things to know about Blue Cross Blue Shield. *Becker's Hospital Review*. Retrieved from http://www.beckershospitalreview.com/payer-issues/25-things-to-know-about-blue-cross-blue-shield.html

35 Thomasson, M.A. (2002, July). From sickness to health: The twentieth-century development of U.S. health insurance. *Explorations in Economic History, 39*(3), 233-253. doi: http://dx.doi.org/10.1006/exeh.2002.0788

36 El-Hai, J. (2016, July 26). How railway surgeons advance medicine. *Discover*. Retrieved from http://discovermagazine.com/2016/jul-aug/doctors-derailed

37 El-Hai, J. (2016, July 26). How railway surgeons advance medicine. *Discover*. Retrieved from http://discovermagazine.com/2016/jul-aug/doctors-derailed

38 El-Hai, J. (2016, July 26). How railway surgeons advance medicine. *Discover*. Retrieved from http://discovermagazine.com/2016/jul-aug/doctors-derailed

39 El-Hai, J. (2016, July 26). How railway surgeons advance medicine. *Discover*. Retrieved from http://discovermagazine.com/2016/jul-aug/doctors-derailed

40 Baltimore and Ohio Employees Relief Association records: 1880-1990. (n.d.) George Washington University, Special Collections Research Center. Retrieved from https://beta.worldcat.org/archivegrid/data/124054187

41 Mosley, G.B. (2008, May). The U.S. health care non-system. *AMA Journal of Ethics, 10*(5), 324-331. Retrieved from http://journalofethics.ama-assn.org/2008/05/mhst1-0805.html

42 Thomasson, M.A. (2002, July). From sickness to health: The twentieth-century development of U.S. health insurance. *Explorations in Economic History, 39*(3), 233-253. doi: http://dx.doi.org/10.1006/exeh.2002.0788

43 Thomasson, M.A. (2002, July). From sickness to health: The twentieth-century development of U.S. health insurance. *Explorations in Economic History, 39*(3), 233-253. doi: http://dx.doi.org/10.1006/exeh.2002.0788

44 Roosevelt, F. D. (1942, Oct. 3). Executive order 9250 establishing the Office of Economic Stabilization. In G. Peters & J.T. Wooley (Eds.), *The American Presidency Project* [Online]. Retrieved from http://www.presidency.ucsb.edu/ws/index.php?pid=16171

45 Roosevelt, F. D. (1942, Oct. 3). Executive order 9250 establishing the Office of Economic Stabilization. In G. Peters & J.T. Wooley (Eds.), *The American Presidency Project* [Online]. Retrieved from http://www.presidency.ucsb.edu/ws/index.php?pid=16171

46 Thomasson, M.A. (2002, July). From sickness to health: The twentieth-century development of U.S. health insurance. *Explorations in Economic History, 39*(3), 233-253. doi: http://dx.doi.org/10.1006/exeh.2002.0788

47 Thomasson, M.A. (2002, July). From sickness to health: The twentieth-century development of U.S. health insurance. *Explorations in Economic History, 39*(3), 233-253. doi: http://dx.doi.org/10.1006/exeh.2002.0788

48 Blumberg, A., & Davidson, A. (Hosts). (2009, Oct. 22). Accidents of history created U.S. health system [Radio broadcast episode]. Retrieved from http://www.npr.org/templates/story/story.php?storyId=114045132

49 Thomasson, M.A. (2002, July). From sickness to health: The twentieth-century development of U.S. health insurance. *Explorations in Economic History, 39*(3), 233-253. doi: http://dx.doi.org/10.1006/exeh.2002.0788

50 Reed, L. S. (1965, Dec.). Private health insurance in the United States: An overview

[PDF document]. *SSA Bulletin*. Retrieved from https://www.ssa.gov/policy/docs/ssb/v28n12/v28n12p3.pdf

51   Ballard, D. J., & Hopkins, R. S. (2009, Aug. 18). Kimball, Justin Ford. In R. M. Mullner (Eds.), Encyclopedia of health services research (pp. 678) [Online]. doi: http://dx.doi.org/10.4135/9781412971942

52   Reed, L. S. (1965, Dec.). Private health insurance in the United States: An overview [PDF document]. *SSA Bulletin*. Retrieved from https://www.ssa.gov/policy/docs/ssb/v28n12/v28n12p3.pdf

53   Reed, L. S. (1965, Dec.). Private health insurance in the United States: An overview [PDF document]. *SSA Bulletin*. Retrieved from https://www.ssa.gov/policy/docs/ssb/v28n12/v28n12p3.pdf

54   Reed, L. S. (1965, Dec.). Private health insurance in the United States: An overview [PDF document]. *SSA Bulletin*. Retrieved from https://www.ssa.gov/policy/docs/ssb/v28n12/v28n12p3.pdf

55   Reed, L. S. (1965, Dec.). Private health insurance in the United States: An overview [PDF document]. *SSA Bulletin*. Retrieved from https://www.ssa.gov/policy/docs/ssb/v28n12/v28n12p3.pdf

56   Social Security Administration. (n.d.). Historical background and development of Social Security. Retrieved from https://www.ssa.gov/history/briefhistory3.html

57   Social Security Administration. (n.d.). Historical background and development of Social Security. Retrieved from https://www.ssa.gov/history/briefhistory3.html

58   Kooijman, J. (1999). – And the pursuit of national health: The incremental strategy toward national health insurance in the United States of America [PDF document]. Retrieved from https://pure.uva.nl/ws/files/3296481/34860_UBA003000107_008.pdf

59   Epstein, L. A. (1964). Income of the aged in 1962: First findings of the 1963 Survey of the Aged [PDF document]. Reprinted in the *Social Security Bulletin*, *51*(3). Retrieved from https://www.ssa.gov/policy/docs/ssb/v51n3/v51n3p9.pdf

60   The Henry J. Kaiser Family Foundation. (2015, Apr. 21). Medicare and Medicaid at 50 [Video file]. Retrieved from https://youtu.be/f9NUCvrrRz4

61   The Henry J. Kaiser Family Foundation. (2015, Apr. 21). Medicare and Medicaid at 50 [Video file]. Retrieved from https://youtu.be/f9NUCvrrRz4

62   The Henry J. Kaiser Family Foundation. (2015, Apr. 21). Medicare and Medicaid at 50 [Video file]. Retrieved from https://youtu.be/f9NUCvrrRz4

63   Centers for Disease Control and Prevention (CDC). (2010). Table 22. Life expectancy at birth, at 65 years of age, and at 75 years of age, by race and sex: United States, selected years 1900-2007 [PDF document]. Retrieved from https://www.cdc.gov/nchs/data/hus/2010/022.pdf

64   The Henry J. Kaiser Family Foundation. (2012, Dec. 20). The story of Medicare: A timeline [Video file]. Retrieved from https://www.youtube.com/watch?v=693XQSujAh8

65   The Henry J. Kaiser Family Foundation. (2015, Apr. 21). Medicare and Medicaid at 50 [Video file]. Retrieved from https://youtu.be/f9NUCvrrRz4

66   Anderson, S. (2016, Oct. 26). A brief history of Medicare in America. Retrieved from https://www.medicareresources.org/basic-medicare-information/brief-history-of-medicare/

67   Centers for Medicare & Medicaid Services (CMS). (n.d.) Medicare enrollment

dashboard. Retrieved February 21, 2017 from https://www.cms.gov/Research-Statistics-Data-and-Systems/Statistics-Trends-and-Reports/Dashboard/Medicare-Enrollment/Enrollment%20Dashboard.html

68   Centers for Medicare & Medicaid Services (CMS). (n.d.). November 2016 Medicaid and CHIP Enrollment Data Highlights. Retrieved February 21, 2017 from https://www.medicaid.gov/medicaid/program-information/medicaid-and-chip-enrollment-data/report-highlights/index.html

69   Centers for Medicare & Medicaid Services (CMS). (n.d.). National Health Expenditures 2015 Highlights [PDF document]. Retrieved from https://www.cms.gov/research-statistics-data-and-systems/statistics-trends-and-reports/nationalhealthexpenddata/downloads/highlights.pdf

70   Sultan, J. (2015, May 1). Believe it or not, the government is driving healthcare innovation. *Xconomy*. Retrieved from http://www.xconomy.com/seattle/2015/05/01/believe-it-or-not-the-government-is-driving-healthcare-innovation/#

71   Thomasson, M.A. (2002, July). From sickness to health: The twentieth-century development of U.S. health insurance. *Explorations in Economic History, 39*(3), 233-253. doi: http://dx.doi.org/10.1006/exeh.2002.0788

72   Mosley, G.B. (2008, May). The U.S. health care non-system. *AMA Journal of Ethics, 10*(5), 324-331. Retrieved from http://journalofethics.ama-assn.org/2008/05/mhst1-0805.html

73   Reed, L. S. (1965, Dec.). Private health insurance in the United States: An overview [PDF document]. *SSA Bulletin.* Retrieved from https://www.ssa.gov/policy/docs/ssb/v28n12/v28n12p3.pdf

74   McKesson Corporation. (n.d.). What healthcare payment models exist? Retrieved from http://www.mckesson.com/population-health-management/resources/what-payment-models-exist/

75   National Council on Disability. (2013). Appendix B. A brief history of managed care. Retrieved from http://www.ncd.gov/publications/2013/20130315/20130513_AppendixB

76   Social Security Administration (SSA). (1974). Health Maintenance Organization Act of 1973 [PDF document]. *Social Security Administration Bulletin,* 37(3). Retrieved from https://www.ssa.gov/policy/docs/ssb/v37n3/v37n3p35.pdf

77   Social Security Administration (SSA). (1974). Health Maintenance Organization Act of 1973 [PDF document]. *Social Security Administration Bulletin,* 37(3). Retrieved from https://www.ssa.gov/policy/docs/ssb/v37n3/v37n3p35.pdf

78   The Henry J. Kaiser Family Foundation. (2015). 2015 Employer health benefits survey, Exhibit 5.1, Distribution of health plan enrollment for covered workers, by plan type, 1988-2015 [PNG file]. Retrieved from http://kff.org/report-section/ehbs-2015-section-five-market-shares-of-health-plans/

79   Arnett, R. H., Cowell, C. S., Davidoff, L. M. & Freeland, M. S. (1985). Health spending trends in the 1980's: Adjusting to financial incentives. *Health Care Financing Review, 6*(3), 1-26. Retrieved from https://www.ncbi.nlm.nih.gov/pmc/articles/PMC4191479/

80   Alliance for Health Reform. (2006, April). HSAs and high-deductible health plans: A primer [PDF document]. Retrieved from http://www.allhealth.org/publications/pub_3.pdf

81   West, W. J. (2013). HSAs: The sure win with health care reform [PDF document]. Retrieved from http://healthequity.com/ppacawebinars/images/ppacaandhsas.pdf

82   Centers for Medicare & Medicaid Services (CMS). (n.d.). The fee for not having

health insurance. Retrieved from https://www.healthcare.gov/fees/fee-for-not-being-covered/

83   Centers for Medicare & Medicaid Services (CMS). (n.d.). What marketplace health insurance plans cover. Retrieved from https://www.healthcare.gov/coverage/what-marketplace-plans-cover/

84   Jost, T. (2016, Feb. 29). Affordability: The most urgent health reform issue for ordinary Americans [Blog post]. Retrieved from http://healthaffairs.org/blog/2016/02/29/affordability-the-most-urgent-health-reform-issue-for-ordinary-americans/

85   U.S. Department of the Treasury. Internal Revenue Service (IRS). (2016). 26 CFR 601.602: Tax forms and instructions (Also: Part 1, §§ 1, 223), Rev. Proc. 2016-28. Retrieved from https://www.irs.gov/pub/irs-drop/rp-16-28.pdf

86   The Henry J. Kaiser Family Foundation. (2016). 2016 Employer health benefits survey. Retrieved from http://kff.org/health-costs/report/2016-employer-health-benefits-survey/

87   Herman, B. (2014, Jan. 9). 9 drivers of high healthcare costs in the U.S. *Becker's Hospital CFO*. Retrieved from http://www.beckershospitalreview.com/finance/9-drivers-of-high-healthcare-costs-in-the-u-s.html

88   Centers for Disease Control and Prevention (CDC). (n.d.). Health, United States, 2015 – Health Insurance, Table 105. No health insurance coverage among persons under age 65, by selected characteristics: United States, selected years 1984-2014 [PDF document]. Retrieved from https://www.cdc.gov/nchs/data/hus/2015/105.pdf

89   Centers for Disease Control and Prevention (CDC). (2016, Feb. 23). Chronic diseases: the leading causes of death and disability in the United States. Retrieved from https://www.cdc.gov/chronicdisease/overview/#sec1

90   Centers for Medicare & Medicaid Services (CMS). (n.d.). National health expenditure data, historical. Retrieved from https://www.cms.gov/research-statistics-data-and-systems/statistics-trends-and-reports/nationalhealthexpenddata/nationalhealthaccountshistorical.html

91   Centers for Medicare & Medicaid Services (CMS). (n.d.). National health expenditure projections 2016-2025, Forecast Summary [PDF document]. Retrieved from https://www.cms.gov/Research-Statistics-Data-and-Systems/Statistics-Trends-and-Reports/NationalHealthExpendData/Downloads/proj2016.pdf

92   Centers for Medicare & Medicaid Services (CMS). (n.d.). The nation's health dollar ($3.2 trillion), calendar year 2015: where it came from [PDF document]. Retrieved from https://www.cms.gov/Research-Statistics-Data-and-Systems/Statistics-Trends-and-Reports/NationalHealthExpendData/Downloads/PieChartSourcesExpenditures2015.pdf

93   Centers for Medicare & Medicaid Services (CMS). (n.d.). National health expenditures 2015 highlights [PDF document]. Retrieved from https://www.cms.gov/Research-Statistics-Data-and-Systems/Statistics-Trends-and-Reports/NationalHealthExpendData/Downloads/highlights.pdf

94   The Henry J. Kaiser Family Foundation. (2013, March 13). Concentration of health care spending in the U.S. population, 2010 [PowerPoint slide]. Retrieved from http://kff.org/health-costs/slide/concentration-of-health-care-spending-in-the-u-s-population-2010/

95   The Henry J. Kaiser Family Foundation. (2012, May 1). Health care costs: A primer,

Figure 6. Distribution of Averages Spending per Person, 2009. Retrieved from http://kff.org/report-section/health-care-costs-a-primer-2012-report/

96   Centers for Disease Control and Prevention (CDC). (2010). Health, United States, 2010, Table 22. Life expectancy at birth, at 65 years of age, and at 75 years of age, by race and sex: United States, selected years 1900-2007 [PDF document]. Retrieved from https://www.cdc.gov/nchs/data/hus/2010/022.pdf

97   Centers for Disease Control and Prevention (CDC). (2015). Health, United States, 2015, Table 15. Life expectancy at birth, at age 65, and at age 75, by sex, race, and Hispanic origin: United States, selected years 1900-2014 [PDF document]. Retrieved from https://www.cdc.gov/nchs/hus/contents2015.htm#015

98   U.S. Department of Health and Human Services. Administration for Community Living (ACL). (n.d.). Aging Statistics. Retrieved from https://aoa.acl.gov/Aging_Statistics/Index.aspx

99   U.S. Department of Health and Human Services. Administration for Community Living (ACL). (n.d.). Aging Statistics. Retrieved from https://aoa.acl.gov/Aging_Statistics/Index.aspx

100   Congressional Budget Office (CBO). (n.d.). Medicare. Retrieved from https://www.cbo.gov/topics/retirement/medicare

101   Centers for Medicare & Medicaid Services (CMS). (n.d.). National health expenditures 2015 highlights [PDF document]. Retrieved from https://www.cms.gov/Research-Statistics-Data-and-Systems/Statistics-Trends-and-Reports/NationalHealthExpendData/Downloads/highlights.pdf

102   Congressional Budget Office (CBO). (n.d.). 10-Year Budget Projections, January 2017, Table 1-2 [Excel spreadsheet]. Retrieved from https://www.cbo.gov/about/products/budget-economic-data#1

103   Congressional Budget Office (CBO). (n.d.). 10-Year Budget Projections, January 2017, Table 1-2 [Excel spreadsheet]. Retrieved from https://www.cbo.gov/about/products/budget-economic-data#1

104   Squires, D., Anderson, C. & The Commonwealth Fund. (2015, October). U.S. health care from a global perspective: Spending, use of services, prices, and health in 13 countries, Exhibit 1. Health care spending as a percent of GDP, 1980 – 2013. Retrieved from http://www.commonwealthfund.org/publications/issue-briefs/2015/oct/us-health-care-from-a-global-perspective

105   Squires, D., Anderson, C. & The Commonwealth Fund. (2015, October). U.S. health care from a global perspective: Spending, use of services, prices, and health in 13 countries, Exhibit 9. Select population health outcomes and risk factors. Retrieved from http://www.commonwealthfund.org/publications/issue-briefs/2015/oct/us-health-care-from-a-global-perspective

106   Squires, D., Anderson, C. & The Commonwealth Fund. (2015, October). U.S. health care from a global perspective: Spending, use of services, prices, and health in 13 countries, Exhibit 9. Select population health outcomes and risk factors. Retrieved from http://www.commonwealthfund.org/publications/issue-briefs/2015/oct/us-health-care-from-a-global-perspective

107   Centers for Disease Control and Prevention (CDC). (n.d.). Deaths and mortality, 2014 data. Retrieved from https://www.cdc.gov/nchs/fastats/deaths.htm

108   Centers for Disease Control and Prevention (CDC). (n.d.). Deaths and mortality, 2014 data. Retrieved from https://www.cdc.gov/nchs/fastats/deaths.htm

109 Centers for Disease Control and Prevention (CDC). (n.d.). Chronic Disease Overview. Retrieved from https://www.cdc.gov/chronicdisease/overview/

110 Centers for Disease Control and Prevention (CDC). (n.d.). Chronic Disease Overview. Retrieved from https://www.cdc.gov/chronicdisease/overview/

111 Ward, B. W., Schiller, J. S., & Goodman, R. A. (2014). Multiple chronic conditions among US adults: A 2012 update. *Preventing Chronic Dis*ease 2014;11:130389. doi: http://dx.doi.org/10.5888/pcd11.130389

112 Centers for Disease Control and Prevention (CDC). (n.d.). At a glance 2015: National Center for Chronic Disease Prevention and Health Promotion [PDF document]. Retrieved from https://www.cdc.gov/chronicdisease/resources/publications/aag/pdf/2015/nccdphp-aag.pdf

113 Engle, M. K. (2014, June 17). Protecting consumers from false and deceptive advertising of weight-loss products, prepared statement of the Federal Trade Commission [PDF document]. Retrieved from https://www.ftc.gov/system/files/documents/public_statements/316321/140617falsedecepweightloss.pdf

114 Centers for Disease Control and Prevention (CDC). (n.d.). Adult obesity facts. Retrieved from https://www.cdc.gov/obesity/data/adult.html

115 Trust for America's Health & the Robert Wood Johnson Foundation. (n.d.) Obesity rates & trends overview. Retrieved from http://stateofobesity.org/obesity-rates-trends-overview/

116 Trust for America's Health & the Robert Wood Johnson Foundation. (n.d.) Obesity rates & trends overview. Retrieved from http://stateofobesity.org/obesity-rates-trends-overview/

117 Chatterjee, A., Kubendran, S., King, J. & DeVol, R. (2014, Jan. 29). Checkup time: Chronic disease and wellness in America [PDF document]. Retrieved from http://www.milkeninstitute.org/publications/view/618

118 Centers for Disease Control and Prevention (CDC). (n.d.). Adult obesity facts. Retrieved from https://www.cdc.gov/obesity/data/adult.html

119 Cawley, J., & Meyerhoefer, C. (2012). The medical care costs of obesity: an instrumental variables approach. *Journal of Health Economics, 31*(1): 219-230. doi: 10.1016/j.jhealeco.2011.10.003. and Finkelstein, E.A., Trogdon, J. G., Cohen, J. S. & Dietz, W. (2009). Annual medical spending attributable to obesity. *Health Affairs, 38*(5): w822-w831. Retrieved from http://content.healthaffairs.org/content/28/5/w822.abstract

120 Harvard T.H. Chan School of Public Health. (n.d.). Sleep deprivation and obesity. Retrieved from https://www.hsph.harvard.edu/nutritionsource/sleep/

121 Centers for Disease Control and Prevention (CDC). (n.d.). Hypertension. Retrieved from https://www.cdc.gov/nchs/fastats/hypertension.htm

122 Centers for Disease Control and Prevention (CDC). (n.d.). High blood pressure facts. Retrieved from https://www.cdc.gov/bloodpressure/facts.htm

123 Centers for Disease Control and Prevention (CDC). (n.d.). Heart disease fact sheet. Retrieved from https://www.cdc.gov/dhdsp/data_statistics/fact_sheets/fs_heart_disease.htm

124 Centers for Disease Control and Prevention (CDC). (n.d.). Deaths and mortality, 2014 data. Retrieved from https://www.cdc.gov/nchs/fastats/deaths.htm

125 Centers for Disease Control and Prevention (CDC). (2016, Dec.) Mortality in the United States, 2015. *National Center for Health Statistics Data Brief No. 267.* Retrieved

from https://www.cdc.gov/nchs/products/databriefs/db267.htm

126 Centers for Disease Control and Prevention (CDC). (n.d.). Heart disease fact sheet. Retrieved from https://www.cdc.gov/dhdsp/data_statistics/fact_sheets/fs_heart_disease.htm

127 Mozaffarian, D., Benjamin, E. J., Go, A. S., Arnett, D. K., Blaha, M. J., Cushman, M., ... Turner, M. B. (2016, Jan. 26). Heart disease and stroke statistics—2016 update: A report from the American Heart Association. *Circulation, 133*(4):e38-360. doi: 10.1161/CIR.0000000000000350

128 Dieleman, J. L., Baral, R., Birger, M., Bui, A.L., Bulchis, A., Chapin, A., ... Murray, C. J. L. (2016, Dec. 27). US spending on personal health care and public health, 1996-2013. *JAMA, 2016; 316*(24):2627-2646. doi:10.1001/jama.2016.16885

129 Dieleman, J. L., Baral, R., Birger, M., Bui, A.L., Bulchis, A., Chapin, A., ... Murray, C. J. L. (2016, Dec. 27). US spending on personal health care and public health, 1996-2013. *JAMA, 2016; 316*(24):2627-2646. doi:10.1001/jama.2016.16885

130 American Diabetes Association. (n.d.). Statistics about diabetes. Retrieved from http://www.diabetes.org/diabetes-basics/statistics/

131 Diabetes Research Institute Foundation. (n.d.). What is type 1 diabetes? Retrieved from https://www.diabetesresearch.org/what-is-type-one-diabetes

132 Diabetes Research Institute Foundation. (n.d.). What is type 2 diabetes? Retrieved from https://www.diabetesresearch.org/what-is-type-two-diabetes

133 Mayo Clinic. (n.d.). Diseases and conditions, diabetes, causes. Retrieved from http://www.mayoclinic.org/diseases-conditions/diabetes/basics/causes/con-20033091

134 Mayo Clinic. (n.d.). Diseases and conditions, diabetes, causes. Retrieved from http://www.mayoclinic.org/diseases-conditions/diabetes/basics/causes/con-20033091

135 Centers for Disease Control and Prevention (CDC). (2016). Health, United States Spotlight, Health Status and Determinants, Spring 2016 [PDF document]. Retrieved from https://www.cdc.gov/nchs/data/hus/hus_spotlight_spring16.pdf

136 Menke, A., Casagrande, S., Geiss, L., & Cowie, C. C. (2015, Sept. 8). Prevalence of and trends in diabetes among adults in the United States, 1988-2012. *JAMA. 2015; 314*(10):1021-1029. doi:10.1001/jama.2015.10029

137 Dieleman, J. L., Baral, R., Birger, M., Bui, A.L., Bulchis, A., Chapin, A., ... Murray, C. J. L. (2016, Dec. 27). US spending on personal health care and public health, 1996-2013. *JAMA, 2016; 316*(24):2627-2646. doi:10.1001/jama.2016.16885

138 Dieleman, J. L., Baral, R., Birger, M., Bui, A.L., Bulchis, A., Chapin, A., ... Murray, C. J. L. (2016, Dec. 27). US spending on personal health care and public health, 1996-2013. *JAMA, 2016; 316*(24):2627-2646. doi:10.1001/jama.2016.16885

139 Dieleman, J. L., Baral, R., Birger, M., Bui, A.L., Bulchis, A., Chapin, A., ... Murray, C. J. L. (2016, Dec. 27). US spending on personal health care and public health, 1996-2013. *JAMA, 2016; 316*(24):2627-2646. doi:10.1001/jama.2016.16885

140 Dieleman, J. L., Baral, R., Birger, M., Bui, A.L., Bulchis, A., Chapin, A., ... Murray, C. J. L. (2016, Dec. 27). US spending on personal health care and public health, 1996-2013. *JAMA, 2016; 316*(24):2627-2646. doi:10.1001/jama.2016.16885

141 American Kidney Fund. (n.d.). Kidney failure/ESRD. Retrieved from http://www.kidneyfund.org/kidney-disease/kidney-failure/

142 American Kidney Fund. (n.d.). Kidney failure/ESRD. Retrieved from http://www.kidneyfund.org/kidney-disease/kidney-failure/

143 American Nephrology Nurses' Association (ANNA). (2015). Overview: Brief

history of Medicare end-stage renal disease (ESRD) reimbursement [PDF document]. Retrieved from https://www.annanurse.org/download/reference/health/esrdReimbursementFactSheet.pdf

144 United States Renal Data System (USRDS). (2016). Annual data report, Chapter 11: Medicare expenditures for persons with ESRD, highlights. Retrieved from https://www.usrds.org/2016/view/v2_11.aspx

145 National Institute of Health (NIH). National Institute of Diabetes and Digestive and Kidney Diseases NIDDK). (n.d.). Kidney disease statistics for the United States. Retrieved from https://www.niddk.nih.gov/health-information/health-statistics/Pages/kidney-disease-statistics-united-states.aspx

146 United States Renal Data System (USRDS). (2016). Annual data report, Chapter 11: Medicare expenditures for persons with ESRD, highlights. Retrieved from https://www.usrds.org/2016/view/v2_11.aspx

147 Mayo Clinic. (n.d.). Diseases and conditions, alcohol use disorder. Retrieved from http://www.mayoclinic.org/diseases-conditions/alcohol-use-disorder/basics/complications/con-20020866

148 Centers for Disease Control and Prevention (CDC). National Center for Health Statistics (NCHS). (n.d.). Alcohol use. Retrieved from https://www.cdc.gov/nchs/fastats/alcohol.htm

149 Ward, B. W., Clarke, T. C., Nugent, C. N., & Schiller, J. S. (2016, May). Early release of selected estimates based on data from the 2015 National Health Interview Survey, National Center for Health Statistics (NCHS) [PDF document]. Retrieved from https://www.cdc.gov/nchs/data/nhis/earlyrelease/earlyrelease201605.pdf

150 Centers for Disease Control and Prevention (CDC). (n.d.). Excessive drinking is draining the U.S. economy. Retrieved from https://www.cdc.gov/features/costsofdrinking/

151 Centers for Disease Control and Prevention (CDC). (n.d.). Excessive drinking is draining the U.S. economy. Retrieved from https://www.cdc.gov/features/costsofdrinking/

152 Centers for Disease Control and Prevention (CDC). (n.d.). Smoking & tobacco use, health effects of cigarette smoking. Retrieved from https://www.cdc.gov/tobacco/data_statistics/fact_sheets/health_effects/effects_cig_smoking/

153 Centers for Disease Control and Prevention (CDC). (n.d.). Smoking & tobacco use, health effects of cigarette smoking. Retrieved from https://www.cdc.gov/tobacco/data_statistics/fact_sheets/health_effects/effects_cig_smoking/

154 Centers for Disease Control and Prevention (CDC). (n.d.). Smoking & tobacco use,, tobacco-related mortality. Retrieved from https://www.cdc.gov/tobacco/data_statistics/fact_sheets/health_effects/tobacco_related_mortality/

155 Centers for Disease Control and Prevention (CDC). (n.d.). Smoking & tobacco use, fast facts. Retrieved from https://www.cdc.gov/tobacco/data_statistics/fact_sheets/fast_facts/

156 Centers for Disease Control and Prevention (CDC). National Center for Health Statistics (NCHS). (n.d.). Smoking. Retrieved from https://www.cdc.gov/nchs/fastats/smoking.htm

157 Centers for Disease Control and Prevention (CDC). National Center for Health Statistics (NCHS). (2016, May). Early release of selected estimates based on data from the 2015 National Health Interview Survey, Figure 8.1. Prevalence of current smoking

among adults aged 18 and over: United States, 1997-2015 [PDF document]. Retrieved from https://www.cdc.gov/nchs/nhis/releases/released201605.htm#8

158 Healthcare.gov. (n.d.). How insurance companies set health premiums. Retrieved from https://www.healthcare.gov/how-plans-set-your-premiums/

159 Centers for Disease Control and Prevention (CDC). National Center for Health Statistics (NCHS). (n.d.). Therapeutic drug use. Retrieved from https://www.cdc.gov/nchs/fastats/drug-use-therapeutic.htm

160 Partnership for Drug-Free Kids. (2013, June 20). Almost 70 percent of Americans take at least one prescription medication, study finds. Retrieved from http://www.drugfree.org/news-service/almost-70-percent-of-americans-take-at-least-one-prescription-medication-study-finds/

161 Eaddy, M. T., Cook, C. L., O'Day, K., Burch, S. P., & Cantrell, C. R. (2012). How patient cost-sharing trends affect adherence and outcomes: A literature review. *Pharmacy and Therapeutics, 37*(1), 45–55. Retrieved from https://www.ncbi.nlm.nih.gov/pmc/articles/PMC3278192/

162 Iuga, A. O., & McGuire, M. J. (2014). Adherence and health care costs. *Risk Management and Healthcare Policy, 7*, 35–44. doi: http://doi.org/10.2147/RMHP.S19801

163 IMS Institute for Healthcare Informatics. (2013). Avoidable costs in US health care [PDF document]. Retrieved from http://www.imshealth.com/deployedfiles/imshealth/Global/Content/Corporate/IMS%20Institute/RUOM-2013/IHII_Responsible_Use_Medicines_2013.pdf

164 National Association of Health Underwriters (NAHU). (2015, June). Healthcare cost drivers [PDF document]. Retrieved from http://cqrcengage.com/nahu/file/9x9J1nKIq2D/NAHU_WhitePaper_Cost_Final_060815.pdf

165 Scipioni, J. (2016, Dec. 8). Life expectancy drops, heart disease is up: Here's what researchers blame. *FOX Business*. Retrieved from http://www.foxbusiness.com/features/2016/12/08/life-expectancy-drops-heart-disease-is-up-here-s-what-researchers-blame.html

166 Loprinzi, P. D., Branscum, A., Hanks, J., & Smit, E. (2016, Feb. 20). Healthy lifestyle characteristics and their joint association with cardiovascular disease biomarkers in US adults [Published online ahead of print February 20, 2016]. *Mayo Clinic Proceedings* doi:10.1016/j.mayocp.2016.01.009

167 Beck, J. (2016, March 23). Less than 3 percent of Americans live a 'healthy lifestyle': Depressing statistics from a new study. *The Atlantic*. Retrieved from https://www.theatlantic.com/health/archive/2016/03/less-than-3-percent-of-americans-live-a-healthy-lifestyle/475065/

168 Loprinzi, P. D., Branscum, A., Hanks, J., & Smit, E. (2016, Feb. 20). Healthy lifestyle characteristics and their joint association with cardiovascular disease biomarkers in US adults [Published online ahead of print February 20, 2016]. *Mayo Clinic Proceedings* doi:10.1016/j.mayocp.2016.01.009

169 Dixon–Fyle, S., Gandhi, S., Pellathy, T., & Spatharou, A. (2012). Changing patient behavior: The next frontier in healthcare value [PDF document]. *Health International*, 64–73. Retrieved from http://healthcare.mckinsey.com/sites/default/files/791750_Changing_Patient_Behavior_the_Next_Frontier_in_Healthcare_Value.pdf

170 Centers for Medicare & Medicaid Services (CMS). (2015). National Health

Expenditure (NHE) summary including share of GDP, CY 1960-2015 [Excel file]. Retrieved from https://www.cms.gov/research-statistics-data-and-systems/statistics-trends-and-reports/nationalhealthexpenddata/nationalhealthaccountshistorical.html

171 Committee on the Learning Health Care System in America, Institute of Medicine. (2013). Chapter 3, Imperative: Achieving greater value in health care. In Smith, M., Saunders, R., Stuckhardt, L. et al., (Eds.), Best care at lower cost: The path to continuously learning health care in America. Washington, DC: National Academies Press (U.S.). Available from: https://www.ncbi.nlm.nih.gov/books/NBK207222/

172 The Henry J. Kaiser Family Foundation. (n.d.). Health Insurance Status, Health Insurance Coverage of the Total Population, 2013 to 2015 [Data set]. Retrieved from http://kff.org/other/state-indicator/total-population/?dataView=1&activeTab=graph&currentTimeframe=0&startTimeframe=2&selectedDistributions=medicaid--medicare&selectedRows=%7B%22wrapups%22:%7B%22united-states%22:%7B%7D%7D%7D&sortModel=%7B%22colId%22:%22Location%22,%22sort%22:%22asc%22%7D

173 Centers for Medicare & Medicaid Services (CMS). (n.d.). National health expenditures 2015 highlights [PDF document]. Retrieved from https://www.cms.gov/Research-Statistics-Data-and-Systems/Statistics-Trends-and-Reports/NationalHealthExpendData/Downloads/highlights.pdf

174 Beach, E. (n.d.). The History of Flat Screen TVs. Techwalla. Retrieved from https://www.techwalla.com/articles/the-history-of-flat-screen-tvs

175 Centers for Disease Control and Prevention (CDC). (n.d.). Antibiotics aren't always the answer. Retrieved from https://www.cdc.gov/features/getsmart/

176 Centers for Disease Control and Prevention (CDC). (n.d.). Antibiotics aren't always the answer. Retrieved from https://www.cdc.gov/features/getsmart/

177 Costhelper.com. (n.d.). Breast augmentation cost. Retrieved from http://health.costhelper.com/breast-augmentation.html

178 Realself.com. (n.d.). Breast augmentation cost. Retrieved from https://www.realself.com/breast-augmentation/cost

179 Buildmybod.com. (n.d.). Retrieved March 12, 2017, from https://www.buildmybod.com/

180 Buildmybod.com. (n.d.). Retrieved March 12, 2017, from https://www.buildmybod.com/

181 Reid, G. (2013, Oct. 20). Defending the chargemaster. Healthcare Finance. Retrieved from http://www.healthcarefinancenews.com/news/defending-chargemaster

182 Brill, S. (2013, April 4). Bitter pill: Why medical bills are killing us. Time. Retrieved from http://time.com/198/bitter-pill-why-medical-bills-are-killing-us/

183 Brill, S. (2013, April 4). Bitter pill: Why medical bills are killing us. Time. Retrieved from http://time.com/198/bitter-pill-why-medical-bills-are-killing-us/

184 American Hospital Association (AHA), Trends in Hospital Financing, Chart 4.6 Aggregate Hospital Payment-to-Cost Ratios for Private Payers, Medicare and Medicaid, 1994-2014, http://www.aha.org/research/reports/tw/chartbook/ch4.shtml

185 Brill, S. (2013, April 4). Bitter pill: Why medical bills are killing us. Time. Retrieved from http://time.com/198/bitter-pill-why-medical-bills-are-killing-us/

186 Centers for Medicare & Medicaid Services (CMS). (2014, Aug. 4). Fiscal year 2015 policy and payment changes for inpatient stays in acute-care hospitals and long-term care hospitals. Retrieved from https://www.cms.gov/Newsroom/MediaReleaseDatabase/Fact-sheets/2014-Fact-sheets-items/2014-08-04.html

187 Centers for Medicare & Medicaid Services (CMS). (2014, Aug. 4). Fiscal year 2015 policy and payment changes for inpatient stays in acute-care hospitals and long-term care hospitals. Retrieved from https://www.cms.gov/Newsroom/ MediaReleaseDatabase/Fact-sheets/2014-Fact-sheets-items/2014-08-04.html

188 Centers for Medicare & Medicaid Services (CMS). (2014, Aug. 4). Fiscal year 2015 policy and payment changes for inpatient stays in acute-care hospitals and long-term care hospitals. Retrieved from https://www.cms.gov/Newsroom/ MediaReleaseDatabase/Fact-sheets/2014-Fact-sheets-items/2014-08-04.html

189 Centers for Medicare and Medicaid Services (CMS). (n.d.). Provider reimbursement manual (PRM), 15-1 (Part 1), Chapter 21, 2102.4 Charges. Retrieved from https:// www.cms.gov/Regulations-and-Guidance/Guidance/Manuals/Paper-Based-Manuals. html

190 Centers for Medicare and Medicaid Services (CMS). (n.d.). Provider Reimbursement Manual (PRM), 15-1 (Part 1), Chapter 22, 2102.1 Reasonable costs. Retrieved from https://www.cms.gov/Regulations-and-Guidance/Guidance/Manuals/Paper-Based-Manuals.html

191 Dietsche, E. (2016, Jan. 14). 60 things to know about the hospital industry, 2016. *Becker's Hospital Review*. Retrieved from http://www.beckershospitalreview.com/ lists/50-things-to-know-about-the-hospital-industry-2016.html

192 Hilsenrath, P., Eakin, C., & Fischer, K. (2015, April 10). Price-transparency and cost accounting: Challenges for health care organizations in the consumer-driven era. *Inquiry: The Journal of Healthcare Organization, Provision, and Financing, 52,* 1-5. doi: 10.1177/0046958015574981

193 Hilsenrath, P., Eakin, C., & Fischer, K. (2015, April 10). Price-transparency and cost accounting: Challenges for health care organizations in the consumer-driven era. *Inquiry: The Journal of Healthcare Organization, Provision, and Financing, 52,* 1-5. doi: 10.1177/0046958015574981

194 Cleverly, W. O. (2008). Effective hospital pricing strategy [PDF document]. Retrieved from https://www.cleverleyassociates.com/Library/EffectiveHospitalPricingStrategy.pdf

195 Cleverly, W. O. (2008). Effective hospital pricing strategy [PDF document]. Retrieved from https://www.cleverleyassociates.com/Library/EffectiveHospitalPricingStrategy.pdf

196 American Customer Satisfaction Index (ACSI). (2014, Nov. 18). Frustration over fees takes a bite out of banks, but credit union satisfaction remains strong. In *ASCI Finance and Insurance Report, 2014* [PDF document]. Retrieved from http://www. theacsi.org/news-and-resources/customer-satisfaction-reports/report-archive/acsi-finance-and-insurance-report-2014

197 American Customer Satisfaction Index (ACSI). (2014, Nov. 18). Frustration over fees takes a bite out of banks, but credit union satisfaction remains strong. In *ASCI Finance and Insurance Report, 2014* [PDF document]. Retrieved from http://www. theacsi.org/news-and-resources/customer-satisfaction-reports/report-archive/acsi-finance-and-insurance-report-2014

198 American Customer Satisfaction Index (ACSI). (2014, Nov. 18). Frustration over fees takes a bite out of banks, but credit union satisfaction remains strong. In *ASCI Finance and Insurance Report, 2014* [PDF document]. Retrieved from http://www. theacsi.org/news-and-resources/customer-satisfaction-reports/report-archive/acsi-finance-and-insurance-report-2014

199 Kristof, N. (2009, Sept. 2). Health Care That Works. *The New York Times*. Retrieved

from http://www.nytimes.com/2009/09/03/opinion/03kristof.html

200 U.S. Department of Health and Human Services (HHS). About the Affordable Care Act. Retrieved from https://www.hhs.gov/healthcare/about-the-aca/index.html

201 American Customer Satisfaction Index (ACSI). (2016). *ASCI Finance and Insurance Report, 2016.* Retrieved from http://www.theacsi.org/news-and-resources/customer-satisfaction-reports/reports-2016/acsi-finance-and-insurance-report-2016/acsi-finance-and-insurance-report-2016-download

202 American Customer Satisfaction Index (ACSI). (2014, Nov. 18). Frustration over fees takes a bite out of banks, but credit union satisfaction remains strong. In *ASCI Finance and Insurance Report, 2014* [PDF document]. Retrieved from http://www.theacsi.org/news-and-resources/customer-satisfaction-reports/report-archive/acsi-finance-and-insurance-report-2014

203 Centers for Medicare & Medicaid Services (CMS). (n.d.). The Center for Consumer Information & Insurance Oversight, Medical loss ratio. Retrieved from https://www.cms.gov/CCIIO/Programs-and-Initiatives/Health-Insurance-Market-Reforms/Medical-Loss-Ratio.html

204 Kirchhoff, S. M. (2014, August 26). Medical loss ratio requirements under the Patient Protection and Affordable Care Act (ACA): Issues for Congress [PDF document]. Retrieved from https://fas.org/sgp/crs/misc/R42735.pdf

205 Kirchhoff, S. M. (2014, August 26). Medical loss ratio requirements under the Patient Protection and Affordable Care Act (ACA): Issues for Congress [PDF document]. Retrieved from https://fas.org/sgp/crs/misc/R42735.pdf

206 Kirchhoff, S. M. (2014, August 26). Medical loss ratio requirements under the Patient Protection and Affordable Care Act (ACA): Issues for Congress [PDF document]. Retrieved from https://fas.org/sgp/crs/misc/R42735.pdf

207 The Henry J. Kaiser Family Foundation. (2012, Feb. 29). Explaining health care reform: Medical loss ratio (MLR). Retrieved from http://kff.org/health-reform/fact-sheet/explaining-health-care-reform-medical-loss-ratio-mlr/

208 Centers for Medicare & Medicaid Services (CMS). (n.d.). The Center for Consumer Information & Insurance Oversight, Medical loss ratio. Retrieved from https://www.cms.gov/CCIIO/Programs-and-Initiatives/Health-Insurance-Market-Reforms/Medical-Loss-Ratio.html

209 The Henry J. Kaiser Family Foundation. (2012, Feb. 29). Explaining health care reform: Medical loss ratio (MLR). Retrieved from http://kff.org/health-reform/fact-sheet/explaining-health-care-reform-medical-loss-ratio-mlr/

210 Kirchhoff, S. M. (2014, August 26). Medical loss ratio requirements under the Patient Protection and Affordable Care Act (ACA): Issues for Congress [PDF document]. Retrieved from https://fas.org/sgp/crs/misc/R42735.pdf

211 Norman, J. (2015, Sept. 14). Americans' views of pharmaceutical industry take a tumble. *Gallup.* Retrieved from http://www.gallup.com/poll/185432/americans-views-pharmaceutical-industry-tumble.aspx?g_source=pharmaceutical+industry&g_medium=search&g_campaign=tiles

212 Gallup. (2016, Aug. 3-7). *Business and Industry Sector Ratings.* Retrieved from http://www.gallup.com/poll/12748/business-industry-sector-ratings.aspx

213 Gallup. (2016, Aug. 3-7). *Business and Industry Sector Ratings.* Retrieved from http://www.gallup.com/poll/12748/business-industry-sector-ratings.aspx

214 Centers for Medicare & Medicaid Services (CMS). (n.d.). National health

expenditures 2015 highlights [PDF document]. Retrieved from https://www.
cms.gov/Research-Statistics-Data-and-Systems/Statistics-Trends-and-Reports/
NationalHealthExpendData/Downloads/highlights.pdf

215 Cummings, E.E., & Sanders, B. (2014, Oct. 2). Ranking member Cummings and
Chairman Sanders investigate staggering price increases for generic drugs [PDF
document]. Retrieved from http://www.sanders.senate.gov/download/face-sheet-on-
generic-drug-price-increases?inline=file

216 Cummings, E.E., & Sanders, B. (2014, Oct. 2). Ranking member Cummings and
Chairman Sanders investigate staggering price increases for generic drugs [PDF
document]. Retrieved from http://www.sanders.senate.gov/download/face-sheet-on-
generic-drug-price-increases?inline=file

217 Long, H. (2016, Aug. 25). Here's what happened to AIDS drug that spiked 5,000%.
CNN Money. Retrieved from http://money.cnn.com/2016/08/25/news/economy/
daraprim-aids-drug-high-price/

218 Long, H. (2016, Aug. 25). Here's what happened to AIDS drug that spiked 5,000%.
CNN Money. Retrieved from http://money.cnn.com/2016/08/25/news/economy/
daraprim-aids-drug-high-price/

219 Mukherjee, S. (2016, Sept. 21). Mylan's CEO tells Congress the EpiPen price hike was
'fair.' *Fortune*. Retrieved from http://fortune.com/2016/09/21/mylan-ceo-epipen-price-
hike/

220 Mukherjee, S. (2016, Sept. 21). Mylan's CEO tells Congress the EpiPen price hike was
'fair.' *Fortune*. Retrieved from http://fortune.com/2016/09/21/mylan-ceo-epipen-price-
hike/

221 International Federation of Health Plans (IFHP). (2015). 2015 comparative price
report, variation in medical and hospital prices by country [PDF document].
Retrieved from http://static1.squarespace.com/static/518a3cfee4b0a77d03a62c98/t/
57d3ca9529687f1a257e9e26/1473497751062/2015+Comparative+Price+Repo
rt+09.09.16.pdf

222 Lee, T. T., Gluck, A. R., & Curfman, G. (2016, Sept. 19). The politics of Medicare and
drug-price negotiation (updated) [Blog post]. *Health Affairs Blog*. Retrieved from
http://healthaffairs.org/blog/2016/09/19/the-politics-of-medicare-and-drug-price-
negotiation/

223 Brill, S. (2013, April 4). Bitter pill: Why medical bills are killing us. *Time*. Retrieved
from http://time.com/198/bitter-pill-why-medical-bills-are-killing-us/

224 Pharmaceutical Research and Manufacturers of America (PhRMA). (2017, Jan. 23).
America's biopharmaceutical companies launch groundbreaking, multi-year initiative
heralding new era of medicine. Retrieved from http://www.phrma.org/press-release/
america-s-biopharmaceutical-companies-launch-groundbreaking-multi-year-
initiative-heralding-new-era-of-medicine

225 Pharmaceutical Research and Manufacturers of America (PhRMA). (2017, Jan. 23).
America's biopharmaceutical companies launch groundbreaking, multi-year initiative
heralding new era of medicine. Retrieved from http://www.phrma.org/press-release/
america-s-biopharmaceutical-companies-launch-groundbreaking-multi-year-
initiative-heralding-new-era-of-medicine

226 Lechleiter, J. (2015, May 19). Debunking the five big myths about 'Big Pharma.'
Forbes. Retrieved from https://www.forbes.com/sites/johnlechleiter/2015/05/19/
debunking-the-five-big-myths-about-big-pharma/#500f2a3847bc

227 Hoyer, M., & Alonso-Zaldivar, R. (2016, Oct. 28). Lack of choice in health insurance markets a growing problem. *U.S. News & World Report*. Retrieved from https://www.usnews.com/news/news/articles/2016-10-28/lack-of-choice-in-health-insurance-markets-a-growing-problem

228 Vanamburg, D. (2015, Dec. 22). Consumers weigh in: Choice matters for health coverage. *ACSI Matters*. Retrieved from https://acsimatters.com/2015/12/22/consumers-weigh-in-choice-matters-for-health-coverage/

229 Ingold, J. (2017, Feb. 11). A judge blocked the Anthem-Cigna health insurance merger. What does that mean for Colorado? *The Denver Post*. Retrieved from http://www.denverpost.com/2017/02/11/anthem-cigna-health-insurance-merger-blocked-colorado-impact/

230 McCoy, K. (2017, Jan. 23). Aetna-Humana $37B merger blocked over fear it would harm consumers. *USA Today*. Retrieved from http://www.usatoday.com/story/money/2017/01/23/aetna-humana-37b-merger-blocked-over-fear-would-harm-consumers/96948570/

231 Pauly, M. (2015, June 23). What's driving health insurers' merger mania? *Knowledge@Wharton* podcast [Audio file]. Retrieved from http://knowledge.wharton.upenn.edu/article/whats-driving-health-insurers-merger-mania/

232 Skillrud, I., Gerhardt, W., & Shukla, M. (2014). The great consolidation: The potential for rapid consolidation of health systems [PDF document]. *Deloitte Center for Health Solutions*. Retrieved from https://www2.deloitte.com/us/en/pages/life-sciences-and-health-care/articles/great-consolidation-health-systems.html

233 Irving Levin Associates, Inc. (2015, March 31). Newly published report: 2014 health care services M&A market sees growth in deal volume and value of transactions. Retrieved from http://www.businesswire.com/news/home/20150331006369/en/Newly-Published-Report-2014-Health-Care-Services#.VRv4s-FKZsZ

234 Skillrud, I., Gerhardt, W., & Shukla, M. (2014). The great consolidation: The potential for rapid consolidation of health systems [PDF document]. *Deloitte Center for Health Solutions*. Retrieved from https://www2.deloitte.com/us/en/pages/life-sciences-and-health-care/articles/great-consolidation-health-systems.html

235 Centers for Medicare & Medicaid Services (CMS). (n.d.). Women's Health and Cancer Rights Act (WHCRA). Retrieved from https://www.cms.gov/CCIIO/Programs-and-Initiatives/Other-Insurance-Protections/whcra_factsheet.html

236 Newport, F. (2016, May 16). Majority in U.S. support idea of Fed-funded healthcare system. *Gallup*. Retrieved from http://www.gallup.com/poll/191504/majority-support-idea-fed-funded-healthcare-system.aspx

237 Newport, F. (2016, March 11). American public opinion and Sanders' proposal for single-payer healthcare system. *Gallup*. Retrieved from http://www.gallup.com/opinion/polling-matters/189902/american-public-opinion-sanders-proposal-single-payer-healthcare-system.aspx?g_source=healthcare&g_medium=search&g_campaign=tiles

238 McCarthy, J. (2015, Nov. 23). In U.S., 51% say government should ensure healthcare coverage. *Gallup*. Retrieved from http://www.gallup.com/poll/186782/say-gov-ensure-healthcare-coverage.aspx?g_source=government%20healthcare&g_medium=search&g_campaign=tiles

239 Gallup. (n.d.). Healthcare system, Responsibility for health insurance, 2000-2016. Retrieved from http://www.gallup.com/poll/4708/healthcare-system.aspx

240 Friedman, E. (2011, April 5). The law that changed everything—and it isn't the one you think. *Hospitals&HealthNetworks (H&HN)*. Retrieved from http://www.hhnmag. com/articles/5010-the-law-that-changed-everything-and-it-isn-t-the-one-you-think

241 Consolidated Omnibus Budget Reconciliation Act of 1985 (COBRA), H.R. 3128, 99th Cong. (1985-1986). Retrieved from https://www.congress.gov/bill/99th-congress/ house-bill/3128

242 Friedman, E. (2011, April 5). The law that changed everything—and it isn't the one you think. *Hospitals&HealthNetworks (H&HN)*. Retrieved from http://www.hhnmag. com/articles/5010-the-law-that-changed-everything-and-it-isn-t-the-one-you-think

243 Friedman, E. (2011, April 5). The law that changed everything—and it isn't the one you think. *Hospitals&HealthNetworks (H&HN)*. Retrieved from http://www.hhnmag. com/articles/5010-the-law-that-changed-everything-and-it-isn-t-the-one-you-think

244 Friedman, E. (2011, April 5). The law that changed everything—and it isn't the one you think. *Hospitals&HealthNetworks (H&HN)*. Retrieved from http://www.hhnmag. com/articles/5010-the-law-that-changed-everything-and-it-isn-t-the-one-you-think

245 The Henry J. Kaiser Family Foundation. (n.d.) Timeline: History of health reform in the U.S. [PDF document]. Retrieved from https://kaiserfamilyfoundation.files. wordpress.com/2011/03/5-02-13-history-of-health-reform.pdf

246 Emtala.com. (n.d.). Special note: What is the 250-yard rule and how does it affect these issues? Retrieved from http://www.emtala.com/250yard.htm

247 Gindi, R. M., Cohen, R. A., & Kirzinger, W. K. (2012, May). Emergency room use among adults aged 18–64: Early release of estimates from the National Health Interview Survey, January–June 2011 [PDF document]. Retrieved from https://www. cdc.gov/nchs/data/nhis/earlyrelease/emergency_room_use_january-june_2011.pdf

248 Meyer, H. (2016, March 26). Why patients still need EMTALA. *Modern Healthcare*. Retrieved from http://www.modernhealthcare.com/article/20160326/ MAGAZINE/303289881

249 AHC Media. (2016, July 1). EDs still tagged with EMTALA violations. Retrieved from https://www.ahcmedia.com/articles/138046-eds-still-tagged-with-emtala-violations

250 Zuabi, N., Weiss, L. D., & Langdorf, M. I. (2016). Emergency Medical Treatment and Labor Act (EMTALA) 2002-15: Review of Office of Inspector General Patient Dumping Settlements. *Western Journal of Emergency Medicine, 17*(3), 245–251. doi: http://doi.org/10.5811/westjem.2016.3.29705

251 Friedman, T. L. (1993, Jan. 26). Hilllary Clinton to head panel on health care. *The New York Times*. Retrieved from http://www.nytimes.com/1993/01/26/us/hillary-clinton-to-head-panel-on-health-care.html

252 Friedman, T. L. (1993, Jan. 26). Hilllary Clinton to head panel on health care. *The New York Times*. Retrieved from http://www.nytimes.com/1993/01/26/us/hillary-clinton-to-head-panel-on-health-care.html

253 The Henry J. Kaiser Family Foundation. (n.d.) Timeline: History of health reform in the U.S. [PDF document]. Retrieved from https://kaiserfamilyfoundation.files. wordpress.com/2011/03/5-02-13-history-of-health-reform.pdf

254 C-SPAN. (2009, July 20). *"Harry and Louise" health care advertisements* [Video file]. Retrieved from https://www.youtube.com/watch?v=CwOX2P4s-Iw

255 C-SPAN. (2009, July 20). *"Harry and Louise" health care advertisements* [Video file]. Retrieved from https://www.youtube.com/watch?v=CwOX2P4s-Iw

256 C-SPAN. (2009, July 20). *"Harry and Louise" health care advertisements* [Video file].

Retrieved from https://www.youtube.com/watch?v=CwOX2P4s-Iw

257   Thomasson, M.A. (2002, July). From sickness to health: The twentieth-century development of U.S. health insurance. *Explorations in Economic History, 39*(3), 233-253. doi: http://dx.doi.org/10.1006/exeh.2002.0788

258   Oberlander, J. (2007). Learning from failure in health care reform. *New England Journal of Medicine, 357*(17), 1677-1679. Retrieved from http://www.nejm.org/doi/full/10.1056/NEJMp078201#t=article

259   Gotbaum, R. (2007). Interview with Jonathan Oberlander on the lessons of the failed Clinton health care plan of 1993 [Audio file]. *NEJM Podcast.* Supplement to the *New England Journal of Medicine, 2007; 357*; 1677-1679. Retrieved from http://www.nejm.org/action/showMediaPlayer?doi=10.1056%2FNEJMp078201&aid=NEJMp078201_attach_1&area=

260   Kapur, S. (2016, Jan. 22). How 'Hillarycare' did, and didn't, lead to Obamacare. *Bloomberg.* Retrieved from https://www.bloomberg.com/politics/articles/2016-01-22/how-hillarycare-did-and-didn-t-lead-to-obamacare

261   Kapur, S. (2016, Jan. 22). How 'Hillarycare' did, and didn't, lead to Obamacare. *Bloomberg.* Retrieved from https://www.bloomberg.com/politics/articles/2016-01-22/how-hillarycare-did-and-didn-t-lead-to-obamacare

262   Health Insurance Portability and Accountability Act of 1996 (HIPAA), Public Law 104-191. (1996). Retrieved from https://www.gpo.gov/fdsys/pkg/PLAW-104publ191/pdf/PLAW-104publ191.pdf

263   Health Insurance Portability and Accountability Act of 1996 (HIPAA), Public Law 104-191. (1996). Retrieved from https://www.gpo.gov/fdsys/pkg/PLAW-104publ191/pdf/PLAW-104publ191.pdf

264   U.S. Department of Health and Human Services. (2003). OCR Privacy Brief: Summary of the HIPAA Privacy Rule [PDF document]. Retrieved from https://www.hhs.gov/hipaa/for-professionals/privacy/laws-regulations/

265   Health Insurance Portability and Accountability Act of 1996 (HIPAA), Public Law 104-191, Part 7 § 701. (1996). Retrieved from https://www.gpo.gov/fdsys/pkg/PLAW-104publ191/pdf/PLAW-104publ191.pdf

266   Health Insurance Portability and Accountability Act of 1996 (HIPAA), Public Law 104-191, Title III, Subtitle A. (1996). Retrieved from https://www.gpo.gov/fdsys/pkg/PLAW-104publ191/pdf/PLAW-104publ191.pdf

267   Health Insurance Portability and Accountability Act of 1996 (HIPAA), Public Law 104-191, Title III, Subtitle F, Administrative Simplification. (1996). Retrieved from https://www.gpo.gov/fdsys/pkg/PLAW-104publ191/pdf/PLAW-104publ191.pdf

268   Hincks, J. (2016, Dec. 28). Donald Trump says 'nobody knows exactly what' going on' because of computers. *Time.* Retrieved from http://time.com/4619337/donald-trump-age-of-computer-technology-internets/

269   Bradley, K. (2012, Jan. 18). Top five rejections related to HIPAA version 5010. *The Daily Practice.* Retrieved from http://dailypracticeblog.com/top-5-rejections-related-to-hipaa-version-5010/

270   Natale, C. (2012, Jan. 26). HIPAA 5010: What's triggering denials and rejections. *Healthcare IT News.* Retrieved from http://www.healthcareitnews.com/blog/hipaa-5010-whats-triggering-denials-and-rejections

271   Health Insurance Portability and Accountability Act of 1996 (HIPAA), Public Law 104-191, Title III, Subtitle F, Administrative Simplification. (1996). Retrieved from

https://www.gpo.gov/fdsys/pkg/PLAW-104publ191/pdf/PLAW-104publ191.pdf

272   U.S. Department of Health and Human Services. Office for Civil Rights (OCR). (2013, March). HIPAA administrative simplification, regulation text, 45 CFR Parts 160, 162 and 164, unofficial version, as amended through March 26, 2013 [PDF document]. Retrieved from https://www.hhs.gov/hipaa/for-professionals/privacy/laws-regulations/combined-regulation-text/index.html

273   U.S. Department of Health and Human Services. Office of the Secretary. (2013, Jan. 25.) 45 CFR Parts 160 and 164, Modifications to the HIPAA Privacy, Security, Enforcement, and Breach Notification Rules under the Health Information Technology for Economic and Clinical Health Act and the Genetic Information Nondiscrimination Act: Other Modifications to the HIPAA Rules. *Federal Register*, Vol. 78, No. 17. Retrieved from https://www.gpo.gov/fdsys/pkg/FR-2013-01-25/pdf/2013-01073.pdf

274   U.S. Department of Health and Human Services. Office of the Secretary. (2013, Jan. 25.) 45 CFR Parts 160 and 164, Modifications to the HIPAA Privacy, Security, Enforcement, and Breach Notification Rules under the Health Information Technology for Economic and Clinical Health Act and the Genetic Information Nondiscrimination Act: Other Modifications to the HIPAA Rules. *Federal Register*, Vol. 78, No. 17. Retrieved from https://www.gpo.gov/fdsys/pkg/FR-2013-01-25/pdf/2013-01073.pdf

275   The Henry J. Kaiser Family Foundation. (2012, May). Massachusetts health care reform: Six years later [PDF document]. Retrieved from https://kaiserfamilyfoundation.files.wordpress.com/2013/01/8311.pdf

276   The Henry J. Kaiser Family Foundation. (2012, May). Massachusetts health care reform: Six years later [PDF document]. Retrieved from https://kaiserfamilyfoundation.files.wordpress.com/2013/01/8311.pdf

277   Baker, M. L. (2004, April 30). Bush creates post to lead medical-records switch. *eWeek*. Retrieved from http://www.eweek.com/enterprise-apps/bush-creates-post-to-lead-medical-records-switch

278   Roberts, D. W. (2010, July 6). The impact of national policy on health information technology [PowerPoint document]. HIT Program Classroom Lecture. University of California San Diego, Extension. San Diego.

279   Healthit.gov. (n.d.). EHR incentives & certification: EHR incentive payment timeline. Retrieved from https://www.healthit.gov/providers-professionals/ehr-incentive-payment-timeline

280   Healthit.gov. (n.d.). EHR incentives & certification: EHR incentive payment timeline. Retrieved from https://www.healthit.gov/providers-professionals/ehr-incentive-payment-timeline

281   Healthit.gov. (n.d.). EHR incentives & certification: EHR incentive payment timeline. Retrieved from https://www.healthit.gov/providers-professionals/ehr-incentive-payment-timeline

282   Henry, J., Pylypchuk, Y., Searcy T. & Patel V. (2016, May). Adoption of electronic health record systems among U.S. non-federal acute care hospitals: 2008-2015. *ONC Data Brief 35*. Retrieved from https://dashboard.healthit.gov/evaluations/data-briefs/non-federal-acute-care-hospital-ehr-adoption-2008-2015.php

283   Healthit.gov. (n.d.). What are the advantages of electronic health records? Retrieved from https://www.healthit.gov/providers-professionals/faqs/what-are-advantages-electronic-health-records

284 Coleman, K. (2016, Oct. 26). Aging consumers without subsidies hit hardest by 2017 Obamacare premium & deductible spikes. *HealthPocket*. Retrieved from https://www.healthpocket.com/healthcare-research/infostat/2017-obamacare-premiums-deductibles#.WNn_svkrI2w

285 Coleman, K. (2016, Oct. 26). Aging consumers without subsidies hit hardest by 2017 Obamacare premium & deductible spikes. *HealthPocket*. Retrieved from https://www.healthpocket.com/healthcare-research/infostat/2017-obamacare-premiums-deductibles#.WNn_svkrI2w

286 Centers for Medicare & Medicaid Services (CMS). (n.d.) Medicaid, eligibility. Retrieved from https://www.medicaid.gov/medicaid/eligibility/index.html

287 The Henry J. Kaiser Family Foundation. (2017, Jan. 1). Status of state action on the Medicaid expansion decision. Retrieved from http://kff.org/health-reform/state-indicator/state-activity-around-expanding-medicaid-under-the-affordable-care-ac t/?currentTimeframe=0&selectedRows=%7B%22wrapups%22:%7B%22united-states%22:%7B%7D%7D%7D&sortModel=%7B%22colId%22:%22Location%22,%22s ort%22:%22asc%22%7D

288 Garfield, R., & Damico, A. (2016, Oct. 19). The coverage gap: Uninsured poor adults in states that do not expand Medicaid. The Henry J. Kaiser Family Foundation. Retrieved from http://kff.org/uninsured/issue-brief/the-coverage-gap-uninsured-poor-adults-in-states-that-do-not-expand-medicaid/

289 American Hospital Association (AHA). (2016). Table 4.1 Aggregate total hospital margins and operating margins; percentage of hospitals with negative total margins; and aggregate non-operating gains as a percentage of total net revenue, 1994-2014 [PDF document]. In *Trendwatch Chartbook 2016*. Retrieved from http://www.aha.org/research/reports/tw/chartbook/2016/table4-1.pdf and U.S. Department of Health and Human Services. Office of the Assistant Secretary for Planning and Evaluation. (2015, March 23). Insurance expansion, hospital uncompensated care and the Affordable Care Act [PDF document]. Retrieved from https://aspe.hhs.gov/system/files/pdf/139226/ib_UncompensatedCare.pdf

290 Brill, S. (2013, April 4). Bitter pill: Why medical bills are killing us. *Time*. Retrieved from http://time.com/198/bitter-pill-why-medical-bills-are-killing-us/

291 House GOP. (n.d.). The American Health Care Act (AHCA). Retrieved March 26, 2017 from https://housegop.leadpages.co/healthcare/

292 American Health Care Act of 2017 (AHCA), H.R. 1628, 115th Cong. (2017-2018). Retrieved from https://www.congress.gov/bill/115th-congress/house-bill/1628

293 Congressional Budget Office. (2017, March 13). Cost estimate, American Health Care Act [PDF document]. Retrieved from https://www.cbo.gov/sites/default/files/115th-congress-2017-2018/costestimate/americanhealthcareact.pdf

294 Congressional Budget Office. (2017, March 13). Cost estimate, American Health Care Act [PDF document]. Retrieved from https://www.cbo.gov/sites/default/files/115th-congress-2017-2018/costestimate/americanhealthcareact.pdf

295 Schoen, J.W. (2017, March 7). Here's the price tag for GOP health care plan: $600 billion. *CNBC*. Retrieved from http://www.cnbc.com/2017/03/07/heres-the-price-tag-for-gop-health-care-plan-600-billion.html

296 Radford, P. (2017, March 7). RyanCare! Or is it TrumpCare? [Blog post]. *Real-World Economics Review Blog (RWER)*. Retrieved from https://rwer.wordpress.com/2017/03/07/ryancare-or-is-it-trumpcare/

297   Auter, Z. (2017, Jan. 9). US uninsured rate holds at low of 10.9% in fourth quarter. *Gallup*. Retrieved from http://www.gallup.com/poll/201641/uninsured-rate-holds-low-fourth-quarter.aspx

298   Auter, Z. (2017, Jan. 9). US uninsured rate holds at low of 10.9% in fourth quarter. *Gallup*. Retrieved from http://www.gallup.com/poll/201641/uninsured-rate-holds-low-fourth-quarter.aspx

299   American Hospital Association (AHA). (2017, March 8). America's hospitals and health systems, Letter to Congress [PDF document]. Retrieved from http://www.aha.org/advocacy-issues/letter/2017/170308-aha-health-orgs-american-healthcare-act.pdf

300   DeBonis, M., O'Keefe, E., & Costa, R. (2017, March 24). GOP health-care bill: House Republican leaders abruptly pull their rewrite of the nation's health-care law. *The Washington Post*. Retrieved from https://www.washingtonpost.com/powerpost/house-leaders-prepare-to-vote-friday-on-health-care-reform/2017/03/24/736f1cd6-1081-11e7-9d5a-a83e627dc120_story.html?utm_term=.8cdea9e442a5

301   Bryan, B. (2017, May 4). Senate Republicans signal they plan to scrap bill the House just passed and write their own. *Business Insider*. Retrieved from http://www.businessinsider.com/senate-plan-for-healthcare-bill-ahca-2017-5

302   Pellathy, T., & Singhal, S. (2010, March). Revisiting healthcare payments: An industry still in need of overhaul [PDF document]. McKinsey & Company. Retrieved from http://healthcare.mckinsey.com/sites/default/files/776489_Revisiting_Healthcare_Payments_An_Industry_Still_in_Need_of_Overnaul.pdf

303   The Henry J. Kaiser Family Foundation. (2016, Sept. 14). Cumulative increases in health insurance premiums, general annual deductibles, and workers' earnings, 2011-2016. *2016 Employer Health Benefits Survey*. Retrieved from http://kff.org/health-costs/report/2016-employer-health-benefits-survey/

304   The Henry J. Kaiser Family Foundation. (2016, Sept. 14). Percentage of covered workers with a general annual deductible for single coverage, 2006-2016. *2016 Employer Health Benefits Survey*. Retrieved from http://kff.org/health-costs/report/2016-employer-health-benefits-survey/

305   The Henry J. Kaiser Family Foundation. (2016, Sept. 14). Average general annual deductible for covered workers enrolled in single coverage, 2006-2016. *2016 Employer Health Benefits Survey*. Retrieved from http://kff.org/health-costs/report/2016-employer-health-benefits-survey/

306   Margolis, J., & Pope, C. (2010, April). Perspective on patient payments. *MGMA Connexion*. Retrieved from https://www.mgma.com/Libraries/Assets/Practice%20Resources/Publications/MGMA%20Connexion/2010/Perspective-on-patient-payments-MGMA-Connexion-April-2010.pdf

307   Miliard, M. (2015, Aug. 12). Revenue cycle vendors rush to innovate amid consumer changes in healthcare: Experts say existing systems are not really capable of dealing with the revenue cycle shift. *HealthcareFinance*. Retrieved from http://www.healthcarefinancenews.com/news/revenue-cycle-vendors-rush-innovate-amid-consumer-changes-healthcare

308   The Henry J. Kaiser Family Foundation. (2016, Sept. 14). Average annual workplace family health premiums rise modest 3% to $18,142 in 2016: More workers enroll in high-deductible plans with savings option over past two years. Retrieved from http://kff.org/health-costs/press-release/average-annual-workplace-family-health-premiums-rise-modest-3-to-18142-in-2016-more-workers-enroll-in-high-deductible-plans-with-savings-option-over-past-two-years/

309 The Henry J. Kaiser Family Foundation. (2016, Sept. 14). Average annual workplace family health premiums rise modest 3% to $18,142 in 2016: More workers enroll in high-deductible plans with savings option over past two years. Retrieved from http:// kff.org/health-costs/press-release/average-annual-workplace-family-health-premiums-rise-modest-3-to-18142-in-2016-more-workers-enroll-in-high-deductible-plans-with-savings-option-over-past-two-years/

310 The Henry J. Kaiser Family Foundation. (2016, Sept. 14). Average annual workplace family health premiums rise modest 3% to $18,142 in 2016: More workers enroll in high-deductible plans with savings option over past two years. Retrieved from http:// kff.org/health-costs/press-release/average-annual-workplace-family-health-premiums-rise-modest-3-to-18142-in-2016-more-workers-enroll-in-high-deductible-plans-with-savings-option-over-past-two-years/

311 The Henry J. Kaiser Family Foundation. (2016, Sept. 14). Summary of findings. *2016 Employer Health Benefits Survey*. Retrieved from http://kff.org/report-section/ehbs-2016-summary-of-findings/

312 The Henry J. Kaiser Family Foundation. (2016, Sept. 14). Average general annual deductible for covered workers enrolled in single coverage, 2006-2016. *2016 Employer Health Benefits Survey*. Retrieved from http://kff.org/health-costs/report/2016-employer-health-benefits-survey/

313 Board of Governors of the Federal Reserve System. (2016, May). Report on the economic well-being of U.S. households in 2015. Retrieved from https://www.federalreserve.gov/2015-report-economic-well-being-us-households-201605.pdf

314 Board of Governors of the Federal Reserve System. (2016, May). Report on the economic well-being of U.S. households in 2015. Retrieved from https://www.federalreserve.gov/2015-report-economic-well-being-us-households-201605.pdf

315 Collins, S. R., Rasmussen, P. W., Doty, M. M., Beutel, S. & The Commonwealth Fund. (2014, Nov.). Too high a price: out-of-pocket health care costs in the United States: Findings from the Commonwealth Fund Health Care Affordability Tracking Survey, September-October, 2014 [PDF document]. Retrieved from http://www.commonwealthfund.org/~/media/files/publications/issue-brief/2014/nov/1784_collins_too_high_a_price_out_of_pocket_tb_v2.pdf

316 Claxton, G., Rae, M. & Panchal, N. (2015, Feb.). Consumer assets and patient cost sharing [PDF document]. Issue Brief, The Henry J. Kaiser Family Foundation. Retrieved from http://files.kff.org/attachment/issue-brief-consumer-assets-and-patient-cost-sharing

317 Fronstin, P. (2013, Dec.) Findings from the 2013 EBRA/Greenwald & Associates Consumer Engagement in Health Care Survey. *EBRI Issue Brief, No. 393*. Retrieved from https://www.ebri.org/pdf/briefspdf/EBRI_IB_012-13.No393.CEHCS.pdf

318 DiJulio, B., Kirzinger, A., Wu, B., & Brodie, M. (2017, March 2). Data note: Americans' challenges with health care costs. The Henry J. Kaiser Family Foundation. Retrieved from http://kff.org/health-costs/poll-finding/data-note-americans-challenges-with-health-care-costs/

319 Silverman, E. (2016, Nov. 15). Most doctors don't cite cost as a factor when deciding treatments. *STAT*. Retrieved from https://www.statnews.com/pharmalot/2016/11/15/doctors-cost-treatments/

320 Fingar, K. R., Stocks, C., Weiss, A. J. & Steiner, C. A. (2014, Dec.) Most frequent operating room procedures performed in U.S. hospitals, 2003-2012. *Healthcare Cost*

and Utilization Project (HCUP), Statistical Brief #186. Retrieved from https://www.
hcup-us.ahrq.gov/reports/statbriefs/sb186-Operating-Room-Procedures-United-
States-2012.jsp

321 Fronstin, P. (2013, Dec.) Findings from the 2013 EBRA/Greenwald & Associates
Consumer Engagement in Health Care Survey. *EBRI Issue Brief, No. 393.* Retrieved
from https://www.ebri.org/pdf/briefspdf/EBRI_IB_012-13.No393.CEHCS.pdf

322 U.S. Department of Health and Human Services. Office of the Assistant Secretary for
Planning and Evaluation (ASPE). (2017, Jan. 26). Poverty guidelines. Retrieved from
https://aspe.hhs.gov/poverty-guidelines

323 The Henry J. Kaiser Family Foundation. (2016, Nov. 1). Explaining health care reform:
Questions about health insurance subsidies. Retrieved from http://kff.org/health-
reform/issue-brief/explaining-health-care-reform-questions-about-health/

324 The Henry J. Kaiser Family Foundation. (2015). Distribution of total population
by federal poverty level, United States. Retrieved from http://kff.org/other/state-
indicator/distribution-by-fpl/?currentTimeframe=0&sortModel=%7B%22colId%22:%
22Location%22,%22sort%22:%22asc%22%7D

325 The Henry J. Kaiser Family Foundation. (2015). Distribution of total population
by federal poverty level, United States. Retrieved from http://kff.org/other/state-
indicator/distribution-by-fpl/?currentTimeframe=0&sortModel=%7B%22colId%22:%
22Location%22,%22sort%22:%22asc%22%7D

326 Garfield, R., & Damico, A. (2016, Oct. 19). The coverage gap: Uninsured poor adults
in states that do not expand Medicaid. The Henry J. Kaiser Family Foundation.
Retrieved from http://kff.org/uninsured/issue-brief/the-coverage-gap-uninsured-
poor-adults-in-states-that-do-not-expand-medicaid/

327 Garfield, R., & Damico, A. (2016, Oct. 19). The coverage gap: Uninsured poor adults
in states that do not expand Medicaid. The Henry J. Kaiser Family Foundation.
Retrieved from http://kff.org/uninsured/issue-brief/the-coverage-gap-uninsured-
poor-adults-in-states-that-do-not-expand-medicaid/

328 Advisory Board. (2016, Feb. 26). Even with ACA, some hospitals face the bad
debt blues. *Daily Briefing.* Retrieved from https://www.advisory.com/daily-
briefing/2016/02/26/even-with-aca-some-hospitals-face-bad-debt

329 U.S. Census Bureau. (2016, Sept. 15). Median household income in the United States:
2015. Retrieved from https://www.census.gov/library/visualizations/2016/comm/
cb16-158_median_hh_income_map.html

330 The Kaiser Family Foundation and the Health Research & Educational Trust (HRET).
(2015). Employer Health Benefits, 2015, Annual Survey. Retrieved from http://files.
kff.org/attachment/report-2015-employer-health-benefits-survey

331 Eyestone, J., & Rozen, M. (2016, May 3). Patient payment optimization: Practical
considerations for optimizing patient payment processes and performance. Retrieved
from https://commercial.jpmorganchase.com/pages/commercial-banking/executive-
connect/patient-payment-optimization

332 Capio Partners. (n.d.). A patient-friendly approach to collecting from
the underinsured. Retrieved from http://www.hfma.org/brg/pdf/
collectingfromtheunderinsured.pdf

333 Bayley, M., Calkins, S., Levine, E., & Machado-Pereira, M. (2013, May). Hospital
revenue cycle operations: Opportunities created by the ACA [PDF document].
Retrieved from http://healthcare.mckinsey.com/sites/default/files/793544_Hospital_
Revenue_Cycle_Operations.pdf

334 TransUnion. (2016, June). TransUnion Healthcare Report [PDF document]. Retrieved from http://www.transunioninsights.com/studies/healthcare/files/Healthcare_Report_June_2016_Final.pdf

335 TransUnion. (2016, June). TransUnion Healthcare Report [PDF document]. Retrieved from http://www.transunioninsights.com/studies/healthcare/files/Healthcare_Report_June_2016_Final.pdf

336 Finn, P., Pellathy, T., & Singhal, S. (2009). U.S. healthcare payments: remedies for an ailing system. In *McKinsey on Payments*, No. 4, April 2009 [PDF document]. Retrieved from http://healthcare.mckinsey.com/sites/default/files/762679_US_healthcare_payments_Remedies_for_an_ailing_system.pdf

337 J.P. Morgan Chase & Co. (2013). Healthcare banking: Key trends in healthcare patient payments [PDF document]. Retrieved from http://www.jpmorgan.com.br/jpmpdf/1320610345938.pdf

338 Availity. (2015, Feb.) The impact of consumerism on provider revenues [PDF document]. Retrieved from https://www.availity.com/-/media/files/availity/resource-library/research-study/availity-consumerism-provider-research-study-availity-mar-2015.pdf

339 Finn, P., Pellathy, T., & Singhal, S. (2009). U.S. healthcare payments: remedies for an ailing system. In *McKinsey on Payments*, No. 4, April 2009 [PDF document]. Retrieved from http://healthcare.mckinsey.com/sites/default/files/762679_US_healthcare_payments_Remedies_for_an_ailing_system.pdf

340 Fifer, J. J. (2014, Sept. 18). Staying ahead of the curve: Revenue cycle change. 2014 MAHAP-MPAA-HFMA, Michigan Revenue Cycle Conference. Retrieved from http://www.mahap.org/2014-2015+Programs

341 The Henry J. Kaiser Family Foundation. (n.d.). Health Insurance Status, Health Insurance Coverage of the Total Population, 2013 to 2015 [Data set]. Retrieved from http://kff.org/other/state-indicator/total-population/?dataView=1&activeTab=graph&currentTimeframe=0&startTimeframe=2&selectedDistributions=medicaid--medicare&selectedRows=%7B%22wrapups%22:%7B%22united-states%22:%7B%7D%7D%7D&sortModel=%7B%22colId%22:%22Location%22,%22sort%22:%22asc%22%7D

342 The Henry J. Kaiser Family Foundation. (n.d.). Health Insurance Status, Health Insurance Coverage of the Total Population, 2013 to 2015 [Data set]. Retrieved from http://kff.org/other/state-indicator/total-population/?dataView=1&activeTab=graph&currentTimeframe=0&startTimeframe=2&selectedDistributions=medicaid--medicare&selectedRows=%7B%22wrapups%22:%7B%22united-states%22:%7B%7D%7D%7D&sortModel=%7B%22colId%22:%22Location%22,%22sort%22:%22asc%22%7D

343 The Henry J. Kaiser Family Foundation. (2016, Sept. 14). Summary of findings. *2016 Employer Health Benefits Survey*. Retrieved from http://kff.org/report-section/ehbs-2016-summary-of-findings/

344 Wade, H., & National Federation of Independent Business (NFIB) Research Foundation. (2016, Aug.). Small business problems & priorities [PDF document]. Retrieved from http://www.nfib.com/assets/NFIB-Problems-and-Priorities-2016.pdf

345 Wade, H., & National Federation of Independent Business (NFIB) Research Foundation. (2016, Aug.). Small business problems & priorities [PDF document]. Retrieved from http://www.nfib.com/assets/NFIB-Problems-and-Priorities-2016.pdf

346 Ross, S. (2016, March 28). 5 Reasons to pay attention to UnitedHealth's financials (UNH). *Investopedia*. Retrieved from http://www.investopedia.com/articles/investing/032816/5-reasons-pay-attention-unitedhealths-financials-unh.asp
347 UnitedHealth Group. (2016). Annual reports & proxy statements. Retrieved from http://www.unitedhealthgroup.com/Investors/AnnualReports.aspx
348 UnitedHealth Group. (2016, July 19). UnitedHealth group reports second quarter results [PDF document]. Retrieved from http://www.unitedhealthgroup.com/~/media/E92CE1B0C91040839E3CB5C75436B1A5.ashx
349 Ross, S. (2016, March 28). 5 Reasons to pay attention to UnitedHealth's financials (UNH). *Investopedia*. Retrieved from http://www.investopedia.com/articles/investing/032816/5-reasons-pay-attention-unitedhealths-financials-unh.asp
350 Cox, C., Long, M., Semanskii, A., Kamal, R., Claxton, G., & Levitt, L. (2016, Nov. 1). 2017 premium changes and insurer participation in the Affordable Care Act's health insurance marketplaces. The Henry J. Kaiser Family Foundation. Retrieved from http://kff.org/health-reform/issue-brief/2017-premium-changes-and-insurer-participation-in-the-affordable-care-acts-health-insurance-marketplaces/
351 Cox, C., Long, M., Semanskii, A., Kamal, R., Claxton, G., & Levitt, L. (2016, Nov. 1). 2017 premium changes and insurer participation in the Affordable Care Act's health insurance marketplaces. The Henry J. Kaiser Family Foundation. Retrieved from http://kff.org/health-reform/issue-brief/2017-premium-changes-and-insurer-participation-in-the-affordable-care-acts-health-insurance-marketplaces/
352 Fitch Ratings. (2017, Mar. 27). ACA inaction hurts exchange enrollment, uncompensated care. Retrieved from https://www.fitchratings.com/site/pr/1021159
353 Fien, A. J. (2016). 2016 MDM market leaders, top pharmaceuticals distributors. Retrieved from https://www.mdm.com/2016-top-pharmaceuticals-distributors
354 Fien, A. J. (2016). 2016 MDM market leaders, top pharmaceuticals distributors. Retrieved from https://www.mdm.com/2016-top-pharmaceuticals-distributors
355 Knaub, J. (2013, April). Technology update: CT—customer expectations after the slice war. *Radiology Today, 14*(4), 16. Retrieved from http://www.radiologytoday.net/archive/rt0413p16.shtml
356 Henry, J., Pylypchuk, Y., Searcy T. & Patel V. (2016, May). Adoption of electronic health record systems among U.S. non-federal acute care hospitals: 2008-2015. *ONC Data Brief 35*. Retrieved from https://dashboard.healthit.gov/evaluations/data-briefs/non-federal-acute-care-hospital-ehr-adoption-2008-2015.php
357 Fry, R. (2016, April 25.). Millennials overtake Baby Boomers as America's largest generation. Pew Research Center. Retrieved from http://www.pewresearch.org/fact-tank/2016/04/25/millennials-overtake-baby-boomers/
358 Finn, P., Pellathy, T., & Singhal, S. (2009). U.S. healthcare payments: remedies for an ailing system. In *McKinsey on Payments*, No. 4, April 2009 [PDF document]. Retrieved from http://healthcare.mckinsey.com/sites/default/files/762679_US_healthcare_payments_Remedies_for_an_ailing_system.pdf
359 Larch, S. M. (2012, Jan. 9). Surviving the Deductible Reset in 2012: How to Collect Deductibles and Improve Self Pay Collections. *Getting Paid*. Retrieved from http://gettingpaid.kareo.com/gettingpaid/2012/01/lets-collect-deductibles-in-2012-tips-for-improving-self-pay-collections/
360 Ellison, A. (2015, Sept. 29). 200 Hospital benchmarks. *Becker's Hospital Review*. Retrieved from http://www.beckershospitalreview.com/lists/200-hospital-benchmarks-2015.html

361 Terhune, C. (2016, Dec. 30). Top Republicans say there's a medical malpractice crisis. Experts say there isn't. *The Washington Post*. Retrieved from https://www.washingtonpost.com/news/to-your-health/wp/2016/12/30/top-republicans-say-theres-a-medical-malpractice-crisis-experts-say-there-isnt/?utm_term=.1cb79e1860b7

362 Price, T. (2010, April 12). *Tom Price visits Fox & Friends to talk about tort reform* [Video file]. Retrieved from https://www.youtube.com/watch?v=tsPph8LbWVQ

363 Jena, A. B., Seabury, S., Lakdawalla, D., & Chandra, A. (2011). Malpractice risk according to physician specialty. *New England Journal of Medicine 365*(7), 629-636. doi: 10.1056/NEJMsa1012370

364 Scott, D., & Kaplan, S. (2016, Nov. 20). What Trump's HHS secretary pick believes about medicine. *STAT*. Retrieved from https://www.statnews.com/2016/11/29/tom-price-hhs-medicine-science/

365 Makary, M. A., & Daniel, M. (2016). Medical error—the third leading cause of death in the U.S. *BMJ* 2016; 353 :i2139. Retrieved from http://www.bmj.com/content/353/bmj.i2139 and Cha, A. E. (2016, May 3). Researchers: Medical errors now third leading cause of death in United States. *The Washington Post*. Retrieved from https://www.washingtonpost.com/news/to-your-health/wp/2016/05/03/researchers-medical-errors-now-third-leading-cause-of-death-in-united-states/?utm_term=.72104a95a10f

366 Stokowski, L. A. (2016, May 26). Who believes that medical error is the third leading cause of hospital deaths? *Medscape*. Retrieved from http://www.medscape.com/viewarticle/863788

367 Nance, J. J. (2008). Why hospitals should fly: The ultimate flight plan to patient safety and quality care. Bozeman, MT: Second River Healthcare Press.

368 Nance, J. J. (2008). Why hospitals should fly: The ultimate flight plan to patient safety and quality care. Bozeman, MT: Second River Healthcare Press.

369 U.S. Constitution. National Archives transcription. Retrieved from https://www.archives.gov/founding-docs/constitution-transcript

370 Healthcare Bluebook. (n.d.). Office visit, new patient, 10 minutes. Retrieved May 5, 2017 from https://healthcarebluebook.com/page_ProcedureDetails.aspx?cftId=218&g=Office+Visit%2c+New+Patient+(~10+min.)

371 Jerant, A., Bertakis, K. D., Fenton, J. J., & Franks, P. (2012). Extended office hours and health care expenditures: A national study. Annals of Family Medicine, *10*(5):388–395. doi: 10.1370/afm.1382

372 Jerant, A., Bertakis, K. D., Fenton, J. J., & Franks, P. (2012). Extended office hours and health care expenditures: A national study. Annals of Family Medicine, *10*(5):388–395. doi: 10.1370/afm.1382

373 Jerant, A., Bertakis, K. D., Fenton, J. J., & Franks, P. (2012). Extended office hours and health care expenditures: A national study. Annals of Family Medicine, *10*(5):388–395. doi: 10.1370/afm.1382

374 Urgent Care Association of America. (n.d.). Industry FAQs. Retrieved from http://www.ucaoa.org/?page=IndustryFAQs

375 Urgent Care Association of America. (n.d.). Industry FAQs. Retrieved from http://www.ucaoa.org/?page=IndustryFAQs

376 Urgent Care Association of America. (2015). 2015 Benchmarking Survey headlines summary. Retrieved from http://c.ymcdn.com/sites/www.ucaoa.org/resource/resmgr/Infographics/2015_BM_Survey_Headlines_Sum.pdf

377 Urgent Care Association of America. (n.d.). Urgency or emergency. Retrieved

from http://c.ymcdn.com/sites/www.ucaoa.org/resource/resmgr/Media/UCAOA-Infographic-UCvsER_FIN.pdf?hhSearchTerms=%22average+and+cost%22

378 Gindi, R. M., Black, L. I., & Cohen, R. A. (2016). Reasons for emergency room use among U.S. adults aged 18–64: National Health Interview Survey, 2013 and 2014. *National Health Statistics Reports, 90*. Retrieved from https://www.cdc.gov/nchs/data/nhsr/nhsr090.pdf

379 Heather L. Farley, et. al., Emergency Medicine Practice Committee, (May 2016), "Emergency Department Crowding: High Impact Solutions," American College of Emergency Physicians (ACEP), https://www.acep.org/search.aspx?searchtext=high%20impact%20solutions/

380 Farley, H. L. & ACEP Emergency Medicine Practice Committee. (2016, May). Emergency department crowding: High impact solutions. Retrieved from https://www.acep.org/search.aspx?searchtext=high%20impact%20solutions/

381 The Henry J. Kaiser Family Foundation. (n.d.). Timeline: History of health reform in the U.S. [PDF document]. Retrieved from https://kaiserfamilyfoundation.files.wordpress.com/2011/03/5-02-13-history-of-health-reform.pdf

382 Emtala.com. (n.d.). Special note: What is the 250-yard rule and how does it affect these issues? Retrieved from http://www.emtala.com/250yard.htm

383 Healthcare Bluebook. (n.d.). Emergency room visit – minor problem. Retrieved May 5, 2017 from https://healthcarebluebook.com/page_ProcedureDetails.aspx?cftId=238&g=Emergency+Room+Visit+-+Minor+Problem

384 Kharasch, S. J., McBride, D. R., Saitz, R. & Myers, W. P. (2016). Drinking to toxicity: college students referred for emergency medical evaluation. *Addiction Science & Clinical Practice, 11*(1), 11. doi: 10.1186/s13722-016-0059-4

385 Centers for Disease Control & Prevention (CDC). (2013). National Hospital Ambulatory Medical Care
Survey: 2013 Emergency Department Summary Tables, Tables 1, 4, 14, 24. Retrieved from https://www.cdc.gov/nchs/fastats/emergency-department.htm

386 Burda, D. (2009, June 14). HCA rolling out emergency-room screening program. *Modern Healthcare*. Retrieved from http://www.modernhealthcare.com/article/20090614/NEWS/306119942

387 Burda, D. (2009, June 14). HCA rolling out emergency-room screening program. *Modern Healthcare*. Retrieved from http://www.modernhealthcare.com/article/20090614/NEWS/306119942

388 Butcher, L. (2013, Jan. 23). Offering non-urgent patients alternatives to emergency care. HFMA. Retrieved from http://www.hfma.org/Content.aspx?id=15263

389 Butcher, L. (2013, Jan. 23). Offering non-urgent patients alternatives to emergency care. HFMA. Retrieved from http://www.hfma.org/Content.aspx?id=15263

390 Butcher, L. (2013, Jan. 23). Offering non-urgent patients alternatives to emergency care. HFMA. Retrieved from http://www.hfma.org/Content.aspx?id=15263

391 Ellison, A., & Marshall, E. (2016, May 11). 150 hospital benchmarks. *Becker's Hospital Review*. Retrieved from http://www.beckershospitalreview.com/lists/150-hospital-benchmarks-2016.html

392 Truven Health Analytics. (2016, Feb. 29). 100 Top Hospitals Study, 2016, 23rd Edition. Retrieved from http://100tophospitals.com/Portals/2/assets/100-Top-Study_web.pdf

393 Centers for Disease Control and Prevention (CDC). National Center for Health Statistics (NCHS). (2015). Table 82. Hospital admissions, average length of stay,

outpatient visits and outpatient surgery, by type of ownership and size of hospital: United States, selected years 1975-2013. In *Health, United States, 2015: With Special Feature on Racial and Ethnic Health Disparities.* Retrieved from https://www.cdc.gov/nchs/data/hus/hus15.pdf#082

394   Skinner, W. (1974, May). The focused factory. *Harvard Business Review.* Retrieved from https://hbr.org/1974/05/the-focused-factory

395   Munnich, E. L., & Parente, S. T. (2014). Procedures take less time at ambulatory surgery centers, keeping costs down and ability to meet demand up. *Health Affairs, 33*(5), 764-769.

396   Morrissey, W. M., Pryor, R. W., & Krishnaswamy, A. (2016, Nov. 17). Using data and analytics to improve clinical and financial performance. *Leadership+.* Retrieved from http://www.hfma.org/Leadership/Archives/2016/Fall/Using_Data_and_Analytics_to_Improve_Clinical_and_Financial_Performance/

397   Morrissey, W. M., Pryor, R. W., & Krishnaswamy, A. (2016, Nov. 17). Using data and analytics to improve clinical and financial performance. *Leadership+.* Retrieved from http://www.hfma.org/Leadership/Archives/2016/Fall/Using_Data_and_Analytics_to_Improve_Clinical_and_Financial_Performance/

398   Morrissey, W. M., Pryor, R. W., & Krishnaswamy, A. (2016, Nov. 17). Using data and analytics to improve clinical and financial performance. *Leadership+.* Retrieved from http://www.hfma.org/Leadership/Archives/2016/Fall/Using_Data_and_Analytics_to_Improve_Clinical_and_Financial_Performance/

399   Morrissey, W. M., Pryor, R. W., & Krishnaswamy, A. (2016, Nov. 17). Using data and analytics to improve clinical and financial performance. *Leadership+.* Retrieved from http://www.hfma.org/Leadership/Archives/2016/Fall/Using_Data_and_Analytics_to_Improve_Clinical_and_Financial_Performance/

400   Morrissey, W. M., Pryor, R. W., & Krishnaswamy, A. (2016, Nov. 17). Using data and analytics to improve clinical and financial performance. *Leadership+.* Retrieved from http://www.hfma.org/Leadership/Archives/2016/Fall/Using_Data_and_Analytics_to_Improve_Clinical_and_Financial_Performance/

401   Nance, J. J. (2008). Why hospitals should fly: The ultimate flight plan to patient safety and quality care. Bozeman, MT: Second River Healthcare Press.

402   D'Onfro, J. (2014, May 10). 14 Quirky things you didn't know about Amazon. *Business Insider.* Retrieved from http://www.businessinsider.com/amazon-jeff-bezos-facts-story-history-2014-5

403   Media Excerpts. (2013, Nov. 24). *Obama: (Healthcare.gov) the same way you'd shop on Kayak or Amazon* [Video file]. Retrieved from https://www.youtube.com/watch?v=XoBpA8ThXAM

404   Esupiñán, J., Fengler, K., & Kaura, A. (2014). The birth of the healthcare consumer: growing demands for choice, engagement and experience. Strategy&. Retrieved from https://www.strategyand.pwc.com/media/file/The-birth-of-the-healthcare-consumer.pdf

405   Esupiñán, J., Fengler, K., & Kaura, A. (2014). The birth of the healthcare consumer: growing demands for choice, engagement and experience. Strategy&. Retrieved from https://www.strategyand.pwc.com/media/file/The-birth-of-the-healthcare-consumer.pdf

406   Esupiñán, J., Fengler, K., & Kaura, A. (2014). The birth of the healthcare consumer: growing demands for choice, engagement and experience. Strategy&. Retrieved from

https://www.strategyand.pwc.com/media/file/The-birth-of-the-healthcare-consumer.pdf

407 Centers for Medicare & Medicaid Services (CMS). (2016, March). EHR incentive programs in 2015 through 2017, patient electronic access [PDF document]. Retrieved from https://www.cms.gov/Regulations-and-Guidance/Legislation/EHRIncentivePrograms/Downloads/2016_PatientElectronicAccess.pdf

408 Centers for Medicare & Medicaid Services (CMS). (2016, March). EHR incentive programs in 2015 through 2017, patient electronic access [PDF document]. Retrieved from https://www.cms.gov/Regulations-and-Guidance/Legislation/EHRIncentivePrograms/Downloads/2016_PatientElectronicAccess.pdf

409 Ranta, K. (2015, June 11). An introduction to the history of dental insurance [Blog post]. *Solstice Oral & Vision Health Blog.* Retrieved from http://blog.solsticebenefits.com/solstice-member-blog/an-introduction-to-the-history-of-dental-insurance

410 National Association of Dental Plans. (n.d.). Who has dental benefits? Retrieved from http://www.nadp.org/Dental_Benefits_Basics/Dental_BB_1.aspx

411 Fontinelle, A. (2016, Nov. 10). Should you bite on dental insurance? *Investopedia.* Retrieved from http://www.investopedia.com/articles/pf/07/dental-insurance.asp

412 Centers for Medicare & Medicaid Services (CMS). (n.d.). Your Medicare coverage, dental services. Retrieved from https://www.medicare.gov/coverage/dental-services.html

413 Neal, D., & Govan, C. (2013, July). US dental price variation and transparency research (LA County report) [PDF document]. Emperica. Retrieved from https://d3ppyoxr8wczcq.cloudfront.net/media/LA%20Region%20Health%20Care%20Price%20Transparency%20Study_%20070313.pdf

414 Neal, D., & Govan, C. (2013, July). US dental price variation and transparency research (LA County report) [PDF document]. Emperica. Retrieved from https://d3ppyoxr8wczcq.cloudfront.net/media/LA%20Region%20Health%20Care%20Price%20Transparency%20Study_%20070313.pdf

415 Neal, D., & Govan, C. (2013, July). US dental price variation and transparency research (LA County report) [PDF document]. Emperica. Retrieved from https://d3ppyoxr8wczcq.cloudfront.net/media/LA%20Region%20Health%20Care%20Price%20Transparency%20Study_%20070313.pdf

416 Temkin Group. (2016, March). 2016 Temkin Experience Ratings. Retrieved from http://temkingroup.com/research-reports/2016-temkin-experience-ratings/

417 Vecchione, A. (2014, May 21). Which barcode system is right for you? EMR vendors driving BCMA selection. *HealthcareITNews.* Retrieved from http://www.healthcareitnews.com/news/which-barcode-system-right-you

418 Adapted from Donna L. Montaldo (23 August 2016), Pros and Cons of Supermarket Loyalty Programs: Do Shoppers Really Save? https://www.thebalance.com/the-pros-and-cons-of-grocery-store-loyalty-programs-940240

419 Montaldo, D. L. (2016, Aug. 23). Pros and cons of supermarket loyalty programs: Do shoppers really save? Retrieved from https://www.thebalance.com/the-pros-and-cons-of-grocery-store-loyalty-programs-940240

420 Hyken, S. (2017, Jan. 7). Ten customer service and customer experience trends for 2017. *Forbes.* Retrieved from https://www.forbes.com/sites/shephyken/2017/01/07/10-customer-service-and-customer-experience-cx-trends-for-2017/#18dbec4a75e5

421 Health Research Institute. (2015, May). Money matters: Billing and payment for a new

health economy [PDF document]. PricewaterhouseCoopers. Retrieved from http://www.pwc.com/us/en/health-industries/health-research-institute/publications/pdf/pwc-hri-healthcare-billing-and-payments.pdf

422 Gawande, A. (2012, Aug. 13). Big med: Restaurant chains have managed to combine quality control, cost control and innovation. Can health care? The New Yorker. Retrieved from http://www.newyorker.com/magazine/2012/08/13/big-med

423 Gawande, A. (2012, Aug. 13). Big med: Restaurant chains have managed to combine quality control, cost control and innovation. Can health care? The New Yorker. Retrieved from http://www.newyorker.com/magazine/2012/08/13/big-med

424 Gawande, A. (2012, Aug. 13). Big med: Restaurant chains have managed to combine quality control, cost control and innovation. Can health care? The New Yorker. Retrieved from http://www.newyorker.com/magazine/2012/08/13/big-med

425 Shah, N. R., Davis, A. C., Gould, M. K. & Kanter, M. H. (2017, Feb. 5), Predictive analytics to determine next year's highest-cost patients. NEJM Catalyst. Retrieved from http://catalyst.nejm.org/predictive-analytics-determine-next-years-highest-cost-patients/

426 Gawande, A. (2012, Aug. 13). Big med: Restaurant chains have managed to combine quality control, cost control and innovation. Can health care? The New Yorker. Retrieved from http://www.newyorker.com/magazine/2012/08/13/big-med

427 American Pet Products Association. (n.d.). APPA Pet Industry Market Size and Ownership Statistics. Retrieved May 4, 2017 from http://www.americanpetproducts.org/press_industrytrends.asp

428 American Pet Products Association. (n.d.). APPA Pet Industry Market Size and Ownership Statistics. Retrieved May 4, 2017 from http://www.americanpetproducts.org/press_industrytrends.asp

429 Does Your Dog Need An MRI? (n.d.). Animal Wellness Magazine. Retrieved from https://animalwellnessmagazine.com/does-he-need-an-mri/

430 Does Your Dog Need An MRI? (n.d.). Animal Wellness Magazine. Retrieved from https://animalwellnessmagazine.com/does-he-need-an-mri/

431 Smialek, J. (2016, Sept. 27). Your pet's vet bill offers insight into rising U.S. healthcare costs: Climbing vet bills suggest it's not just regulation and insurance behind health care cost inflation. Bloomberg. Retrieved from https://www.bloomberg.com/news/articles/2016-09-27/your-pet-s-vet-bill-offers-insight-into-rising-u-s-healthcare-costs

432 North American Pet Health Insurance Association. (n.d.). History of pet health insurance. Retrieved from https://naphia.org/industry/history/

433 Olen, H. (2016, Sept. 27). The cost of pet health care could be rising faster than the cost of human health care [Blog post]. Slate. Retrieved from http://www.slate.com/blogs/moneybox/2016/09/27/the_cost_of_pet_health_care_could_be_rising_faster_than_the_cost_of_human.html

434 dvm360.com. (2016, Dec. 6). Pet insurance: Fact and fiction. Retrieved from http://veterinarybusiness.dvm360.com/pet-insurance-fact-and-fiction

435 Einav, L., Finkelstein, A., & Gupta, A. (2016, September). Is American pet health care (also) uniquely inefficient? NBER Working Paper No. w22669. Available at SSRN: https://ssrn.com/abstract=2843382

436 Einav, L., Finkelstein, A., & Gupta, A. (2016, September). Is American pet health care (also) uniquely inefficient? NBER Working Paper No. w22669. Available at SSRN: https://ssrn.com/abstract=2843382

437 Einav, L., Finkelstein, A., & Gupta, A. (2016, September). Is American pet health care (also) uniquely inefficient? *NBER Working Paper No. w22669*. Available at SSRN: https://ssrn.com/abstract=2843382

438 Einav, L., Finkelstein, A., & Gupta, A. (2016, September). Is American pet health care (also) uniquely inefficient? *NBER Working Paper No. w22669*. Available at SSRN: https://ssrn.com/abstract=2843382

439 dvm360.com. (2009, Aug. 1) Veterinarians offer alternative payment methods to cash-strapped clients. Retrieved from http://veterinarybusiness.dvm360.com/veterinarians-offer-alternative-payment-methods-cash-strapped-clients#

440 dvm360.com. (2015, Jan. 5) Keep your options open for veterinary clients' payments. Retrieved from http://veterinarybusiness.dvm360.com/keep-your-options-open-veterinary-clients-payment

441 HealthFirst Financial. (n.d.). Do you need help with medical expenses? HealthFirst Financial is here for you. Retrieved from https://www.healthfirstfinancial.com/

442 ClearBalance. (2016, Sept. 14). ClearBalance consumerism study finds patients seek affordable healthcare financing. Retrieved from http://www.clearbalance.org/clearbalance-consumerism-study-finds-patients-seek-affordable-healthcare-financing/

443 CareCredit. (n.d.). Here for you ... and your whole family. Retrieved from www.carecredit.com

444 CareCredit. (n.d.). Here for you ... and your whole family. Retrieved from www.carecredit.com

445 CareCredit. (n.d.). Here for you ... and your whole family. Retrieved from www.carecredit.com

446 Pollitz, K. (2017, Feb. 22). High-risk pools for uninsurable individuals. The Henry J. Kaiser Family Foundation. Retrieved from http://kff.org/health-reform/issue-brief/high-risk-pools-for-uninsurable-individuals/

447 Pollitz, K. (2017, Feb. 22). High-risk pools for uninsurable individuals. The Henry J. Kaiser Family Foundation. Retrieved from http://kff.org/health-reform/issue-brief/high-risk-pools-for-uninsurable-individuals/

448 Hall, J. P., & The Commonwealth Fund. (2015, Feb. 13). Why high risk pools (still) won't work. Retrieved from http://www.commonwealthfund.org/publications/blog/2015/feb/why-high-risk-pools-still-will-not-work

449 HealthCare.gov. (n.d.). How to claim an exemption for members of a healthcare sharing ministry. Retrieved from https://www.healthcare.gov/exemptions-tool/#/results/2016/details/healthcare-sharing-ministry

450 HealthCare.gov. (n.d.). How to claim an exemption for members of a healthcare sharing ministry. Retrieved from https://www.healthcare.gov/exemptions-tool/#/results/2016/details/healthcare-sharing-ministry

451 Christian Healthcare Ministries. (2016). Christian Healthcare Ministries Guidelines [PDF document]. Retrieved from http://www.chministries.org/guidelines.aspx

452 Christian Healthcare Ministries. (2016). Christian Healthcare Ministries Guidelines [PDF document]. Retrieved from http://www.chministries.org/guidelines.aspx

453 Christian Healthcare Ministries. (2016). Christian Healthcare Ministries Guidelines [PDF document]. Retrieved from http://www.chministries.org/guidelines.aspx

454 Leonard, K. (2016, Feb. 23). Christians find their own way to replace Obamacare. *U.S. News and World Report*. Retrieved from https://www.usnews.com/news/articles/2016-02-23/membership-for-health-sharing-ministries-soars-under-obamacare

455 Centers for Medicare & Medicaid Services (CMS). (n.d.). What are the value-based programs? Retrieved from https://www.cms.gov/Medicare/Quality-Initiatives-Patient-Assessment-Instruments/Value-Based-Programs/Value-Based-Programs.html

456 Healthcare Financial Management Association (HFMA). (2015). Value-based payment readiness. Retrieved from https://www.hfma.org/value-basedpaymentreadiness/##

457 Centers for Medicare & Medicaid Services (CMS). (n.d.). What are the value-based programs? Retrieved from https://www.cms.gov/Medicare/Quality-Initiatives-Patient-Assessment-Instruments/Value-Based-Programs/Value-Based-Programs.html

458 Centers for Medicare & Medicaid Services (CMS). (n.d.). What are the value-based programs? Retrieved from https://www.cms.gov/Medicare/Quality-Initiatives-Patient-Assessment-Instruments/Value-Based-Programs/Value-Based-Programs.html

459 Centers for Medicare & Medicaid Services (CMS). (n.d.). What are the value-based programs? Retrieved from https://www.cms.gov/Medicare/Quality-Initiatives-Patient-Assessment-Instruments/Value-Based-Programs/Value-Based-Programs.html

460 Centers for Medicare & Medicaid Services (CMS). (n.d.). Readmissions Reduction Program (HRRP). Retrieved from https://www.cms.gov/medicare/medicare-fee-for-service-payment/acuteinpatientpps/readmissions-reduction-program.html

461 Centers for Medicare & Medicaid Services (CMS). (n.d.). The Hospital Readmissions Reduction (HRR) Program. Retrieved from https://www.cms.gov/Medicare/Quality-Initiatives-Patient-Assessment-Instruments/Value-Based-Programs/HRRP/Hospital-Readmission-Reduction-Program.html

462 Centers for Medicare & Medicaid Services (CMS). (n.d.). Readmissions Reduction Program (HRRP). Retrieved from https://www.cms.gov/medicare/medicare-fee-for-service-payment/acuteinpatientpps/readmissions-reduction-program.html

463 Rau, J. (2016, Aug. 2). Medicare's readmission penalties hit new high. *Kaiser Health News*. Retrieved from http://khn.org/news/more-than-half-of-hospitals-to-be-penalized-for-excess-readmissions/

464 Boccuti, C., & Casillas, G. (2017, March 10). Aiming for fewer hospital U-turns: The Medicare Hospital Readmission Reduction Program. The Henry J. Kaiser Family Foundation. Retrieved from http://kff.org/medicare/issue-brief/aiming-for-fewer-hospital-u-turns-the-medicare-hospital-readmission-reduction-program/

465 The Commonwealth Fund. (n.d.). The Affordable Care Act at five years: How the law is changing the delivery of care in the U.S. Retrieved from http://www.commonwealthfund.org/ACAat5/delivery-reform/

466 Centers for Medicare & Medicaid Services (CMS). (n.d.). Accountable Care Organizations (ACO). Retrieved from https://www.cms.gov/Medicare/Medicare-Fee-for-Service-Payment/ACO/index.html?redirect=/Aco/

467 Centers for Medicare & Medicaid Services (CMS). (n.d.). Accountable Care Organizations (ACO). Retrieved from https://www.cms.gov/Medicare/Medicare-Fee-for-Service-Payment/ACO/index.html?redirect=/Aco/

468 Frakt, A. B., & Mayes, R. (2012). Beyond capitation: How new payment experiments seek to find the 'sweet spot' in amount of risk providers and payers bear. *Health Affairs, 31*(9), 1951-1958. Retrieved from http://content.healthaffairs.org/content/31/9/1951.full

469 Frakt, A. B., & Mayes, R. (2012). Beyond capitation: How new payment experiments seek to find the 'sweet spot' in amount of risk providers and payers bear. *Health Affairs, 31*(9), 1951-1958. Retrieved from http://content.healthaffairs.org/content/31/9/1951.full

470 Frakt, A. B., & Mayes, R. (2012). Beyond capitation: How new payment experiments seek to find the 'sweet spot' in amount of risk providers and payers bear. *Health Affairs, 31*(9), 1951-1958. Retrieved from http://content.healthaffairs.org/content/31/9/1951.full

471 Centers for Medicare & Medicaid Services (CMS). (n.d.). The Quality Payment Program overview fact sheet [PDF document]. Retrieved from https://qpp.cms.gov/docs/Quality_Payment_Program_Overview_Fact_Sheet.pdf

472 Centers for Medicare & Medicaid Services (CMS). (n.d.). The Quality Payment Program overview fact sheet [PDF document]. Retrieved from https://qpp.cms.gov/docs/Quality_Payment_Program_Overview_Fact_Sheet.pdf

473 Guterman, S., & The Commonwealth Fund. (2015, April 15). With SGR repeal, now we can proceed with Medicare payment reform. Retrieved from http://www.commonwealthfund.org/publications/blog/2015/apr/repealing-the-sgr

474 Teske, K. (2017, Jan. 13). Your questions about the 2017 MACRA final rule—answered. Advisory Board. Retrieved from https://www.advisory.com/research/physician-practice-roundtable/members/expert-insights/2016/nine-faqs-on-provider-payment-under-macra

475 Centers for Medicare & Medicaid Services (CMS). (n.d.). About the CMS Innovation Center. Retrieved from https://innovation.cms.gov/About

476 Centers for Medicare & Medicaid Services (CMS). (n.d.). Comprehensive Primary Care Plus. Retrieved from https://innovation.cms.gov/initiatives/comprehensive-primary-care-plus

477 Rappleye, E. (2016, April 21). MACRA roadmap: 9 questions on a post-SGR world, answered. *Becker's Hospital CFO*. Retrieved from http://www.beckershospitalreview.com/finance/macra-roadmap-9-questions-on-a-post-sgr-world-answered.html

478 Teske, K. (2017, Jan. 13). Your questions about the 2017 MACRA final rule—answered. Advisory Board. Retrieved from https://www.advisory.com/research/physician-practice-roundtable/members/expert-insights/2016/nine-faqs-on-provider-payment-under-macra

479 InLight EHR. (2016, Dec. 5). Amazing Charts makes five predictions for health IT in 2017. Retrieved from http://www.inlightehr.com/amazing-charts-makes-five-predictions-health-2017/

480 Understanding Rep. Ryan's Plan for Medicare. (2011, April 4). *Kaiser Health News*. Retrieved from http://khn.org/news/ryan-plan-for-medicare-vouchers-vs-premium-support/

481 Understanding Rep. Ryan's Plan for Medicare. (2011, April 4). *Kaiser Health News*. Retrieved from http://khn.org/news/ryan-plan-for-medicare-vouchers-vs-premium-support/

482 Kotlikoff, L. J. (n.d.). The Purple Health Plan. Retrieved from http://www.thepurplehealthplan.org/node/2

483 Kotlikoff, L. J. (2017, Jan. 18). The Republicans' healthcare answer—The Purple Health Plan. *Forbes*. https://www.forbes.com/sites/kotlikoff/2017/01/18/the-republicans-healthcare-answer-the-purple-health-plan/#142635563b87

484 Centers for Medicare & Medicaid Services (CMS). (n.d.). National health expenditure data, historical. Retrieved from https://www.cms.gov/research-statistics-data-and-systems/statistics-trends-and-reports/nationalhealthexpenddata/nationalhealthaccountshistorical.html

485 Keehan, S. P., Poisal, J. A., Cuckler, G. A., Sisko, A. M., Smith, S. D., Madison, A. J., …
Lizonitz, J. M. (2016). National Health Expenditure Projections, 2015-25: Economy,
prices and aging expected to shape spending and enrollment. *HealthAffairs, 35*(8),
1522-1531. Retrieved from http://content.healthaffairs.org/content/35/8/1522.abstract

486 Kotlikoff, L. J. (2017, Jan. 18). The Republicans' healthcare answer—The Purple Health
Plan. *Forbes.* https://www.forbes.com/sites/kotlikoff/2017/01/18/the-republicans-
healthcare-answer-the-purple-health-plan/#142635563b87

487 Merhar, C. (2014, Jan. 21). How to set up a healthcare Voucher Program [Blog post].
Small Business Employee Benefits and HR Blog, Zane Benefits. Retrieved from
https://www.zanebenefits.com/blog/health-care-voucher-program

488 Tsugawa, Y. (2014, May 12). Pros and cons of healthcare voucher system [Blog
post]. *Health Policy Buzz Blog.* Retrieved from https://healthpolicybuzz.wordpress.
com/2014/05/12/three-reasons-why-health-care-voucher-system-does-not-work/

489 Tsugawa, Y. (2014, May 12). Pros and cons of healthcare voucher system [Blog
post]. *Health Policy Buzz Blog.* Retrieved from https://healthpolicybuzz.wordpress.
com/2014/05/12/three-reasons-why-health-care-voucher-system-does-not-work/

490 Davis, K. (2012, Dec. 8). A voucher-based system for Medicare is not a solution
for healthcare. *Huffington Post.* Retrieved from http://www.huffingtonpost.com/
kennethdavis/medicare-vouchers_b_1947804.html

491 Davis, K. (2012, Dec. 8). A voucher-based system for Medicare is not a solution
for healthcare. *Huffington Post.* Retrieved from http://www.huffingtonpost.com/
kennethdavis/medicare-vouchers_b_1947804.html

492 Expanded & Improved Medicare For All Act, H.R. 676, 115th Cong. (2017-2018).
Cosponsors. Retrieved from https://www.congress.gov/bill/115th-congress/house-
bill/676/cosponsors

493 Expanded & Improved Medicare For All Act, H.R. 676, 115th Cong. (2017-2018).
History of legislation. Retrieved from https://www.congress.gov/search?q={%22source
%22:%22legislation%22,%22search%22:%22H.R.%20676%22}&searchResultViewType
=expanded

494 Expanded & Improved Medicare For All Act, H.R. 676, 115th Cong. (2017-2018).
History of legislation. Retrieved from https://www.congress.gov/search?q={%22source
%22:%22legislation%22,%22search%22:%22H.R.%20676%22}&searchResultViewType
=expanded

495 Physicians for a National Health Program. (2016, May 5). Beyond the Affordable Care
Act: A physicians' proposal for single-payer healthcare reform. Retrieved from http://
www.pnhp.org/nhi

496 Physicians for a National Health Program. (2017, Jan. 25). Doctors hail reintroduction
of Medicare-for-all bill. Retrieved from http://www.pnhp.org/news/2017/january/
doctors-hail-reintroduction-of-medicare-for-all-bill

497 DiJulio, B., Firth, J., Kirzinger, A., & Brodie, M. (2016, Feb. 25). Kaiser health tracking
poll, Figure 7 Reactions vary depending on what you call it. Retrieved from http://kff.
org/global-health-policy/poll-finding/kaiser-health-tracking-poll-february-2016/

498 Asher, T., Love, M., & Wilson, B. (1966). Wouldn't it be nice [Recorded by The Beach
Boys]. On *Pet Sounds* [CD]. Los Angeles: Capital Records.

499 The Henry J. Kaiser Family Foundation. (n.d.). Health Insurance Status, Health
Insurance Coverage of the Total Population, 2013 to 2015 [Data set]. Retrieved from

http://kff.org/other/state-indicator/total-population/?dataView=1&activeTab=gra
ph&currentTimeframe=0&startTimeframe=2&selectedDistributions=medicaid--
medicare&selectedRows=%7B%22wrapups%22:%7B%22united-states%22:%7B%7D%
7D%7D&sortModel=%7B%22colId%22:%22Location%22,%22sort%22:%22asc%22%
7D

500   Grob, R., Schlesinger, M., Grubstein, L. & Pollitz, K. (2014). Taking stock and
      taking steps: a report from the field after the first year of marketplace consumer
      assistance under the ACA. The Henry J. Kaiser Family Foundation and Robert Wood
      Johnson Foundation. Retrieved from http://files.kff.org/attachment/taking-stock-and-
      taking-steps-a-report-from-the-field-after-the-first-year-of-marketplace-consumer-
      assistance-under-the-aca-report

501   Grob, R., Schlesinger, M., Grubstein, L. & Pollitz, K. (2014). Taking stock and
      taking steps: a report from the field after the first year of marketplace consumer
      assistance under the ACA. The Henry J. Kaiser Family Foundation and Robert Wood
      Johnson Foundation. Retrieved from http://files.kff.org/attachment/taking-stock-and-
      taking-steps-a-report-from-the-field-after-the-first-year-of-marketplace-consumer-
      assistance-under-the-aca-report

502   Feffer, M. (2016, Sept. 8). Financial wellness success requires proactive HR. Retrieved
      from https://www.shrm.org/resourcesandtools/hr-topics/benefits/pages/financial-
      wellness-success.aspx

503   Feffer, M. (2016, Sept. 8). Financial wellness success requires proactive HR. Retrieved
      from https://www.shrm.org/resourcesandtools/hr-topics/benefits/pages/financial-
      wellness-success.aspx

504   Feffer, M. (2016, Sept. 8). Financial wellness success requires proactive HR. Retrieved
      from https://www.shrm.org/resourcesandtools/hr-topics/benefits/pages/financial-
      wellness-success.aspx

505   Mobile Future. (2016, Feb. 4). The rise of mobile: 11.6 billion mobile-connected
      devices by 2020 [Blog post]. Retrieved from http://mobilefuture.org/the-rise-of-
      mobile-11-6-billion-mobile-connected-devices-by-2020/

506   Mobile Future. (2016, Feb. 4). The rise of mobile: 11.6 billion mobile-connected
      devices by 2020 [Blog post]. Retrieved from http://mobilefuture.org/the-rise-of-
      mobile-11-6-billion-mobile-connected-devices-by-2020/

507   Mobile Future. (2016, Feb. 4). The rise of mobile: 11.6 billion mobile-connected
      devices by 2020 [Blog post]. Retrieved from http://mobilefuture.org/the-rise-of-
      mobile-11-6-billion-mobile-connected-devices-by-2020/

508   HealthCare.gov. (n.d.). How to pick a health insurance plan: The 'metal' categories:
      Bronze, Silver, Gold & Platinum. Retrieved from https://www.healthcare.gov/choose-
      a-plan/plans-categories/#catastrophic

509   Healthcare.gov. (n.d.). How insurance companies set health premiums. Retrieved
      from https://www.healthcare.gov/how-plans-set-your-premiums/

510   HealthCare.gov. (n.d.). Preventive care benefits for adults. Retrieved from https://
      www.healthcare.gov/preventive-care-adults/

511   U.S. Department of Health and Human Services. U.S. Food & Drug Administration
      (FDA). Menu labeling requirements. Retrieved May 3, 2017 from https://www.
      fda.gov/Food/GuidanceRegulation/GuidanceDocumentsRegulatoryInformation/
      LabelingNutrition/ucm515020.htm

512   Pollitz, K., & Rae, M. (2016, May 19). Workplace wellness programs characteristics

and requirements. The Henry J. Kaiser Family Foundation. Retrieved from http://kff. org/private-insurance/issue-brief/workplace-wellness-programs-characteristics-and-requirements/

513   Pollitz, K., & Rae, M. (2016, May 19). Workplace wellness programs characteristics and requirements. The Henry J. Kaiser Family Foundation. Retrieved from http://kff. org/private-insurance/issue-brief/workplace-wellness-programs-characteristics-and-requirements/

514   WellSteps. (n.d). WellSteps solutions work: Scientific evidence that WellSteps solutions are effective [PDF document]. Retrieved from https://www.wellsteps.com/images/ stories/wellsteps/wellsteps_solutions_work.pdf

515   WellSteps. (n.d). WellSteps solutions work: Scientific evidence that WellSteps solutions are effective [PDF document]. Retrieved from https://www.wellsteps.com/images/ stories/wellsteps/wellsteps_solutions_work.pdf

516   WellSteps. (n.d). WellSteps solutions work: Scientific evidence that WellSteps solutions are effective [PDF document]. Retrieved from https://www.wellsteps.com/images/ stories/wellsteps/wellsteps_solutions_work.pdf

517   WellSteps. (n.d). WellSteps solutions work: Scientific evidence that WellSteps solutions are effective [PDF document]. Retrieved from https://www.wellsteps.com/images/ stories/wellsteps/wellsteps_solutions_work.pdf

518   Transamerica Center for Health Studies® Survey: Millennial Survey: Young Adults' Healthcare Reality (June 2016), https://www.transamericacenterforhealthstudies. org/health-care-research/2016-millennials-survey-highlights ; https://www. transamericacenterforhealthstudies.org/docs/default-source/research/tchs-2016-millennial-survey-embargoed.pdf

519   Transamerica Center for Health Studies. (2016). Transamerica Center for Health Studies® survey: Millennial survey: Young adults' healthcare reality [PDF document]. Retrieved from https://www.transamericacenterforhealthstudies.org/docs/default-source/research/tchs-2016-millennial-survey-embargoed.pdf

520   Transamerica Center for Health Studies. (2016). Transamerica Center for Health Studies® survey: Millennial survey: Young adults' healthcare reality [PDF document]. Retrieved from https://www.transamericacenterforhealthstudies.org/docs/default-source/research/tchs-2016-millennial-survey-embargoed.pdf

521   Transamerica Center for Health Studies. (2016). Transamerica Center for Health Studies® survey: Millennial survey: Young adults' healthcare reality [PDF document]. Retrieved from https://www.transamericacenterforhealthstudies.org/docs/default-source/research/tchs-2016-millennial-survey-embargoed.pdf

522   Saltzman, E., Eibner, C., & The Commonwealth Fund. (2015, Sept. 2). Technical Appendix: Rate banding analysis [PDF document]. Retrieved from http://www. commonwealthfund.org/~/media/files/publications/blog/2015/eibner_rate_banding_tech_append_090215_clean_pf.pdf

523   AARP. (2017, Feb. 1). AARP opposes 'age rating' bill that threatens to drive up health costs. Retrieved from https://press.aarp.org/2017-02-01-AARP-Opposes-Age-Rating-Bill-that-Threatens-to-Drive-Up-Health-Costs

524   AARP. (2017, Feb. 1). AARP opposes 'age rating' bill that threatens to drive up health costs. Retrieved from https://press.aarp.org/2017-02-01-AARP-Opposes-Age-Rating-Bill-that-Threatens-to-Drive-Up-Health-Costs

525   Spiegel, J. (2015, Dec. 19). Why HSAs are underused. *Morningstar*

Magazine. Retrieved from http://ibd.morningstar.com/article/article.
asp?id=733960&CN=brf295,http://ibd.morningstar.com/archive/archive.
asp?inputs=days=14;frmtId=12,%20brf295

526 Spiegel, J. (2015, Dec. 19). Why HSAs are underused. *Morningstar
Magazine*. Retrieved from http://ibd.morningstar.com/article/article.
asp?id=733960&CN=brf295,http://ibd.morningstar.com/archive/archive.
asp?inputs=days=14;frmtId=12,%20brf295

527 Spiegel, J. (2015, Dec. 19). Why HSAs are underused. *Morningstar
Magazine*. Retrieved from http://ibd.morningstar.com/article/article.
asp?id=733960&CN=brf295,http://ibd.morningstar.com/archive/archive.
asp?inputs=days=14;frmtId=12,%20brf295

528 Andrews, M. (2016, Dec. 2). HSA balances climb but benefits reward wealthier
consumers most. *Kaiser Health News*. Retrieved from http://khn.org/news/hsas-
benefits-reward-wealthier-consumers-most/

529 Availity. (2015, Feb.) The impact of consumerism on provider revenues [PDF
document]. Retrieved from https://www.availity.com/-/media/files/availity/resource-
library/research-study/availity-consumerism-provider-research-study-availity-
mar-2015.pdf

530 FirstData. (2015). The unbanked generation: A guide to the financial habits of
Millennials [PDF document]. Retrieved from https://www.firstdata.com/en_us/all-
features/millennials.html

531 Terhune, C. (2016, Dec. 30). Top Republicans say there's a medical malpractice
crisis. Experts say there isn't. *The Washington Post*. Retrieved from https://www.
washingtonpost.com/news/to-your-health/wp/2016/12/30/top-republicans-say-theres-
a-medical-malpractice-crisis-experts-say-there-isnt/?utm_term=.1cb79e1860b7

532 Terhune, C. (2016, Dec. 30). Top Republicans say there's a medical malpractice
crisis. Experts say there isn't. *The Washington Post*. Retrieved from https://www.
washingtonpost.com/news/to-your-health/wp/2016/12/30/top-republicans-say-theres-
a-medical-malpractice-crisis-experts-say-there-isnt/?utm_term=.1cb79e1860b7

533 Centers for Medicare & Medicaid Services (CMS). (n.d.). Medical loss ratio. Retrieved
from https://www.cms.gov/CCIIO/Programs-and-Initiatives/Health-Insurance-
Market-Reforms/Medical-Loss-Ratio.html

534 Mukherjee, S. (2016, Sept. 21). Mylan's CEO tells Congress the EpiPen price hike was
'fair.' *Fortune*. Retrieved from http://fortune.com/2016/09/21/mylan-ceo-epipen-price-
hike/

535 Kissick, W.L., (1994), Medicine's dilemmas: Infinite needs versus finite resources. New
Haven and New London, CT: Yale University Press.

536 Carroll, A. (2012, Oct. 3). The "iron triangle" of health care. *JAMA Forum*. Retrieved
from https://newsatjama.jama.com/2012/10/03/jama-forum-the-iron-triangle-of-
health-care-access-cost-and-quality/

537 Centers for Medicare & Medicaid Services (CMS). (n.d.). Accountable Care
Organizations (ACO). Retrieved fro https://www.cms.gov/Medicare/Medicare-Fee-
for-Service-Payment/ACO/index.html?redirect=/Aco/

538 American Hospital Association (AHA). (n.d.). About. Retrieved from http://www.aha.
org/about/index.shtml

539 American Medical Association (AMA). (n.d.). AMA history. Retrieved from https://
www.ama-assn.org/ama-history

540 American Medical Association (AMA). (2015). Annual Report, 2015. Retrieved from https://www.ama-assn.org/sites/default/files/media-browser/public/about-ama/ama-annual-report.pdf

541 Graham, J. (2016, Dec. 22). 'Like a slap in the face': Dissent roils the AMA, the nation's largest doctor's group. *STAT*. Retrieved from https://www.statnews.com/2016/12/22/american-medical-association-divisions/

542 American College of Emergency Physicians (ACEP). (n.d.). APC (Ambulatory Payment Classifications) FAQ. Retrieved from https://www.acep.org/Clinical---Practice-Management/APC-(Ambulatory-Payment-Classifications)-FAQ/

543 National Conference of State Legislatures. (2017). Children's Health Insurance Program overview. Retrieved from http://www.ncsl.org/research/health/childrens-health-insurance-program-overview.aspx

544 American College of Emergency Physicians (ACEP). (n.d.). APC (Ambulatory Payment Classifications) FAQ. Retrieved from https://www.acep.org/Clinical---Practice-Management/APC-(Ambulatory-Payment-Classifications)-FAQ/

545 Centers for Medicare & Medicaid Services (CMS). (n.d.). Emergency Medical Treatment & Labor Act (EMTALA). Retrieved from https://www.cms.gov/regulations-and-guidance/legislation/emtala/

546 U. S. Department of Labor. (n.d.). Health plans & benefits: ERISA. Retrieved from https://www.dol.gov/general/topic/health-plans/erisa

547 The Henry J. Kaiser Family Foundation. (n.d.). Fee-for-Service. In *Health Reform Glossary*. Retrieved from http://kff.org/glossary/health-reform-glossary/

548 HealthCare.gov. (n.d.). How to claim an exemption for members of a healthcare sharing ministry. Retrieved from https://www.healthcare.gov/exemptions-tool/#/results/2016/details/healthcare-sharing-ministry

549 Health Insurance Portability and Accountability Act of 1996 (HIPAA), Public Law 104-191. (1996). Retrieved from https://www.gpo.gov/fdsys/pkg/PLAW-104publ191/pdf/PLAW-104publ191.pdf

550 U.S. Department of the Treasury. Internal Revenue Service (IRS). (2016). IRS Publication 969, Health Savings Accounts (HSAs). Retrieved from https://www.irs.gov/publications/p969/ar02.html#en_US_2016_publink1000204020

551 U.S. Department of the Treasury. Internal Revenue Service (IRS). (2016). IRS Publication 969, Health Reimbursement Arrangements (HRAs). Retrieved from https://www.irs.gov/publications/p969/ar02.html#en_US_2016_publink1000204194

552 U.S. Department of the Treasury. Internal Revenue Service (IRS). (2016). 26 CFR 601.602: Tax forms and instructions (Also: Part 1, § 1, 223), Rev. Proc. 2016-28. Retrieved from https://www.irs.gov/pub/irs-drop/rp-16-28.pdf

553 Centers for Medicare & Medicaid Services (CMS). (n.d.). The Hospital Readmissions Reduction (HRR) Program. Retrieved from https://www.cms.gov/Medicare/Quality-Initiatives-Patient-Assessment-Instruments/Value-Based-Programs/HRRP/Hospital-Readmission-Reduction-Program.html

554 Centers for Medicare & Medicaid Services (CMS). (n.d.). Readmissions Reduction Program (HRRP). Retrieved from https://www.cms.gov/medicare/medicare-fee-for-service-payment/acuteinpatientpps/readmissions-reduction-program.html

555 World Health Organization (WHO). (n.d.). Classifications, ICD. Retrieved from http://www.who.int/classifications/icd/en/

556 Centers for Medicare & Medicaid Services (CMS). (n.d.). Provider resources, ICD-10.

Retrieved from https://www.cms.gov/medicare/coding/icd10/providerresources.html

557 American Hospital Association (AHA). (n.d.). Long-term care hospitals (LTCHs). Retrieved from http://www.aha.org/advocacy-issues/postacute/ltach/index.shtml

558 Healthit.gov. (n.d.). EHR incentives & certification: What is meaningful use? Retrieved from https://www.healthit.gov/providers-professionals/ehr-incentives-certification

559 Healthit.gov. (n.d.). EHR incentives & certification, meaningful use definition & objectives. Retrieved from https://www.healthit.gov/providers-professionals/meaningful-use-definition-objectives

560 Centers for Medicare & Medicaid Services (CMS). (n.d.). What are the value-based programs? Retrieved from https://www.cms.gov/Medicare/Quality-Initiatives-Patient-Assessment-Instruments/Value-Based-Programs/Value-Based-Programs.html

561 U.S. Department of the Treasury. Internal Revenue Service (IRS). (2016). IRS Publication 969, Medical Savings Accounts (MSA). Retrieved from https://www.irs.gov/publications/p969/ar02.html#en_US_2016_publink1000204110

562 Healthcare.gov. (n.d.). What Marketplace health insurance plans cover. Retrieved from https://www.healthcare.gov/coverage/what-marketplace-plans-cover/

563 Centers for Medicare & Medicaid Services (CMS). (n.d.). Physician Quality Reporting System. Retrieved from https://www.cms.gov/Medicare/Quality-Initiatives-Patient-Assessment-Instruments/PQRS/index.html?redirect=/pqrs/

564 U.S. Department of Health and Human Services. Office of the Secretary. 45 CFR Subtitle A, § 160.103, https://www.gpo.gov/fdsys/pkg/CFR-2010-title45-vol1/pdf/CFR-2010-title45-vol1-sec160-103.pdf

565 Healthcare.gov. (n.d.). UCR (Usual, Customary, and Reasonable. *Glossary*. Retrieved from https://www.healthcare.gov/glossary/UCR-usual-customary-and-reasonable/

566 Colorado Department of Regulatory Agencies (DORA). (n.d.). *Health Insurance Glossary*. Retrieved from https://www.colorado.gov/pacific/dora/health-insurance-glossary

567 U.S. Department of Health and Human Services. (n.d.). About HHS. Retrieved from https://www.hhs.gov/about/index.html#